D1365145

# FOOD FOR LIFE

# FOOD FOR LIFE

## MYRTLE SIEBERT
## EVELYN KERR

### CONTRIBUTING AUTHOR
### PHYLLIS THOMSON

**McGraw-Hill Ryerson Limited**

Toronto   Montreal   New York   Auckland   Bogotá   Caracas
Lisbon   London   Madrid   Mexico   Milan   New Delhi   Paris
San Juan   Singapore   Sydney   Tokyo

FOOD FOR LIFE

Copyright © McGraw-Hill Ryerson Limited, 1994. All rights
reserved. No part of this publication may be reproduced
or transmitted in any form or by any means, or stored in a
data base or retrieval system, without the prior written
permission of McGraw-Hill Ryerson Limited.

ISBN 0-07-551544-X

2 3 4 5 6 7 8 9 10 ML 3 2 1 0 9 8 7 6 5 4

Printed and bound in Canada

Care has been taken to trace ownership of copyright
material contained in this text. The publishers will gladly
accept any information that will enable them to rectify
any reference or credit in subsequent editions.

**Canadian Cataloguing in Publication Data**

Siebert, Myrtle
   Food for life

Includes index.
ISBN 0-07-551544-X

1. Food.  2. Nutrition
I. Kerr, Evelyn.  II. Title.

TX355.S54 1994     641.3     C93-095567-6

PUBLISHER: Janice Matthews
ASSOCIATE EDITOR: Nancy Christoffer
SENIOR SUPERVISING EDITOR: Carol Altilia
PERMISSIONS EDITOR: Jacqueline Donovan
EDITORIAL ASSISTANT: Crystal Shortt
COPY EDITOR: Geraldine Kikuta
ILLUSTRATIONS: Iryna Molodecky
CARTOONS: Cuyler Black
COVER AND INTERIOR DESIGN: Brant Cowie/ArtPlus Limited
ELECTRONIC PAGE MAKE UP: Valerie Van Volkenburg/
                         ArtPlus Limited

This book was manufactured in Canada using acid-free
and recycled paper.

# Contents

# Preface

Written by Canadians for Canadians, *Food for Life* encourages students to explore their food habits and those of their families in relation to cultural, nutritional, psychological, and social factors. Students will understand the important relationship between what they eat and their vitality and performance level, as well as the importance of food choices for their continued well-being.

Unit 1 is directed to students as they become increasingly responsible for their own food choices. It explains their reasons for eating, why they make the food choices they do, and how those choices can be adapted for maximum health.

Unit 2 centres around the kitchen and its management. Many students are responsible for preparing food for themselves and often for others—family members, roommates, or customers in a food service establishment. This unit helps prepare them for working in a kitchen, whether at school, at home, or at work.

Unit 3 was developed around the food groups in *Canada's Food Guide to Healthy Eating*. Basic aspects of grading, buying, storing, and preparing foods are discussed for the variety of foods included in each food group. A short chapter describes some of the Other Foods that are also part of our meals but that, except for water, herbs, and spices, should be consumed in moderate amounts.

Unit 4 begins with an introduction of Canadian food heritage by studying foods of Native peoples and the different regions of Canada. Students then delve into the food habits, eating patterns, traditional foods, and recipes of some of the cultures in our multicultural society. This unit also looks at the global implications of food production and consumption.

Unit 5 explores food as it enters the body and undergoes the digestive process. Students will learn more about making healthy food choices and become aware of the relationship between eating patterns and current health risks.

Key terms in *Food for Life* appear in boldface and are defined in the glossary for student reference. Each unit contains two career sketches which provide information on careers that students may be considering in the food industry. Students will discover many other interesting features as they proceed through the book.

In the end, we hope that students and teachers find *Food for Life* an enjoyable book to read and a valuable learning experience.

# Acknowledgements

Recognition of their assistance, direct and indirect, is made for the following people by Myrtle Siebert:

Frances Clive and Ollie Carpenter, teachers who encouraged the study of home economics beyond high school;

Charlotte Black, instructor and director of the school, who taught the value of management in the classroom, at home, and in daily living;

Muriel Johnson, exceptional teacher, who provided initial experience in choosing and creating learning materials for students;

Leslie Paris, teacher and curriculum coordinator, who provided guidance and support on the program;

Evelyn Kerr, teacher, writer, and long-term associate, who provided support throughout the project;

Jeri Manley, nutritionist, with whom ideas for encouraging healthy food habits in children were developed;

Carolyn Pfortmueller, teacher, friend, and partner for many projects;

Dale Siebert, husband and friend, for consistent support through varied career activities and food experiences.

Evelyn Kerr would like to express her appreciation to Sandy Ulmi at the BC Dairy Foundation; Pat Scarlett at the Beef Information Centre; Pat Rooker; Pat Stearman; and Shirley Ann Brown.

The authors would like the thank the following reviewers for their perceptive comments: Janet Dryden, Merle MacDonald, Helen Siemens, Phyllis Thomson, and Wendy Walker.

Many individuals lent their time and expertise to this text and deserve special credit:

Shrikala Baljekar-Grewal for her contributions in the Indian section;

Thelma Barer-Stein, Ph.D., (author of *You Eat What You Are: A Study of Ethnic Food Traditions*, originally published by McClelland & Stewart and available from Culture Concepts Inc., Toronto) for her review of chapters 11 and 12;

Geraldine Kikuta for her insightful comments and suggestions throughout the project;

Judy Christensen and Yvonne Pinnock for their assistance with the Jamaican section;

Gale Smith, University of British Columbia, for writing chapter 13, Global Food Issues;

Phyllis Thomson for lending her creativity and writing skills;

the individuals who took time from their busy schedules to participate in the career sketches.

To create this text, material from the following organizations has been helpful:

Beef Information Centre
Canadian Cancer Society
Canadian Diabetes Association
Canadian Dietetic Association
Canadian Egg Marketing Agency
Canadian Home Economics Association
Canadian Red Cross Society
Central Vancouver Island Health Unit, British Columbia
Dairy Bureau of Canada
Health and Welfare Canada
Health Canada
Heart and Stroke Foundation of Canada
J.M.P. Marketing, Burnaby, British Columbia
National Eating Disorder Information Centre
National Geographic Society
National Institute of Nutrition
Osteoporosis Society of British Columbia
Save On Foods Stores, British Columbia
Sport Medicine Council of Canada
Vancouver Health Department
Vancouver School Board
Weight Watchers International

# Food Perspectives

Have you ever wondered why you choose to eat some foods and not others? Your choices are based on where you live, your cultural group, your religion, your family patterns, and even outside influences such as friends, advertising, and the media. Health care professionals and governments also try to influence our eating habits. Sometimes our choices are not wise, and we put our bodies at risk of illness. Why would we do this? We eat not only to satisfy physical needs but to fulfill social and emotional needs as well.

In this unit you will learn about factors that might influence your choices of food. When you have read this unit ask yourself whether you are making healthy food choices. Are you choosing food that provides your body with the nutrients it needs? Are you happy and healthy? For many people in the world and in Canada, food and nutrition are not choices but matters of survival. Make your choices count.

# Food Habits and Traditions

## FACTORS THAT INFLUENCE FOOD HABITS

Why do you snack on an apple, while your friend may choose chips? Why does one student bring rice and cooked vegetables, while another brings a roll and salad for lunch? Our food habits are influenced by what we like and by our family heritage. Food traditions in your family came from those in your parents' families. Others, your parents may have developed together. Some traditions have origins in religion; others developed from practices in other countries. All are passed down through the years. They are affected by physical, emotional, and social needs of the people who are eating.

Through the ages, travellers to foreign lands described in their diaries the foods and dietary traditions of the people whose lands they visited. Food has played an important role through the years. The abundance or scarcity of food has often changed the course of history. Chapter 11 describes foods of Native Canadians and of the various groups that have emigrated to Canada.

How might Newfoundland's coastal geography affect its food supply?

Geography • Our nomadic ancestors ate whatever they could find to satisfy their hunger. Available food depended on a variety of conditions, such as climate, soil quality, abundance of water, and the presence of wild game and native plants. When people began to grow crops and raise animals, a more settled lifestyle evolved. As well, bartering with other societies made new foods available. However, barriers such as mountains, rivers, and deserts often made trading difficult.

Geographic location is no longer a major factor determining availability of food in Canada. Refrigeration and improved transportation make it possible to obtain food from all over the world at almost any time of the year.

Trade has become very complex and sometimes has political implications. Some countries with which Canada trades have questionable labour or environmental practices. Canadian laws require that the country of origin be identified on all foods. This information helps people who choose not to buy from these countries make purchasing decisions.

History ◆ History is full of examples of the role that food habits have played in the story of civilization. Here is a list of some of the major factors that have been influential in changing food habits over the years. Can you explain how each has been able to affect food habits?

- Discovery of fire.
- Development of agriculture.
- Migration, travel, exploration, and trade.
- Introduction of a monetary system.
- Industrialization and urbanization.
- Increased population.
- Improved standard of living.
- Improved education.
- Advanced science and technology.
- Improved knowledge of medicine and nutrition.

Religion ◆ Ancient societies sought to please their gods with sacrifices or ceremonies and rituals that centred on the food that was essential for life. Eventually, most societies and cultures developed special ceremonies associated with the various steps of obtaining or producing food. Certain members of the community took charge for directing these rites. The guidelines for these ceremonies continue to be handed down to successive spiritual leaders.

Our food habits have been influenced greatly by the formal religions of the world. For example, the Buddhist practice of not eating meat is based on the belief that animals possess a spiritual as well as a physical existence. Therefore all creatures must be treated with respect and not be eaten. In Buddhist teachings, humans are considered to be part of nature, not its superior. Christian beliefs, on the other hand, describe humans as different from and superior to all other animals. They believe that everything on earth is provided for human use. These are two examples of differing attitudes about eating meat. Many other foods are also a part of religious practice.

*Did you know that Hopi Indians use corn in ceremonies as a symbol representing life? During the name-giving ceremony, a perfect ear of white corn is passed four times over a twenty-day-old baby while it is fed a blue corn mush, considered by the Hopi to be holy.*

Sometimes it is the absence of food that is important. For example, during **Ramadan** those of Muslim faith do not eat between the hours of sun-up to sundown. This is called fasting, a practice common to many religions.

## REASONS FOR EATING

### Physical Needs ◆ Your body needs certain nutrients to function properly and supply it with energy. For more about meeting physical needs see pages 16–18. Many people eat more than their physical needs require; others do not eat enough. Hunger tells us when to eat. But with snacking, some people seldom have an opportunity to experience how a completely empty stomach feels.

### Hunger ◆ When was the last time you felt really hungry? Hunger is a physical sensation that tells the brain it is time to eat. People who listen to their bodies when they are functioning at peak performance levels will recognize and respond to the sensation of hunger. These people eat only as much as required to reach **satiety**, or a full feeling.

Food banks store donated food to help feed those who would otherwise not have enough to eat. Do you have a food bank in your community?

Unfortunately, many of us are driven to eat by other influences. These include time schedules, advertising, psychological reasons, social acceptability, and because food has been prepared and is ready to eat. Eating when one is not really hungry can lead to overeating and diseases related to poor eating habits. On the other hand, some people ignore the sensation of hunger in their efforts to lose weight. Then, when they finally do eat, they may overeat. Ignoring hunger and overeating are both poor habits that can lead to health problems.

### Senses ◆ How are sensory organs — eyes, nose, tongue, and ears — used in relation to food? Food attractively arranged on the plate with an assortment of colours, aromas, textures, and flavours is more appealing. Smells influence appetite by triggering the flow of juices from the salivary glands. When you enjoy the taste of a food you want to eat more. The sound of food being cooked or eaten may entice you; for example, food frying or chips being crunched.

Information about sensory reactions is often used to present the most appealing plate of food possible. Advertisers, chefs, and cooks carefully consider the combination of colour, shape, texture, consistency, and flavour when dealing with food.

Taste is largely a learned response. The **taste buds**, small sensors on the tongue, develop over time. Children grow up learning to like the flavour of foods that are part of their culture. People raised in a Polynesian culture, for example, will have a learned taste for *poi*. Poi is a starchy staple with the taste and consistency of paste. It is made from the root of the taro plant. If you never learned to like poi as a young child, you probably would not enjoy its taste and consistency now.

Adults who were not accustomed as children to the taste of foods such as pickles, olives, and avocados, for example, may learn eventually to appreciate their flavours. To see first-hand that taste is a learned response, watch as an infant is introduced to new foods. A food such as pureed carrots may receive an unfavourable reaction at first, but the child may soon grow to enjoy it.

**Psychological Needs** ◆ Psychological needs are feelings of lacking or wanting something that cause us to behave as we do. They are not associated with the body but with the mind. There are many complex psychological reasons for eating, but food habits are learned. Infants and children learn their basic attitudes toward food from early methods of feeding. Food can be a source of *affection*, *security*, and *satisfaction* or a demonstration of pleasant human interaction.

The reverse of these feelings can also be experienced. The *power* that others have over the food supply can be used as a reward or punishment. If the parent expects the entire meal to be eaten before treats are allowed, young children soon learn that their demands for candy can be met by eating their meal. Eating can also be a source of power over others. In families where young people feel powerless they may, in their frustration, resort to not eating to have some control over a part of their life. Eventually, the struggle can develop into an eating disorder.

Why does a person eat an ice cream cone on a hot day when a big meal has already satisfied any feeling of hunger? Is it for *reward*, to give *comfort*, to relieve *stress,* or is it perhaps a demonstration of *revolt*? Does the human body have any real need for coffee or cola drinks that some people seem to crave? And what about popcorn, chocolate bars, whipped cream, and potato chips? They can hardly be considered important for the nutrients supplied, but when we like them, the eating gives us *pleasure*.

The way food is prepared and served is an expression of the cook's individuality. Food preparation can also be a demonstration of *love*, *affection*, *power*, *status*, and *affluence*. What a person chooses to eat or not eat is another means of self-expression and, in extreme cases, of revolt. A young person refusing dinner may be exerting *independence*. Food combinations used in family recipes and meals that are part of special occasions express *tradition* or *custom*, and provide *security*. These are important factors in satisfying a person's psychological needs for food. Have you experienced any of the needs mentioned here? What are some others?

## Social Needs

Social needs are being met when a group gathers in a home or restaurant. It is less important what food or beverage is ordered or how hungry each person may be. Food shared with good friends symbolizes their friendship and trust.

Whether you are drinking coffee, tea, water, or another beverage, a coffee break is a time to relax with your friends.

The planning of parties for all ages invariably involves choosing the food to be served. Teams often go out together after playing a game of baseball, hockey, or soccer. Public meetings routinely offer coffee and tea, sometimes with cookies or doughnuts. It is likely the people are not eating because of any physical need for food. A break during any activity that brings people together is a good opportunity to visit and talk. Coffee breaks among workers, in addition to the mental and physical break, are more important for the social opportunity than for the actual coffee or other beverage being enjoyed.

## Food Symbolism

**Prestige** is involved in the serving of certain foods. A prestigious object indicates reputation, influence, or social status. While other factors contribute to the prestige of certain foods, it is frequently associated with monetary value or scarcity of the food item. For example, it could be argued that caviar, at such high cost, is not good value unless prestigious foods are valued.

It is ironic that the **status** assigned to some foods in many cases means that people of higher economic levels or higher status receive food of lower nutritional value. White flour has been a prestigious food from the time of the Egyptians and Romans. Only the poor used the coarsely ground whole grain, which has more nutrition. In various parts of Asia, white rice has greater prestige than brown rice. Brown rice, which is rich in thiamin, is eaten by those who cannot afford to purchase the polished grain. Unfortunately, people of lower economic levels sometimes aspire to the same inadequate diets of those with status. With the new awareness for the need to make healthier food choices, however, the trend seems to be changing.

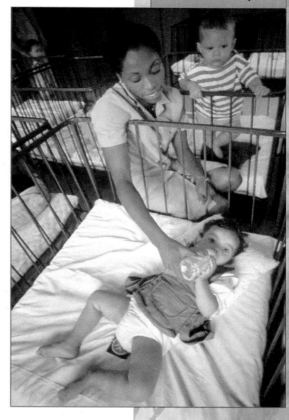

Although infant formula is often given high status, babies should be breast-fed instead, if possible. List the reasons why.

Another status-related example is the use of prepared infant formula instead of breast milk in developing countries. Believing they are giving their child the best possible nourishment, poor people often spend limited money to buy the formula. Then they are unable to satisfy other important needs like food for the mother and family. Unfortunately, often only polluted water is available to mix with the formula, which makes the baby sick. The mother would have been better advised to continue the natural process and breast-feed her child. World help organizations are now focussing on teaching mothers about the value of breast-feeding and the importance of hygiene.

Food is a means of communicating other symbolic factors. It may express *affection*, *friendship*, *hospitality*, *neighbourliness*, or *comfort* and *sympathy* in times of sadness or disaster. There are many examples:

- A person prepares or offers a favourite food to a child.
  
  It might be as an expression of love or to console an injury or hurt feelings.

- Friends and neighbours take prepared food to the family of the deceased.
  
  Feeding those who are grieving gives them strength and encouragement to go on. A physical demonstration by supportive friends makes the pain more bearable. As well, the preparation gives the friends something to do.

- A neighbour brings fresh baking or another home-cooked offering to a person or family new to the community.

  The message of the food is one of goodwill to the newcomer.

- A child prepares breakfast or another meal for a parent or family member.

  This may be a demonstration of love or the child showing his or her knowledge and skills.

- A small amount of food or sweets is presented at a shrine. It may be in a garden, house, or special temple.

  Many cultures present offerings to the gods as symbols of "sacrifices." Once these sacrifices often took the form of an animal being killed.

- Businessperson invites a client for a meal.

  This may be an offering of friendship, demonstrated hospitality, or just an expected business practice. The meaning implied depends on the circumstances of the association, the culture of those involved, and the location of the meal, whether at home or in a restaurant.

  It is generally accepted that the sharing of food creates a symbolic bond between people who share the food and those who receive it.

## FOOD FOR SPECIAL OCCASIONS

When you think of a special occasion or religious celebration in your family, you can probably name the kind of food or beverage traditionally served. Consider the importance of food at such events as Christmas, Thanksgiving, Easter, New Year, Hanukkah, Shavuot, Ramadan, the Mid Autumn Festival, the Dragon Boat Festival, or at a christening, Bar Mitzvah, Bat Mitzvah, birthday, graduation, confirmation, wedding, or funeral.

**Feasts** are given as celebrations of relationships among the diners, as with marriage feasts. Food served at festivals, feasts, and parties is more elaborate than we usually eat, but it is also traditional or inherited from the past. Memories of good food last, so lavish foods help make the feast unforgettable.

A **potlatch**, a lavish feast given by First Nations people of Canada's Northwest coast, is an example of a cultural feast. The best available fish and game meat are served in traditional ways. For both the host and the guests at the potlatch, there is a complex set of expectations, or rules, of appropriate behaviour. Each person attending the feast is presented with gifts by

Christmas Kuchen (above) and Santa Lucia Crown (below) are baked for special occasions. What special food does your family bake?

the chief or host. Gifts traditionally given are food and possessions. The better the food and the greater the value of the gifts, the greater the status of the host. The eventual result is a redistribution of wealth among the guests.

Usually festive foods are served only on festive days. If the festival is a reoccurring one, the food served is always the same. Part of the value of festive foods is the time required for their preparation as well as their richness. An English Christmas cake and brandy soaked Christmas pudding are heavy, sweet, and rich, not like usual desserts. Many families serve turkey for Christmas dinner, others make pyrohy, still other families expect roast duck or ham. Most of these foods require a long time to prepare.

Special cookies are made for guests at Italian weddings. The huge selection of different designs and recipes takes a long time to prepare. The greater the assortment and quantity available for tasting, the greater the culinary talent of the makers. Norwegian cooks make *crullers* for Christmas. These thin, delicately flavoured sugar cookies are rolled with a special iron and deep-fried. They also take a long time to make and must be handled carefully as they break easily.

Chapter 12 describes foods served in some of the countries that people living in Canada came from originally. There are many cultural traditions followed here that began elsewhere. Can you think of a cultural tradition that has continued the same way in Canada? Other traditions have been adapted and have become truly Canadian.

An example of a tradition that has been adapted in Canada is the preparation and serving of cake. A visitor to a home in Germany will be served freshly-made cake soon after his or her arrival. The guest is thus recognized and the importance of the visit acknowledged. Family members celebrating a birthday or a wedding anniversary also enjoy a cake in Germany. In Canada, the tradition continues in a modified way. Birthday celebrants are presented with a birthday cake. This custom has extended to most Canadian families regardless of their country of origin. It has become a North American tradition.

A birthday cake can help make a birthday a special day. How does your family celebrate birthdays?

However, in Canada a visit is not always acknowledged with cake. For people who value the German traditions, not being served cake by the hostess may be seen as showing disrespect for the visitor.

The widespread practice of having a special wedding cake has different customs associated with it. English and Canadian wedding cakes were first made heavy and rich like Christmas cake. They were decorated with extra hard white icing originally used to support the pillars that separated the layers. The custom continues today. The ritual of the cutting of the wedding cake took hold in the 1930s. The groom cut the cake with a large, beribboned knife. Now the wedded pair perform the task together. Small pieces of wrapped cake are given to each guest to take home, where the ritual continues. Guests place their pieces of cake under their pillows on the wedding night and make a wish for the new couple.

You can see the difference between cultures when you are invited to the home of someone from another culture to celebrate a festive occasion. For example, foods served on New Year's day vary from culture to culture. These differences are also evident in regular meals. Some people traditionally serve rice with every main meal. Perhaps your family serves potatoes. What happens when two people from different cultural backgrounds marry? Unless they are both comfortable with one meal pattern, they will need to make adjustments, keeping important parts from both cultures.

## CHANGING FOOD HABITS

Professionals, including doctors, nutritionists, and dietitians, know how very difficult it is to change food habits. Eating patterns and attitudes toward food are established early and, whether good or bad, may last a lifetime. We are influenced by family habits, cultural practice, media advertising, and new ideas being promoted.

Television can be a very powerful but negative influence on a child's eating habits. Increasing numbers of children influenced by advertising are growing up overweight. A lot of television advertisements focus on snacking. Sugar- and/or fat-rich breakfast cereals, cookies, candy, gum, and snacks make up about two-thirds of the televised food advertising directed at children. These advertisements have subtle ways of leading children to believe that the product is not only delicious and fun to eat but even good for them. Have you witnessed children insisting that their parents buy a certain product they have seen on television?

Are you aware of any changes that need to be made in your food habits or those of some family members? Because food habits are very personal, even small suggestions of menu changes will sometimes be interpreted as a personal attack. If you try to get your friends to change their food habits, you will probably be under attack. You may be committed to changing or improving your food habits, but how can you stay on track when everyone else is eating chips and drinking pop? Here are some possibilities.

- Eat three planned meals so that you will not be hungry when others are eating less healthy snacks.

- Bring your friends home, if possible, to eat a meal that you have prepared.

- Suggest an active social event to shift the focus from food.

Similarly, an attempt by a family member to make changes in the foods served may be met with resistance. You may have seen this happen at home. A gradual approach to change will produce the best results. After all, it has taken a good many years with careful conditioning of advertisers to get family members to where they are now.

When introducing new foods or new recipes it is a good idea not to try too many items at once. Team the new idea with an old favourite. Combine an unfamiliar vegetable with one everyone likes. Family members will be more likely to try a new food when they are not expected to make a meal of it. If you are trying a new vegetarian recipe, serve it first as a side dish with meat if other family members are not vegetarian. If the new recipe is well received the first time, you might try it another time without a meat dish.

It is fun to try new recipes and doing so relieves the cook from boredom and makes meals more interesting for everyone. Proceed with caution. Something new each week is a safe guideline. When you start making healthy improvements to familiar meals, remember that eating patterns are part of our heritage.

Experimenting with vegetables can be fun. Think of two new ways to prepare vegetables for your family.

# FOOD AND WELLNESS

Wellness is a term that takes in all aspects of your physical and emotional health. It is more than absence of disease; it strives for an enhanced quality of life. Here are the aspects that work together in achieving wellness.

Lifestyle • **Lifestyle** is the way you choose to live your life. It includes your typical habits, recreational choices, and your attitudes. Lifestyle also includes the pattern of behaviour affecting health. An individual usually has control over his or her lifestyle. Lifestyle includes many aspects of choosing and eating food; it includes the foods you select and the social and emotional setting in which you eat. It is the number and timing of meals and snacks, and the pattern of beverage consumption.

## CAREER SKETCH

Earl Geddes, farmer, with his son Mattew, daughter Sohmer, and wife Helen-Ann

EARL GEDDES was born and raised on a farm at Pilot Mound, Manitoba. After graduating from high school he enrolled in the faculty of Agriculture at the University of Manitoba. He completed the two-year diploma course in 1972.

He had already gained farming experience on the family farm as he grew up. At an early age he became expert in the art of driving tractors and harvesters as well as managing the cattle operation. Through the 4-H program he learned how to prepare cattle for exhibition and competition at county and provincial fairs as well as the Calgary Stampede.

In 1973 Geddes purchased 178 hectares of the land that his grandfather's uncles had settled in 1887. He has since increased the farm to 405 hectares. Geddes grows varieties of wheat, barley, oats, flax, canola, as well as feed for his purebred Charolais beef cattle.

Geddes states, "One of the benefits of farming is that the required activity varies from day to day and season to season." In the winter months he must battle the cold weather but is able to take time to attend farm meetings and take courses to upgrade his knowledge of farm issues. February and March are calving season, which means constant attention to the cattle. A few minutes in Manitoba's cold weather can freeze the ears or tail on a new-born calf. Family members Helen-Ann, Sohmer, and Mattew help check on the cows on a regular basis, even throughout the night.

In the spring, machinery is overhauled for the coming planting season. May is probably the busiest and most critical time of year for a cattle and grain operation. "Every effort is made to get the crop planted as early as possible to ensure the maximum growing season."

With the summer months comes haying season. Geddes and his family put in long hours to put up their hay in the best quality possible.

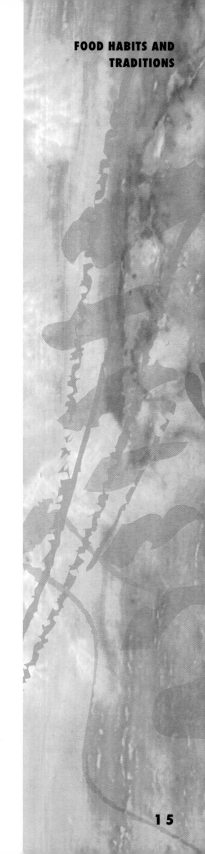

July gives them a short break, but harvesting equipment needs to be checked and readied for the harvesting of the other crops in August and September. "Weather is the greatest contributor to harvest success. If there is a warm, dry fall, the harvest will be enjoyable and much easier. If it is wet and cool, the quality of the grain and the enjoyment go down dramatically." Everyone pitches in to run combines and trucks and bale straw and second cut of hay.

In the fall the grain is taken to market and some of the bills can be paid. The cows are brought home and the calves are weaned off milk and started on feed. In October Geddes starts planning for next year's crop by applying fertilizer and crop protection materials. The farm meetings start again. Throughout the year all family members take part, using their particular skills.

When asked about the most rewarding aspects of farming, Geddes says it is "the ability to see the response to decisions that I make. The farm responds to the amount of energy and effort that is put into it, and I reap the benefit or the loss according to my desire to work. Many occupations never deliver that type of visual output.

"Without a doubt the most challenging aspect of farming is the weather—not enough rain, too much rain, too hot, early frost, too windy, and on and on. I have no control over the weather. All of the planning and preparation that I do to produce a crop can be wiped out by a hail storm or an early frost. I can educate myself to understand new technology, I can learn more about markets to make the right planting decisions, but I cannot control the weather."

Geddes has many duties other than those directly on the farm. He is currently under contract to the Federal Deputy Minister of Agriculture and Agri-Food. He is developing a consultative process for federal, provincial, and farm organizations to meaningfully interact in the development of farm and food policy. He played a large part in establishing Keystone Agricultural Producers Inc., Manitoba's largest general farm organization. He has also served on many other farm committees and organizations.

According to Geddes, "Farming is no longer something you can do if you drop out of school. It is a highly technical and business-driven occupation, and the skills to function in this reality are a must. It is an occupation that is chosen as a life career without the expectation of changing careers five or six times through your life as many other careers are. Farming is rewarding, but a very risky business with a high level of stress throughout the year. This should be a consideration one takes into account before making this career decision."

Nutrition ◆ The more you understand what making wise food choices does for you, the easier it is to feel better and still enjoy what you eat. Understanding the value of the key nutrients is only the beginning.

Physical Fitness ◆ Healthy internal organs and external body fitness make you alert and give you stamina. Physical fitness involves knowing what each part of the body is used for and how to take care of it. Most adults know more about taking care of their cars than their bodies.

Environment ◆ Environment related to wellness means recognizing how the space at home, at school, and at work affect you and your mood. Check for fresh air circulation, quality of drinking water, quality of lighting, waste disposal, and sound or air pollution.

Communication ◆ Communication refers to the exchange of information by talking and in writing, as well as the use of body language. Being aware of these aspects will remove the risk of being misunderstood when you are communicating. Well developed interpersonal skills go a long way in contributing to your state of wellness.

Your body movements can reinforce what you say to others. What forms of body language do you use when you speak?

Stress Management ◆ Some **stress** is important to keeping you active and productive. Stress exists in many forms and is, to a degree, individual. A busy schedule may leave a person feeling pressured and unable to cope. But that is not the only kind of stress the body endures. Lifting exerts stress on the muscles and heart. Digestion of some foods stresses the digestive system. Personal conflict gives emotional stress. The challenge of stress is to have the right amount and to know how to prevent burnout when there is too much stress in your life.

Responsibility for Yourself ◆ You need to take responsibility for all of your actions, including your wellness. To make wise, responsible choices you need to know your options and how each option will affect you. It is not helpful to point a finger elsewhere when something does not turn out as you wanted.

This text emphasizes three interrelated areas: food choices, physical activity, and body mass. In each area you have an opportunity to take responsibility for yourself and make changes that will contribute to your wellness.

1. Make nutritious food choices.

   Eating food to meet the body's need for nutrients is essential to maintaining good health. Patterns of physical activity affect food needs also. Your aim is to have the energy to do all the things you want to do and feel good while doing them.

   A car needs fuel for energy and oil to keep it running smoothly. It also needs to be maintained regularly to keep it working well and maximize performance. Similarly, you need to take care of your body by making informed choices so that you can be the best you can be.

2. Follow a pattern of regular physical activity.

   Physical activity is important because it helps maintain a normal body mass, muscle tone, and cardiovascular fitness. When the body operates at its peak performance level a person has better stamina and energy reserves for periods of stress. A physically active life will help give you vitality for anything that comes your way.

   The physical activities a person engages in depends as much on the person's attitude toward exercise as it does on available opportunities. But a person must have the will to make changes in his or her exercise pattern and continue exercising regularly.

   Exercise is an important part of your lifestyle choices. If you have a strong desire to include exercise in your daily routine, you will find a way. You probably know someone who was told to walk regularly to prevent a life-threatening emergency such as heart attack or stroke. Did that person start walking? Changing a routine is a matter of revising goals and setting priorities. You have an early opportunity to establish healthy lifestyle habits. Choose a physical activity that appeals to you. This way you will stick with it. You will be toning muscles and developing all the body systems that will make you more alert and effective in whatever you do. You will also be using up extra energy value of the foods you enjoy eating.

   Physical activity is an important part of healthy living. Name five sports or physical activities you enjoy.

3. Maintain an ideal body mass.

   An ideal body mass is something to strive for, but not at the expense of your wellness. It is far more important to feel good and enjoy an active life than to conform to some unrealistic model in a magazine. The ideal mass for you will depend on your body type and stature and will be, to a degree, inherited. See pages 367–371 for Weight Management.

Maintaining a reasonable body mass is important to your health. The risk of cardiovascular disease and diabetes increases in individuals having excess body fat. Too much body weight places additional strain on all organs, resulting in premature wear and tear. But people who are underweight because they do not eat enough will not be getting enough of the necessary nutrients to allow them to function at their best. Appropriate food choices are easily made by selecting from *Canada's Food Guide to Healthy Eating*. See pages 24–25.

## ACHIEVING AN ENERGY BALANCE

*Energy intake* depends on the energy content of the food. A kilojoule (kJ) is the metric unit for measuring energy content. (One Calorie is equal to approximately 4.2 kJ.) You determine your energy intake through the foods and beverages you select within the framework of *Canada's Food Guide to Healthy Eating*. The energy content of foods within each food group varies widely. This makes it easy to select foods with an energy content suited to your needs.

Energy expenditure depends on basic body needs and patterns of physical activity. **Basal metabolism** is the food energy (kJ) needed for the body to perform the basic functions that keep your body alive. For example, breathing, blood circulation, maintaining normal body temperature, and growth all require energy. The speed at which your body carries out these processes is known as your **metabolic rate**. Basal metabolism is based on more or less fixed factors, such as age, sex, body build, and rate of metabolism.

How do this man's energy needs differ from the energy needs of someone who works in an office?

Your total energy needs are a combination of basal metabolism and physical activity. Physical activity includes movement, such as walking, running, physical work, and recreational activities. A person whose schooling or job keeps him or her seated will require fewer kilojoules than one who depends on body strength to do a job. Recreational activities like racquet sports will use up more energy than cards or video games. The amount of physical exercise a person engages in is a personal decision.

What choices do you make?

• Walk to school or take the bus.

• Use the stairs or take the elevator.

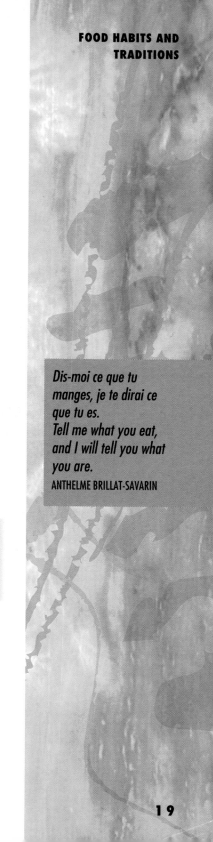

- Join a sports team or just "hang out."
- Swim or read a book at the beach.
- Go for a bike ride or watch television.
- Go to a school dance or play video games at the mall.

The more active choice will use more energy to balance energy intake.

ENERGY INTAKE ————  ———— ENERGY EXPENDITURE

CONSTANT
BODY MASS

Energy intake (food eaten) and energy expenditure (energy used) work like a seesaw or teeter-totter. They must be in balance to maintain a constant body mass.

To decrease body mass (lose kilograms), either decrease the number of kilojoules eaten (better choices, smaller portions, fewer extras) or increase exercise to increase energy used.

To increase body mass (gain kilograms), increase the number of kilojoules consumed.

It may be healthier to be more active, making a conscious effort to get more exercise, than to reduce the foods you eat and deprive your body of nutrients it needs.

*Dis-moi ce que tu manges, je te dirai ce que tu es.*
Tell me what you eat, and I will tell you what you are.
ANTHELME BRILLAT-SAVARIN

**Meal Frequency** ◆ *Canada's Food Guide to Healthy Eating* does not state a specific number of meals a day, nor does it suggest meal patterns. For good nutrition and vitality, food should be eaten throughout the day without long delays. A traditional "three meals a day" is perfectly acceptable, but there is no scientific reason to make it a rigid rule. The number and timing of meals and snacks depends on personal preferences. Meal frequency is a lifestyle decision.

KEY TERMS

Use the words listed below to complete the following statements in your notebook.

wellness          basal metabolism
ritual            taste buds
potlatch          prestige
satiety           symbol

1. To celebrate birthdays many families have a _____ of serving cake.

2. _____ is reached when you no longer feel hungry.

3. Certain _____ on the tongue are specialized to sense sweet or salty flavours.

4. Ancient cultures used food as a _____ to represent life.

5. Foods held in high regard by a culture are said to have _____.

6. A west coast Native practice that includes a lavish feast and gift giving by the host is called a _____ .

7. _____ is a term used to describe a healthy state of being.

8. _____ is the food energy needed by the body to perform basic functions.

FOCUS YOUR KNOWLEDGE

1. Briefly describe the conditions that controlled the availability of food for our nomadic ancestors.

2. List five historical factors that have affected your food habits.

3. Describe how religion plays a role in food habits.

4. What kinds of food symbolism have you noticed in your family?

5. Briefly describe three indications of an individual's wellness level

6. How is an energy balance achieved?

## ☀ DEMONSTRATE YOUR KNOWLEDGE

1. With a partner test your taste buds with sweet, sour, bitter, and salty foods. Create a diagram that shows which part of the tongue best senses each flavour.

2. Prepare a food that your family traditionally serves at a special occasion.

3. Prepare an open-faced sandwich that appeals to all of the senses. Serve it to a partner and have him or her evaluate the results.

4. Prepare a food that has a symbolic meaning. Give it to a partner. Have your partner determine the symbolic meaning.

## ☀ APPLY YOUR KNOWLEDGE

1. If you were to prepare a feast to celebrate a special occasion, what foods would you serve? Prepare a menu for your feast.

2. Analyze a television advertisement for food to determine which needs for food are being targetted.

3. Make a list of your food habits. According to the information in this chapter, determine which of these habits could be changed for the better. Prepare a realistic plan to change these habits.

4. Chart your physical activity for a week. Include any activity that burns energy for more than 10 minutes at a time.

5. In pairs, choose a topic that interests you both. In front of another pair of partners, communicate your thoughts on the topic to your partner. Use appropriate body language. Have the pair judge your effectiveness at communication. Then switch roles and evaluate the other pair.

# Personal Food Choices

## PERSONAL FOOD CHOICES

Most of the Canadian population has moved from rural to urban living. Fewer Canadians now work long hours in coal mines or on farms, or labour in forests or on the sea. Recipes from earlier times were rich and filling and supplied the food energy needed for hard, physical work. But lifestyles in this generation are seldom as strenuous.

Today people have a genius for inventing ways to save human energy and make life easier. Convection ovens cook more food in less time. Microwave ovens save time as well as electrical power. Prepared foods of all kinds reduce the time and effort spent in the kitchen. A dishwasher speeds clean-up. A change to an easier lifestyle with less hard work dictates that we learn to choose foods containing less energy, but supplying the nutrients needed by our body.

There are some excellent new cookbooks by well-informed authors that have recipes suited to healthier eating. Some include nutritional content along with the directions and number of servings. Often magazines and newspapers also feature healthy recipes. Some of your favourite family recipes can be altered easily to reflect your need for decreasing fat, salt, and sugar and increasing whole-grain and fibre content. Pages 88–90 describe this process.

Is your family's lifestyle as physically demanding as this family's? How does the difference affect your food needs?

Choose new recipes and cookbooks carefully. Some recipes that are quick to fix may not meet the nutritional requirements of your family. Any recipe that uses instant mixes, canned soups, frozen foods, or packaged seasonings must be considered carefully. Recipes using partially prepared and packaged foods are consistently more expensive than similar recipes made "from scratch" ingredients. They also often contain more fat, sugar, salt, and additives than you may want to use.

Statistics produced by government ministries and organizations, such as the Heart and Stroke Foundation of Canada, suggest that Canadians are *flunking foods*. More specific information can be found in Chapter 16, Health Risks and Food. Here are some areas where we can improve.

- 27 percent of the population is overweight.
- 15 percent of Canadians have highly elevated blood cholesterol levels.
- 43 percent of all deaths are caused by cardiovascular disease.
- One in four women over 60 years of age is affected by osteoporosis.

To improve the Canadian diet, a revised version of *Canada's Food Guide to Healthy Eating* was released in 1992. This food guide was the result of an extensive process involving consumer research and consultation with over 200 health-related organizations, including professional dietitians, nutritionists, and home economists. The guide is based on these specific guidelines from Health and Welfare Canada.

1. Enjoy a *variety* of foods.
2. Emphasize cereals, breads, other *grain products*, vegetables, and fruit.
3. Choose *lower-fat* dairy products, leaner meats, and foods prepared with little or no fat.
4. Achieve and maintain a *healthy body weight* by enjoying regular physical activity and healthy eating.
5. *Limit* salt, alcohol, and caffeine.

What guidelines from Health and Welfare Canada are these children following?

## YOUR FOOD GUIDE

*Canada's Food Guide to Healthy Eating* is a plan that helps you meet your nutritional needs by following a simple daily eating pattern. It is a reliable guide for nutritious eating for all Canadians aged four and older, with varying food preferences and lifestyles. It recommends that a certain number of servings be chosen daily from each of four food groups:

- Grain Products
- Vegetables and Fruit
- Milk Products
- Meat and Alternatives

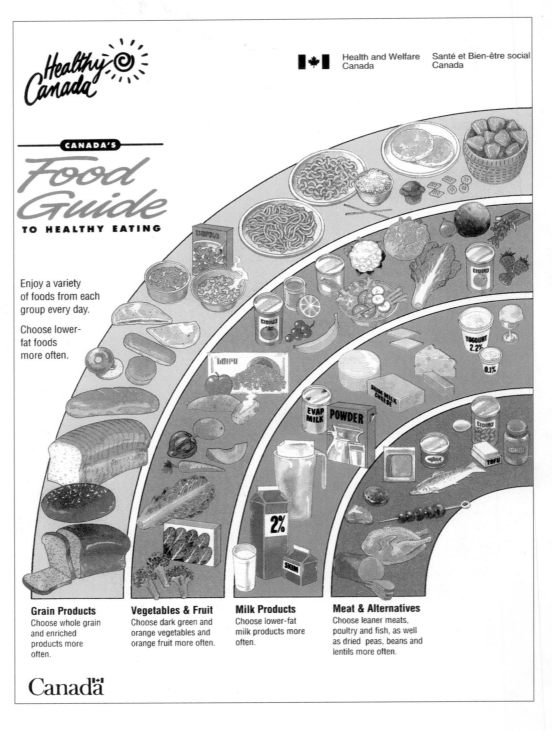

**Healthy Canada**

Health and Welfare Canada    Santé et Bien-être social Canada

**CANADA'S**

# Food Guide

## TO HEALTHY EATING

Enjoy a variety of foods from each group every day.

Choose lower-fat foods more often.

**Grain Products**
Choose whole grain and enriched products more often.

**Vegetables & Fruit**
Choose dark green and orange vegetables and orange fruit more often.

**Milk Products**
Choose lower-fat milk products more often.

**Meat & Alternatives**
Choose leaner meats, poultry and fish, as well as dried peas, beans and lentils more often.

Canada

**CANADA'S**
*Food Guide*
TO HEALTHY EATING
FOR PEOPLE FOUR YEARS AND OVER

### Different People Need Different Amounts of Food

The amount of food you need every day from the 4 food groups and other foods depends on your age, body size, activity level, whether you are male or female and if you are pregnant or breast-feeding. That's why the Food Guide gives a lower and higher number of servings for each food group. For example, young children can choose the lower number of servings, while male teenagers can go to the higher number. Most other people can choose servings somewhere in between.

**Grain Products**
**5–12**
SERVINGS PER DAY

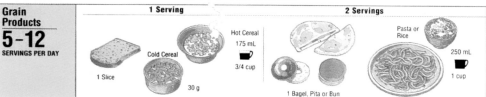

**Vegetables & Fruit**
**5–10**
SERVINGS PER DAY

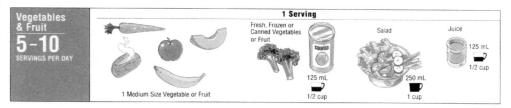

**Milk Products**
SERVINGS PER DAY
Children 4–9 years: 2–3
Youth 10–16 years: 3–4
Adults: 2–4
Pregnant & Breast-feeding
Women: 3–4

### Other Foods

Taste and enjoyment can also come from other foods and beverages that are not part of the 4 food groups. Some of these foods are higher in fat or Calories, so use these foods in moderation.

**Meat & Alternatives**
**2–3**
SERVINGS PER DAY

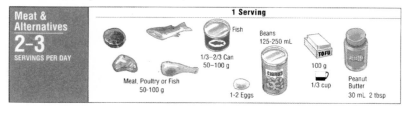

*Enjoy eating well, being active and feeling good about yourself. That's VITALIT*

© Minister of Supply and Services Canada 1992   Cat. No. H39-252/1992E   No changes permitted. Reprint permission not required.
ISBN 0-662-19648-1

These four food groups were chosen because of the amount and type of key nutrients each contributes. Together they form a pattern of good nutrition. Food groups are not interchangeable; each group supplies a particular variety of important nutrients. Because the body's major nutritional needs have been well identified by scientific research, and only certain food groups supply those needs, *Canada's Food Guide to Healthy Eating* simplifies making wise food choices. The number of daily servings from each food group depends on your age, body size, activity level, and whether you are male or female. That is why *Canada's Food Guide to Healthy Eating* gives a lower and higher number of servings for each food group.

*Checklist for Healthy Eating*

When evaluating the foods you eat, give careful consideration to each of these questions. Healthy eaters should be able to answer "yes" to each.

Do you choose a variety of foods from each of the four food groups?

Do you choose foods within the suggested number of servings for all four food groups?

Do you choose whole grain and enriched grain products often?

Do you choose dark green and orange vegetables and orange fruit regularly?

Do you choose lower-fat milk products regularly?

Do you choose leaner meats, poultry, and fish, as well as dried peas, beans, and lentils often?

Do you choose foods from the Other Foods group wisely?

*Like your skin and your nails, good lustrous hair comes from the fuel you feed your body. If you are eating a low-grade fuel (with lots of junk foods...) you are crowding out your appetite for foods your body needs.*
DIAN DINCIN BUCHMAN

## Key Nutrients in *Canada's Food Guide to Healthy Eating*

| Grain Products | + Vegetables and Fruit | + Milk Products | + Meat and Alternatives | = The Food Guide |
|---|---|---|---|---|
| protein | | protein | protein | protein |
| | | fat | fat | fat |
| carbohydrate | carbohydrate | | | carbohydrate |
| fibre | fibre | | | fibre |
| thiamin | thiamin | | thiamin | thiamin |
| riboflavin | | riboflavin | riboflavin | riboflavin |
| niacin | | | niacin | niacin |
| folacin | folacin | | folacin | folacin |
| | | vitamin B12 | vitamin B12 | vitamin B12 |
| | vitamin C | | | vitamin C |
| | vitamin A | vitamin A | | vitamin A |
| | | vitamin D | | vitamin D |
| | | calcium | | calcium |
| iron | iron | | iron | iron |
| zinc | | zinc | zinc | zinc |
| magnesium | magnesium | magnesium | magesium | magnesium |

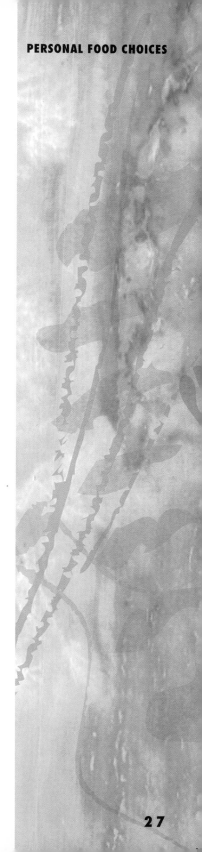

# MEAL PLANNING

There are many good reasons for planning meals and snacks in advance, whether for a day or a week. The main benefits are outlined on the next pages, followed by some guidelines on how to plan. Details on choosing foods that will provide a balanced and appealing combination in the meal are also discussed. For our purposes *meal planning* refers to choosing foods for a number of meals, extending over several days or even weeks. On the other hand, *menu planning* refers to combining foods to make up a single meal.

## Why Plan Your Meals?

1. To provide adequate *nutrition*.
2. To meet the special *needs* of each family member.
3. To control the *money* spent on food.
4. To save *time* and *effort* while shopping, planning, and cooking each meal.
5. To provide meals having more *variety*, colour, and visual appeal.

**What to Consider** ◆ Every meal-planning situation differs from the space used, to the equipment available, to the people being served. As you begin to plan meals for a day, a week, or longer, consider these factors.

1. Plan to provide sufficient *nutrients*.

   Good meal planning will ensure the best possible nutrition for all family members. *Canada's Food Guide to Healthy Eating* is the tool used to plan meals that will supply all the required nutrients.

2. Consider the *people* being served.
   - *Age* and *sex* of people eating.

     As a general rule, males need more food than females. Males have a higher metabolic rate and usually a larger body than females. Younger people require more food because they are growing, and most have a higher metabolic rate than older people. Younger people also usually have a higher activity level. Older people have a gradually decreasing metabolic rate and often are less active. There are many variations on this guideline. See foods for specific populations, pages 333–351, for more information.

   - Personal *likes* and *dislikes*.

     Liking the food you eat makes eating pleasurable. It is a good idea to include only one new food in a meal. This way family members will enjoy most of the meal even if they do not like the new food. Preparing food that is not eaten is a waste of food and the time and energy spent preparing it.

   - *Activity* level of people being served.

     People in some occupations will require meals with a high kilojoule value. Those who do work requiring physical stamina or who take part in active leisure activities need food that supplies more energy than inactive people do.

   - *Number* of people being served.

     When time, equipment, and help are limited, some recipes or kinds of foods are not practical to serve to large numbers of people. Some recipes do not adapt well to a reduction or increase in the number of servings.

   - Special *diets*.

     Any allergies or food intolerances should be considered. Certain foods may need to be restricted for medical or health reasons, such

How might this woman's metabolic rate differ from yours?

as heart disease, cholesterol, or diabetes. See details in Unit 5. There may also be ethnic or religious limitations on what foods can be served. For example, vegetarians and Buddhists do not eat meat; people of Jewish faith have strict dietary laws; and people of the Roman Catholic faith often abstain from eating certain foods during Lent.

3. Consider the *money* available in the budget for food.
   Within the family budget, money available for food is limited. Careful meal planning will stretch the food dollars from one pay period to the next. Sometimes a family includes money spent on eating out within its food budget. There are benefits to considering the money available for food prior to shopping.

   - Food choices can be made to stay within the food budget.
   - Planned shopping will result in minimum waste.
   - Use of foods already on hand, including leftovers, can be planned.
   - Costly spur-of-the-moment shopping can be reduced.

4. Plan to save *time* and *effort*.
   For people with busy lifestyles, food shopping and preparation time is limited. They spend less time in the kitchen than their ancestors did. Most prefer to spend their time doing other things, so using time-saving foods and techniques is popular. Being organized and planning ahead has advantages.

   - It saves time for other things you need or want to do.
   - Shopping can be done less frequently.
   - Everything needed to prepare a meal will be on hand.
   - With the decision of what to prepare already made, making it is easier and takes less time.
   - The required equipment will be available for use.

Business people often have little extra time for cooking. How could meal planning help this woman?

How to Plan Meals ◆ By planning weekly meals, it is possible to serve appetizing, nutritionally balanced meals, make better use of foods on hand, and make fewer shopping trips. Here are the steps for one method of meal planning. For meals to be balanced, they should include foods from three or four food groups.

1. Begin with dinner by choosing the protein food first, then grain products, vegetables, salad, and any appetizer, dessert, or beverage.

2. Next, plan lunch, keeping in mind the use of leftovers and easy-to-prepare foods.

3. Breakfast, the most important meal of the day, should include some form of protein.

4. After the plan is complete, check that the main considerations have been satisfied.
   - Nutrients — *Canada's Food Guide to Healthy Eating.*
   - Special dietary needs, limitations, and number of people.
   - Budget.
   - Available supplies, time, and equipment.
   - Colour, flavour, textures, shapes, temperature, and method of preparation.

Another way is to plan meals for several days at one time as shown in the accompanying diagram. This method would be used in a commercial kitchen or small food service facility, but it works well at home too. Try both to see which method you like best.

1. First, choose the entrees for dinner, lunch, and breakfast for each day from Meat and Alternatives or Milk Products.

2. Choose the starches from Grain Products or Vegetables and Fruit to accompany each of the entrées.

3. Choose required foods from the Vegetables and Fruit group.

4. Check that required Milk Products are supplied.

5. Choose any other snack foods.

6. Check to be sure the correct number of servings of each food group is included for each day.

7. As a last step, choose the condiments and beverages to go with all meals and snacks.

## MENU PLANNING

When deciding which foods to include in a meal, try to visualize what they will look like when served together. The attractive appearance of food stimulates the flow of digestive juices and in this way, prepares the digestive system to do its work. It also increases the enjoyment of a good meal.

# MENU PLANNING BY FOOD GROUP

| MONDAY DATE: | TUESDAY DATE: | WEDNESDAY DATE: |
|---|---|---|
| **Breakfast** Whole-grain cereal Bagel 1/2 grapefruit 2% milk | **Breakfast** Poached egg on whole-wheat toast Orange juice | **Breakfast** Yogurt and berries Bran muffin |
| **AM snack** Yogurt | **AM snack** Banana | **AM snack** Apple |
| **Lunch** Tuna on kaiser roll Cream of corn chowder soup Grapes | **Lunch** Cheese, bacon, and tomato on multigrain bread Carrot sticks Peach | **Lunch** Ham and pea soup Cheese biscuits Raw vegetables Raisin cake |
| **PM snack** Pear | **PM snack** Oatmeal cookies Milk | **PM snack** Taco |
| **Dinner** Beef stew Dumplings Coleslaw Ice cream | **Dinner** Curried shrimp Steamed rice Stir-fried vegetables Milk pudding | **Dinner** Pork chops Noodles Green beans Fruit salad |
| **Evening snack** Trail mix | **Evening snack** Popcorn | **Evening snack** Milkshake |

*Seven days without food makes one weak.*
ANONYMOUS

## What to Consider When Combining Foods for a Meal

### 1. Colour

Colour combinations are very important to the appetizing appearance of a plate of food. Colours need to be chosen carefully, the way a designer would combine colours for a room. A colourless plate of food, such as halibut (a white fish) with mashed potatoes and cauliflower is not appetizing. It could be made more interesting by substituting broccoli or carrots for the cauliflower and boiled potatoes with parsley garnish. At the same time repeated colours are not interesting; bright colours are better used as accents. Colours naturally associated with foods have more appeal than colours not natural to foods. Remember this when using food colouring for cake decorating.

How have colour and shape been used in making this plate of food look attractive?

### 2. Flavour

The goal is to achieve a balance of flavours: sweet, sour, salty, bitter, strong, and spicy. Avoid using two strongly flavoured foods at the same meal. One strong flavour, however, is desirable, and its appetizing aroma will heighten anticipation for the meal (curry, garlic, onion, ham, and cabbage). Bland foods tend to enhance strongly flavoured ones. Examples are plain rice with curry, macaroni with cheese, spaghetti with tomato sauce.

It is a good idea to avoid repeating a flavour twice in a meal, for example, lemon sauce and lemon dessert, or tomato in the salad and grilled tomato garnish. Also avoid too many sweet accompaniments in the main course. Most accompaniments, also known as condiments, add flavour to the meal. Some of these combinations have become traditional:

- Apples with pork
- Mint with lamb
- Lemon with fish
- Cranberries with turkey
- Soy sauce with tempura
- Mustard with ham
- Sambals with curry
- Sour cream with herring
- Chutney with meats

3. Texture

Contrasts of texture are always advisable: hard, soft, chewy, and crisp. Something crisp goes well with a soft food (green salad and macaroni casserole). Similarly, soups are often served with croutons or crackers. A further example is the combination of cooked and raw foods. Most people enjoy the crunchiness of a raw vegetable served with others that are cooked. It is preferable to have only one sauce, gravy, or condiment with a meal to allow it to be distinctive.

4. Shape

The shape and size of foods being served together should be varied. Peas, corn, and carrot rings served at the same meal can be unappealing, as are mashed potatoes and mashed turnip served together. Instead use larger pieces of carrot with corn or peas. Cut turnip in cubes before cooking or serve the potatoes baked whole.

5. Temperature

Contrast in temperature is also a consideration. Even on a hot day, a meal with something hot, such as muffins, biscuits, or rolls, served with a cold salad is enjoyable. In the same way, a cold salad is refreshing when served with an otherwise hot meal. The quality and flavour of most foods are best when served at the correct temperatures. Serving hot foods hot and cold foods cold also minimizes chances for food spoilage that can cause illness.

A hot stew and cold rolls provide a good contrast in temperatures. Think of three other examples.

6. Cooking Method

It is sometimes tempting to cook several foods the same way because it is quick and easy and minimizes clean-up. For example, put several foods in a frying pan and cook them separately or together or put the entire meal in the oven. This is an economical use of energy and utensils. The addition of an uncooked food, such as salad, will make the meal more interesting. Some meals will be much more appealing if a variety of cooking methods is used for different components. A familiar example of overuse of one cooking method is the frequent use by restaurants of the deep-fryer. Sometimes the entire meal is cooked this way leaving a similar flavour and texture to all foods as well as giving a high-fat content to the meal.

# CHOOSING FOODS FOR SIMPLE MEALS

**Breakfast** ◆ A breakfast that consists of a selection from at least three of the food groups is a good way to start the day. Some people who skip breakfast do not understand its importance. Others find it a monotonous and boring meal. Still others have difficulty finding time for breakfast, and if they are not convinced of its value, they will not make the time for it.

During an extended sleep period the functions and processes of the resting body slow down and require nourishment to get going again. Students will be more alert and have an improved attention span during the morning at school after eating a nutritious breakfast. After even a simple breakfast, adults feel better, are more alert, and work more productively. Children learn better at school and are more lively in their play if they have eaten breakfast. People concerned with weight control find a small meal eaten early in the day activates their digestive system and helps them to maintain a healthy eating pattern during the rest of the day. They are less hungry at break or lunch time and can more easily avoid the temptation to overeat.

The quality of a breakfast does not depend on how long it takes to prepare it. However, it should be nutritious enough to supply the nutrients the body requires. If breakfast includes a food that you enjoy, you will be more likely to eat. If you are presented with eggs as the only choice in your household and you do not like eggs, then consider an alternative food. Even leftovers from yesterday's dinner are better than skipping breakfast altogether.

What kinds of foods could you help a younger brother or sister make for breakfast?

Those who choose a highly sweetened baked product such as a doughnut, cinnamon bun, or Danish pastry with coffee or a cola drink may note a drowsiness or reduced energy level later in the morning. This is an indication of a drop in the blood sugar level that follows after eating a high sugar food. The role of **insulin** is to clear extra sugar from the bloodstream, and it is produced in response to eating sugar. When a high sugar food is eaten without other foods that take longer to digest, more insulin than necessary is produced. As a result, the blood sugar level drops lower than the normal level. You feel less energetic because you have less blood sugar available.

A better food choice is a slice of cheese or some form of milk with a less sweet bread product such as a bagel or English muffin. A valuable addition to this "breakfast on the run" is a piece of fruit or fruit juice. Any protein food takes longer to digest than a carbohydrate, and it extends the time over which the breakfast is useful to the body. This keeps the person alert.

If family members make their own breakfast, it becomes the responsibility of the food purchaser to ensure breakfast foods are available. Keeping a choice of good foods on hand that can be combined easily will be helpful. Some teenagers find themselves caught between fixing breakfast for themselves, helping younger members of the family make theirs, and getting to school on time. The following suggestions may be helpful.

## Breakfast Suggestions by Food Group

### Grain Products

Ready-to-eat cereal, cooked cereal, congee or jook, flummery, muesli.
Bread, muffin, biscuit, scone, English muffin, bagel, whole-wheat bun, whole-wheat crackers.
Waffle or pancake — may be heated in a toaster.
Sandwich.

### Vegetables and Fruit

Fresh fruit — apple, berries, canteloupe, grapefruit, grapes, mango, orange, tomato.
Fruit or vegetable juice, unsweetened — apple, grapefruit, orange, tomato.
Canned or frozen fruit, unsweetened.

### Milk Products

Milk — as a beverage (hot or cold) or poured over cooked or ready-to-eat cereal.
Yogurt — plain or combined with your choice of fresh fruit.
Cottage cheese.
Any of the above in a blended drink.
Cheese — preferably lower-fat varieties.

Pease-porridge hot, pease-porridge cold. Pease-porridge in the pot, nine days old.
NURSERY RHYME

## Meat and Alternatives

Egg — cooked in any of many ways or added to blender drink.
Peanut butter, nuts, seeds.
Cold sliced meats or leftover meat from another meal.

Here are some possible combinations for breakfast:

| | |
|---|---|
| Bite-size wheat cereal<br>2% or 1% milk<br>Fresh orange | Whole-wheat toast<br>Plain yogurt<br>Fresh or frozen berries |
| Ground-wheat crackers<br>Cheddar cheese slice<br>Grapefruit juice | Bran muffin<br>Skim milk<br>Green grapes |

Have you ever thought of these breakfast ideas? Try them.

Leftovers — macaroni and cheese, pizza, rice, stir-fry.
Instant breakfast made in a blender.
Grilled cheese sandwich.
Microwave cooked hot cereal.

How does what you eat for lunch at school differ from what you eat for lunch at home?

**Lunch** ◆ Lunch refers to a light meal that is not breakfast or the main meal of the day. Lunch is most often served around noon. You may eat lunch at home, at a restaurant, in the school cafeteria, or during a break between classes. Lunch can also be the meal eaten by a shift worker at any time during the day or night. The English practice of serving a substantial "tea" late in the afternoon might also be considered a lunch. In some countries, such as Italy and France, the noon meal is the main meal of the day, so this would be dinner not lunch.

Lunch should consist of approximately one-quarter to one-third of the nutrients and kilojoules for the day. It will be balanced if you choose foods from three or four of the food groups.

## Lunch Suggestions by Food Group

### Grain Products

Bread — whole-wheat, rye, multigrain, bran.
Rolls or buns — to be made into a bunwich or to accompany salad or soup.
Muffins — especially those made at home with less fat and sugar.
Biscuits, scones, pita bread, couscous.
Loaves made with nuts and/or fruit such as applesauce, banana, currants, dates, pumpkin, raisins.
Whole-grain crackers.
Rice, noodles, or other pasta.

### Vegetables and Fruit

Vegetable salad — with foods added from the Meat and Alternatives group.
Fruit salad — with foods added from the Milk Products group, such as cottage cheese or yogurt.
Vegetables (raw or cooked) — beans, bok choy, broccoli, cabbage, carrots, cauliflower, celery, cucumber, lettuce, peas, peppers, radishes, sprouts, tomatoes, turnip, zucchini.
Vegetable soups, borscht, gazpacho.
Vegetable juice.
Fruit juices — apple, grapefruit, orange, pineapple.
Fruit: *Fresh* — apple, apricot, banana, berries, grapefruit, grapes, kiwi, mango, melon slice, orange, peach, pear, pineapple, plums, pomegranate.
*Dried* — apple, apricot, currents, dates, figs, prunes, raisins.
*Canned* — cherries, peaches, pears, pineapple, plums.

Cafeterias often have fruit salads for sale. What are your favourite fruits at lunch time?

### Milk Products

Milk — preferably 2%, 1%, or skim.
Cheese — Many varieties can be put in sandwiches, on crackers, spread on celery, or served alone.
Cottage cheese or yogurt plain — used to make a dip for vegetables or fruit.
Creamed soups made with milk.
Chenga.
Pastizzi.

### Meat and Alternatives

Peanut butter — Spread on celery or whole-wheat crackers.
Nuts and seeds — Pack in tiny plastic containers.
Cold sliced meat — Wrap meat around a vegetable stick and secure it with a toothpick.
Hard cooked egg, frittata.
Cold, cooked chicken pieces.
Sardines, shrimp, prawns, cold, cooked fish (leftovers).
Baked beans, stew, meat soup, casserole — Pack hot in insulated container or heat in microwave before eating.
Combinations with grain products such as tuna roll, sausage roll, meat pie, Cornish pastie, quiche, pizza, sushi, spring roll, dolma, koufta.

### Sandwich Filling Suggestions

Meat — beef, chicken, pork, turkey, veal — Slice or chop and mix with salad dressing. Add shredded lettuce, bean or alfalfa sprouts, sliced tomato, cucumber, or zucchini.
Fish — tuna, salmon — Mix with salad dressing, add chopped celery, pickles, lettuce, alfalfa sprouts, sliced apple.
Cheese — Slice or grate with salad dressing. For variety add chopped nuts, chopped onion, crushed pineapple, applesauce, lettuce, sprouts, olives, or pickles.
Peanut butter — Use plain or with nuts, seeds, sliced apple, or banana.
Egg — Chop fine and mix with salad dressing. Add any of onion, celery, green pepper, bean or alfalfa sprouts, lettuce, grated carrot, grated cheese.

By using reusable lunch bags and containers, you will be taking action to create a better world.

**Lunch in a Bag** • When lunch is eaten away from home, as in most school and work situations, packing a lunch becomes an important alternative to eating out. People often find sandwiches boring or have insufficient time to prepare a packed lunch. However, the advantage of healthier food choices and lower cost over a purchased lunch make packing a lunch worthwhile. Bringing part of the meal from home and adding cafeteria foods reduces cost and may increase food value.

Here are some helpful suggestions for making packed lunches.

- Set aside a lunch-making area in the kitchen with needed supplies at hand. Include knives, cutting board, plastic wrap, wax paper, bags, small plastic containers, and insulated containers.

- Post a list of ideas on the inside of a cupboard door in the lunch-making area. Include your favourites, other family members' likes and dislikes, and any special food needs or restrictions. Attach a copy of *Canada's Food Guide to Healthy Eating.*

- Juice in single-serving containers can be frozen and placed in the lunch bag. It will thaw by lunch time and will keep the lunch cool at the same time.

- Instead of buying costly individual servings of yogurt or canned fruit, fill your own small container from larger containers or cans. Add fresh fruit to plain yogurt or prepare your own fruit salad. This is more economical than buying individual portions and is usually more nutritious. It is also more environmentally friendly. A very small freezer pack in the bottom of a lunch bag will keep these foods cold.

- Salad dressings for lunch box salads and small quantities of nuts, seeds, or dried fruit will travel well in small, clean, airtight containers.

- Pack the lunch carefully so it will still be appetizing when it is time to eat.
  * Put heavier foods at the bottom to prevent crushing.
  * Wrap each item separately to prevent mingling of flavours and odours.
  * Wrap moist foods such as tomatoes and lettuce separately and add to your sandwich just before you eat.
  * Place a serviette or tissue under rinsed vegetables or fruit to absorb moisture or place in a separate sandwich bag.

- Insulated containers are important to keep hot foods hot and cold foods cold.
  * For hot foods, fill container first with boiling water and allow to stand until the hot food is ready to be packed.
  * For cold foods, fill the container with cold water or with the food to be kept cold, and place in the refrigerator overnight.
  * Wash used containers with warm, soapy water, rinse well, and allow to air dry. If odour is difficult to remove, place 15 mL baking soda in the bottom and fill with hot water. Allow to stand for 30 minutes or more, then wash as usual.

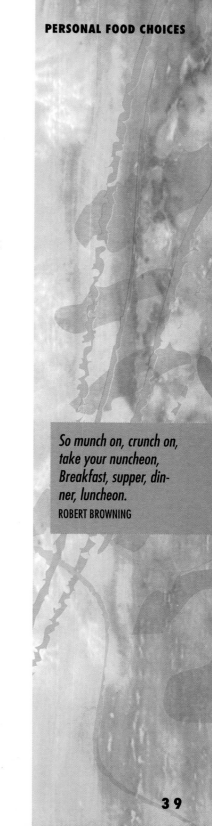

*So munch on, crunch on, take your nuncheon, Breakfast, supper, dinner, luncheon.*
ROBERT BROWNING

## CAREER SKETCH

Dr. Lawrence C.H. Wang, researcher

**D**R. LAWRENCE C.H. WANG was born in China and grew up in Taiwan. He earned his Bachelor of Science degree in Taiwan and his Masters and Doctorate in the United States. After teaching at the University of Oregon for one year, he immigrated to Canada and has taught at the University of Alberta for the past 22 years. He became a Canadian citizen in 1977.

Dr. Wang's current research interests involve energy metabolism and temperature regulation in cold climates. This includes exercise physiology, cold tolerance in humans, hibernation, and hypothermia. He is also interested in the influence of herbal compounds on learning and memory, ageing, exercise, and obesity.

Dr. Wang's interests led to 15 years of research trying to understand the metabolic processes that lead to hypothermia. He credits perseverance and self-confidence in keeping him on his career path. Dr. Wang was rewarded. The result of his years of research was the development of the "Canadian Cold Buster" food bar.

This food bar can provide energy to help keep your body warm in the cold. It is made chiefly with skim milk powder, honey, complex carbohydrates, chocolate, and cocoa powder. It is free of preservatives, artificial sweeteners, and artificial colouring. Each 38-g bar contains 640 kJ (154 Calories), with 3.8 g protein, 3.3 g fat, and 24 g carbohydrates.

After eating this bar a person has twice as much time to seek proper shelter or help before his or her body temperature reaches the dangerous level of 35°C and helplessness due to hypothermia. The bar was acclaimed by the Canadian Institute of Food Science and Technology as "the outstanding new food product for 1992."

Already Dr. Wang has realized his hope "that the bar would save just one life." In 1992 a dogsledder, travelling in sub-zero temperatures, fell into the North Saskatchewan River. He was able to walk the 2 km to shelter, losing only a very small amount of his body temperature, after consuming two Canadian Cold Buster bars. He was quoted as saying, "I'm sure I wouldn't have been able to make that trip if I hadn't eaten the bars."

Dr. Wang has published two patents, four books, and over 100 original scientific research papers in international journals. He has been invited to lecture in over 11 countries and has been recognized with numerous awards. He states, however, that "the most rewarding aspects of my career have been the discovery of new knowledge, and the ability to use such knowledge to create products to benefit humankind and improve the quality of life."

Packed Lunches for Children • Some students are responsible for preparing lunches for younger children. Making a child's lunch every day can be interesting. These comments may help a person faced with the task.

- The lunch bag can provide a link with home as well as show children the foods people eat to be healthy.
- If a child eats an inadequate breakfast, a nutritious morning snack and lunch are especially important.
- The packed lunch should provide about one-quarter to one-third of the day's nutrients for health, growth, and daily activities. Lunch will be balanced if it includes one serving from each food group.
- The food people eat affects their behaviour as well as learning. Hungry children have difficulty concentrating on schoolwork and tend to become restless and moody.

• Lunch cannot nourish if it is not eaten. To ensure packed lunches are eaten, do the necessary homework. Discuss what foods or combinations are favourites and which ones are not acceptable. Variety is important to keep lunch exciting. When children have foods on hand that they will eat, they can be encouraged to make their own lunches.

## Snacks

• **Snacks** are small amounts of food eaten between meals. To many people in Canada snacks, in addition to regular meals, are an important part of their eating pattern. A snack provides a "pick me up" when there is a long period of time between regular meals. Your energy level may be low late in the day indicating that your blood sugar needs to be replenished, much like a car needs additional fuel. Snacking is a big part of most social activities. Snacks are an important part of children's meal patterns since their smaller, growing bodies need more frequent small meals. Some people have special dietary needs for snacks, such as people with diabetes.

Snacks are so important to some people that they have developed a habit of **grazing** throughout the day. Grazing is continuous snacking on whatever foods are available when you are hungry. This pattern of eating can have serious consequences for health unless the foods available are good for you, because grazing involves no preplanning.

An apple is a healthy snack. What do you choose for your snacks? Are they healthy choices?

Snacking may satisfy other needs besides providing nutrients. For some people, snacks may provide relief from unhappiness, loneliness, boredom, or low self-esteem. The snack provides only temporary relief, no matter what food is eaten. Snacking for any of these reasons does not solve the problem. Professional advice is recommended.

Since snacks play an important part in the food habits of Canadians, we need to consider them when we choose foods that supply the nutrients we need using *Canada's Food Guide to Healthy Eating*. We should also be aware of the hazards of unplanned snacking. It is very easy to lose track of how much has been eaten when nibbling is continuous throughout the day. Snacks take the edge off your appetite so that it is difficult to recognize real hunger. Poorly managed snacking is a major cause of weight gain.

It is important to choose snacks that will meet a part of the daily requirement of *Canada's Food Guide to Healthy Eating*.

## Snacking Strategies

- Sometimes a glass of cold water is sufficient. Drinking water often reduces the feeling of hunger and is a healthy alternative to snacking. Most health professionals recommend drinking at least eight glasses of water daily to help cleanse the body. Enhance the flavour by adding a small slice of lemon or lime.

- Snacks should be regarded as small meals and should count nutritionally. They should be chosen from one or more of the four food groups. Most of the snack foods in the Other Foods category are not considered good for snacks as they are generally higher in fat, salt, sugar, and kilojoules.

- For the sake of healthy teeth, avoid choosing sweet, sticky foods as snacks.

- Space snacks carefully between mealtimes to avoid spoiling the next meal. Establishing a cut-off time for snacks before meals is a good idea.

- Some individuals who are irritable late in the afternoon find this problem reduced by having a suitable snack. Studies have shown that late afternoon is a peak period for accidents, child abuse, and behaviour problems associated with low blood sugar.

- Eat some of the foods you would normally eat at a regular meal as a snack. If you did not eat the fruit included with breakfast or lunch, eat it later in the day during a break or after school. Eating part of the meal beforehand is an idea especially helpful for feeding children. Offer a hungry child raw vegetables or a glass of milk while dinner is being prepared.

## Snacking Suggestions

- Keep a jug of cold water in the refrigerator.
- Keep cleaned, finger portions of raw vegetables in the refrigerator.
- Raw peanuts, cashews, sunflower seeds, etc. can be bought in bulk and roasted at home. The result costs less and eliminates a lot of salt.
- Try mixing raisins or currants with nuts and seeds. Dried fruits such as apples, apricots, figs, and prunes can also be a satisfying healthy snack.
- Use frozen orange juice concentrate instead of honey and dried fruit instead of seeds or nuts to make granola.

A glass of cold water is a refreshing drink. What other beverages can be part of a healthy snack?

## Snack Suggestions by Food Group

### Grain Products

Whole-grain crackers other low-salt crackers, puffed wheat.
Bran muffin.
Cornbread made without sugar, honey, or molasses.
Tortillas — Broken and used as dippers.
Pita bread.
Noodles.

### Vegetables and Fruit

All raw vegetables — with or without dip.
All fresh fruit — serve alone or combine in fruit salad.
Unsweetened canned or frozen fruit.
Unsweetened fruit juice or juice popsicles.
Vegetable juice.
Vegetable soups.

### Milk Products

Milk — 1%, 2%, skim, whole, buttermilk.
Eggnog — made with milk, eggs, flavouring.
Blender shakes — made with milk or juice, crushed ice,
    unsweetened fruit.
Creamed soups — good in a mug.
Yogurt or cottage cheese — eat plain or mix with fresh or unsweetened
    canned or frozen fruit. Make into a dip for vegetables by adding
    fresh or dried herbs, such as basil, curry powder, dill, garlic powder,
    parsley, to taste.
Cheese — all kinds. Use soft varieties to stuff celery.

### Meat and Alternatives

Eggs — hard-boiled, devilled, or pickled.
Cold meat — slices, cubes, strips.
Nuts — almonds, cashews, filberts, peanuts, walnuts.

*Did you know that Genghis Khan, the great Mongolian conqueror, believed the extraordinary bravery of his warriors was due to their regular consumption of yogurt?*
DAIRY BUREAU OF CANADA

Seeds — sunflower, sesame, pumpkin, pine. May be flavoured with spices.
Roasted soy beans.
Peanut butter (without sugar) — use as spread or vegetable dip.
Dried beans and peas — cooked garbanzo beans make good nibbles.
Mix with salad dressing to make a bean salad. Try cooked and
mashed for sandwich spread or dip.
Split pea or lentil soup.

*Combinations*

Taco, hot dog, hamburger, sandwich, pizza, samosa, and banh cuon.

| Energy Content of Some Common Snacks | | | |
|---|---|---|---|
| Common Snack | Kilojoules | Alternative Snack | Kilojoules |
| Doughnut | 980 | Plain muffin | 500 |
| Peanuts (125 mL) | 1775 | Popcorn, unbuttered (500 mL) | 450 |
| Ice cream (124 mL) | 565 | Frozen yogurt (30 mL) | 315 |
| Chocolate bar (56 g) | 1190 | Fibre bar (35 g) | 625 |
| Whole milk (250 mL) | 625 | Skim milk (250 mL) | 355 |
| Chocolate cake, iced (1 slice) | 1295 | Angel food cake, plain (1 slice) | 505 |

# MAIN MEALS

Canadians have a wide variety of eating patterns and styles. Some people have a main meal at the end of the work or school day. Others follow the practice of their ancestors in the country of their origin and serve the main meal at noon. A standard pattern of three meals a day is not necessarily the best, or only, acceptable meal pattern. Many people in Canada do very well on a pattern of more frequent, but smaller, meals.

Family traditions and lifestyles determine when the main meal is eaten. For someone working an evening shift, the main meal may need to be in mid-afternoon. If work extends late in the day or into the evening, the main meal might be eaten closer to bedtime or eaten at work. If a school serves a hot

Some families eat their main meal of the day together in the evening. When do you eat your main meal of the day?

*The proverb warns that, "You should not bite the hand that feeds you." But maybe you should, if it prevents you from feeding yourself.*
THOMAS SZASZ

meal at noon it may be a student's main meal of the day. It is usually still called lunch. Ageing citizens sometimes find having their main meal at noon agrees with their slowing digestive systems. It also eliminates sleep problems associated with going to bed with a full stomach.

For many people, no main meal is complete without meat, fish, or poultry. Others are strictly vegetarian and secure their complete proteins by eating combinations of foods from plant sources. In any case, the main meal of the day should supply approximately one-third of the body's energy needs for the day.

## EATING OUT

Generally restaurant owners are including healthier items on their menus. This is a result of a growing demand for fewer fatty foods and a wider choice of vegetables and high carbohydrate foods such as breads, pastas, and rice. Customers' wishes continue to influence what is available in many restaurants. For example, salads are often available in fast-food restaurants. Menus now offer more specialized foods: low-fat salad dressing, broiled chicken instead of deep-fried, salt-free foods, sugar substitutes. Some restaurants have a special designation for meals that are lower in fat, cholesterol, and salt and higher in fibre. In some cases ethnic foods have made contributions that are more healthy.

Despite these trends, eating in a restaurant can still be a challenge for health-conscious people. It is always a good idea to ask the server how individual items are prepared and what comes with them. It is now much more acceptable than in the past to ask for a substitution; for example, a baked potato instead of mashed potato. A careful reading of the menu will tell you what might be available in the kitchen as a substitute. If a tossed side salad is shown on the menu, it should be possible to substitute it for French fries. Sometimes a substitution will cost more than the original accompaniment, but if you will eat it and not the other, it is worth it. Sharing one meal is sometimes possible if two of you want to eat a smaller meal than the restaurant offers.

Here are some suggestions to ensure that the meal you eat in a restaurant is in keeping with the recommendations for healthy eating outlined by *Canada's Food Guide to Healthy Eating*.

- Request whole-wheat buns, bread, and toast. When garlic or cheese bread is served with the meal ask for plain bread or buns instead.

- Use butter sparingly or not at all on rolls or hot bread. To make it easier to resist, ask the server to remove the butter dish.

- Ask for skim or low-fat milk.

- Request that the dressing be served in a separate small dish on the side of the salad plate. Salads are not always nutritious or low in kilojoules. A Caesar salad, for example, offers only one vegetable and contains a lot of fat in the dressing.

- Look for "Heart Smart," "Low Calorie," or other special designations of healthier meal choices. However, do not assume a special designation will be better for you; it may not be. Evaluate the description or ask the server to describe the preparation.

A salad can be a healthy choice when eating in a restaurant.

- Many restaurants now offer vegetarian items on their menus, and some of these are healthy alternatives to the high meat protein, high-fat menu items.

- Order fish, poultry, or meats that have been broiled rather than fried or deep-fried.

- Request that sauces and gravies be served on the side.

- Choose a tomato-based sauce rather than a white sauce for pasta. White sauces are generally much higher in fat because they are made with cream. For the same reason choose a broth-based soup like chicken noodle instead of a cream soup.

- Ask for plain rice or baked potato instead of French fries. Use pepper and plain yogurt rather than butter and sour cream.

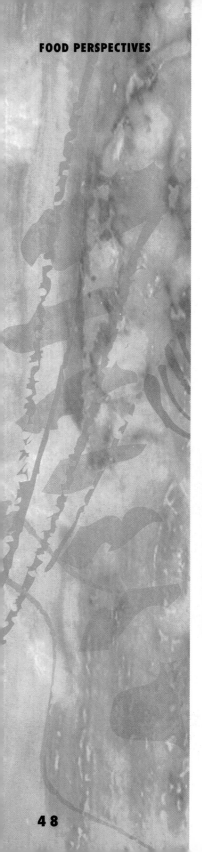

- Choose steamed or stir-fried vegetables rather than sautéed or deep-fried.
- When the portions served are large, consider leaving what you do not need. Some restaurants encourage guests to take home what they are unable to eat and will offer to wrap excess food. Ask the server to do it.
- For dessert, choose sherbet or frozen yogurt instead of ice cream, fresh fruit instead of fruit pie.

Unit 4 describes many foods and recipes that have been brought to Canada over the last 200 years by newcomers. As immigrant groups arrived and adapted their recipes in the new land, foods available in eating establishments also changed and expanded.

Menus presently offered to customers in restaurants and dining rooms across the country use descriptive terms that represent the rich food heritage of other nations.

**Understanding Menus** ◆ This chart lists some common terms found on menus that are of French origin.

| | |
|---|---|
| à la carte | item priced separately and served alone |
| à la king | food served in a rich cream sauce |
| à la mode | served with ice cream |
| amandine | with almonds |
| au gratin | with cheese |
| au jus | with juice, as roast beef with meat juice |
| au lait | with milk |
| du jour | of the day, as soup of the day |
| en brochette | on a skewer, like a shish kebab |
| en croute | meat or vegetable, cooked in a crust |
| flambé | with flames, served to the table flaming |
| Florentine | with spinach |

| | |
|---|---|
| fricassée | meat or poultry stewed and served in a sauce made with its own gravy |
| hors d'oeuvre | appetizer |
| julienne | cut in long, thin strips |
| table d'hôte | one price for the complete meal |
| vinaigrette | with vinegar |

## Reading the Menu

People who regularly eat away from home will have developed their own method of choosing from a restaurant menu. However, for many people eating in a restaurant is reserved for special occasions. For these people the wide assortment of available items and the way they are listed may be puzzling. In fact, reading an unfamiliar menu may be intimidating to anyone. Here are some suggestions that may help when you are next presented with a menu for dinner.

Rather than attempting to read the whole menu from front to back, look first at the entrées, or main course offerings. Look for headings such as From the Grill, Beef and Chicken, Complete Dinners, or the popular term, Main Course. In the accompanying sample menu from an actual restaurant you would check any of the headings from Keg Combos to Prime Rib.

If you have already decided that you want fish for this meal then you would choose from Seafood or Shellfish Classics without needing to read further.

It is important to know what will come with the main course you are considering. At the bottom of this menu it states: "All Keg dinners are served with fresh seasonal vegetables, sourdough bread, and your choice of baked potato, rice pilaf, or Keg fries." Your server will appreciate your having read this to be ready to state which of the three choices you prefer.

Some restaurants do not include vegetables with the dinner. They must be ordered separately from the menu à la carte. À la carte means the items are priced separately. An example on this menu is "Accompaniments." Sometimes the whole meal is priced and ordered that way.

The alternative term is table d'hôte. This means a complete meal offered at a fixed price. The price stated includes appetizer, main course,

"Then you should say what you mean," the March Hare went on. "I do," Alice hastily replied; "at least — at least I mean what I say — that's the same thing, you know."
"Not the same thing a bit!" said the Hatter. "Why, you might just as well say that 'I see what I eat' is the same thing as 'I eat what I see!'"
LEWIS CARROLL

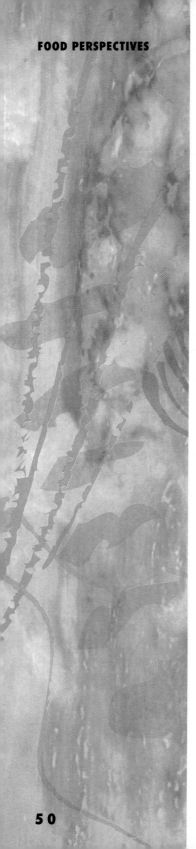

dessert, and beverage. Often this is the best value, but you may not be able to eat that much.

If you have a small appetite you may want to consider a salad with an appetizer instead of an entrée. Tell your server what you would like served to you when others in your group are served their main course. On this menu, the salad bar offers a variety that may be adequate.

Once the main course is decided, if you are able to eat more than the entrée you could consider an appetizer or salad. They will be listed on the first page.

Dessert may be ordered at the same time as the rest of your meal but you may later find you are too full for dessert. The server will usually be happy to return with a dessert menu when the main course has been completed. You can ask for details and choose then.

1. If reduced fat and fewer "empty" kilojoules are your objectives, the salad bar is a good choice, but select items wisely. Select unadorned vegetables and add a modest serving of dressing, or choose items with a minimum of dressing. Beware of hidden kilojoules in potato salad, macaroni salad, cheese.

2. In spite of the delicious flavour, this is a high-fat choice. The dressing, the croutons, and the cheese all contain fat.

3a. A food served *gratinée* means with addition of cheese.

3b. *Creole* indicates hot spices.

## SALADS

**1 Keg Salad Bar**
*Our legendary salad bar features fresh vegetables, fruits, mixed salads and our famous dressings.*
$3.49

**Caesar Salad** **2**
*Crisp romaine with croutons and freshly shredded Parmesan cheese*
$3.49

**Kids Salad Bar**
*Free for those under twelve years of age.*

## STARTERS

**French Onion Soup**
*Topped with Swiss and Parmesan cheese.*
$3.99

**Mushrooms Neptune**
*Six mushroom caps topped with a mixture of crabmeat, cream cheese and spices.*
$5.99

**Scallops & Bacon**
*Six bacon wrapped scallops with cocktail sauce.*
$6.49

**Hot Crab and Artichoke Dip**
*Crabmeat, artichokes, mayo, Parmesan cheese and spices. Served with tortilla chips or sourdough bread for dipping.*
$5.99

**Shrimp Gratinée**
*Pacific white shrimp baked in garlic butter and topped with melted cheese.*
$6.49 **3a**

**Escargot**
*Six escargot stuffed mushroom caps baked in The Keg's unique Cafe de Paris butter.*
$5.99

**Creole Gratinée**
*Pacific white shrimp baked in a spicy Creole butter and topped with melted cheese.*
$6.49 **3b**

**Potato Skins**
*Crispy skins topped with bacon and cheese.*
$5.99

## ACCOMPANIMENTS

**Mushrooms For Two**
$3.49

**Garlic Cheese Toast**
$2.99

## KEG COMBOS

4

### Steak & Lobster
*A 7oz sirloin, mesquite grilled, with a Caribbean lobster tail.*
*$22.99*

### Sirloin Oscar
*A 7oz sirloin, topped with shrimp, crab-meat, asparagus and Bearnaise sauce.*
*$16.99*

### Steak & Crab
*A 7oz sirloin, mesquite grilled, with Alaskan King Crab.*
*$21.99*

## SEAFOOD

### Salmon
*Mesquite grilled Coho fillet. Served with basil mayonnaise.*
*$13.99*

### Halibut
*Mesquite grilled, served with a sweet and spicy red bell pepper sauce.*
*$12.99*

5

### Seafood Fettuccini
*Scallops, shrimp and pasta in a creamy Alfredo sauce.*
*$11.99*

### Keg Sizzle
*Shrimp, scallops, chicken, and fresh vegetables sautéed in a teriyaki sauce. Served "sizzling" to your table over rice pilaf.*
*$13.99*

## SHELLFISH CLASSICS

### Alaskan King Crab
*One pound of steamed crab legs, hot butter for dipping.*
*$22.99*

### Caribbean Lobster Dinner
*Steamed and served with hot butter.*
*$24.99*

## CHICKEN & RIBS

### Teriyaki Chicken
*Marinated, mesquite grilled boneless breast.*
*$11.99*

### Chicken Oscar
*Topped with shrimp, crabmeat, asparagus, and Bearnaise sauce.*
*$14.99*

6

### Chicken Cordon Bleu
*Boneless breast, Black Forest Ham, Swiss cheese.*
*$12.99*

### Chicken Sizzle
*Grade A chicken breast strips and fresh vegetables sautéed in teriyaki sauce. Served "sizzling" to your table over rice pilaf.*
*$11.99*

### BBQ Ribs
*Half rack $11.99    Full rack $16.99*

4. *Béarnaise sauce* is made with melted butter thickened with egg yolks. Its characteristic flavour is achieved by adding a tarragon vinegar mixture.

5. *Fettuccini* is a broad-noodle pasta. *Alfredo sauce* has a cream base with cheese.

6. *Cordon Bleu* refers to the addition of ham and Swiss cheese. Sometimes the boneless meat, not always chicken, is wrapped around these ingredients.

7. Of the choices, the fewest kilo-joules are found in a baked potato. *Rice pilaf* is a tasty baked mixture of rice, seasonings, and finely chopped vegetables such as onions, celery, and green pepper.

### KEG CLASSICS

Keg steaks are aged to perfection, seasoned with Keg spice, then grilled over mesquite charcoal to sear in the natural flavour and tenderness.

**Keg Size Sirloin**
*Centre cut, top sirloin.*
*Served with sautéed mushrooms.*
*10oz $14.99*

**Keg Size Teriyaki**
*Marinated in our famous teriyaki sauce.*
*Served with sautéed mushrooms.*
*10oz $14.99*

**Keg Size New York**
*Naturally grilled with Keg spice.*
*Served with sautéed mushrooms.*
*13oz $17.99*

**Keg Size Prime Rib**
*The traditional cut. Served with*
*sautéed mushrooms.*
*14oz $18.99*

### GREAT STEAKS

**Sirloin**
*Centre cut, top sirloin*
*7oz $11.99*

**Teriyaki Sirloin**
*Marinated in our famous teriyaki sauce.*
*7oz $11.99*

**New York**
*Naturally grilled, with Keg spice*
*10oz $14.99*

**Peppercorn New York**
*Coated in black peppercorns and served*
*with peppercorn sauce.*
*10oz $15.99*

**Filet Mignon**
*Tender filet wrapped with bacon and*
*served with Bearnaise sauce.*
*$14.99*

**New York Steak Sandwich**
*Served open face on garlic bread*
*with sautéed mushrooms.*
*$10.99*

### PRIME RIB

Specially aged, seasoned and slow roasted.
Limited quantities are prepared to ensure top quality.

**Prime Rib Dinner**
*A Keg Tradition!*
*8oz $13.99    10oz $15.99*

7    All Keg dinners are served with fresh seasonal vegetables, sourdough bread, and your choice of baked potato, rice pilaf, or Keg fries.

8. This is an adaptation of the Mexican *Fajita*. You will need to spoon the hot mixture on the *tortilla* yourself and roll it together before eating. A tortilla is a large flat wheat flour pancake.

## SNACK & SHARE

### Hot Chicken Caesar
*Our delicious Caesar salad topped with slices of mesquite grilled chicken.*
$7.99

### Chicken Wings
*Plump wings, deep fried and tossed in a red, hot sauce.*
$6.49

### 8  Chicken Kajitas
*Grilled chicken breast sautéed with green peppers and onions. Served with assorted relishes, cheese and warm flour tortillas to wrap it all up.*
$12.99

### Nachos
*Crisp, hot tortilla chips covered with melted cheese, jalapenos, black olives and chopped tomatoes. Served with guacamole, salsa and sour cream.*
*For Two* $6.99
*For Four* $9.99

### Chicken Strips
*Deep fried in a crispy coating. Served with two dips.*
$6.49   *with fries* $7.99

### Caesar & Chicken Strips
*One order of our tender chicken strips served with a freshly tossed Caesar salad.*
$8.99

### Keg Burger Platter
*100% Grade A chuck burger, grilled and topped with lean, naturally smoked bacon, aged Cheddar cheese, lettuce, fresh tomato and red onion. Served with Keg fries and freshly tossed Caesar salad.*
$8.99

## KEG CONCLUSIONS

### Cheesecake
*Rich, thick and creamy! The Keg's own recipe, topped with fruit.*
$3.99

### Momentary Madness
*Unbelievable!!*
*Ask your server for details.*
$3.99

### Billy Miner Pie
*Mocha ice cream pie with hot fudge.*
$3.99

### Premium Ice Cream
*Ask your server for today's flavour.*
$2.99

### Coffee or Tea
*Freshly brewed decaffeinated coffee is also available.*
$1.29

*The Great Steak*  *and Seafood House*

Abbotsfort 10/93

## ☀ KEY TERMS

Use the words listed below to complete the following statements in your notebook.

meal planning    key nutrients
snacks    grazing
breakfast    lunch
*Canada's Food Guide to Healthy Eating*
menu planning

1. A plan that helps you meet daily nutrient needs is _____ .

2. Protein, carbohydrate, vitamin A, and iron are all _____ .

3. _____ refers to choosing foods for a number of meals.

4. _____ refers to choosing foods to make a single meal.

5. People will be more alert and have an improved attention span if they eat _____ .

6. _____ refers to a light meal often served around noon.

7. Small quantities of food eaten between meals are called _____ .

8. _____ refers to eating whatever is around when you are hungry.

## ☀ FOCUS YOUR KNOWLEDGE

1. In which four areas do Canadians need to improve their health?

2. List the five guidelines from Health and Welfare Canada on which *Canada's Food Guide to Healthy Eating* is based.

3. Explain briefly why it is important to plan meals.

4. Discuss briefly six considerations when combining foods for a meal.

5. Explain why breakfast is such an important meal.

6. Discuss with a partner why the time at which lunch is eaten may vary according to age, culture, or employment.

7. Explain why grazing may lead to health problems.

8. List ten strategies for healthful snacking.

**FOOD PERSPECTIVES**

## ☀ DEMONSTRATE YOUR KNOWLEDGE

1. In small groups, plan a menu for a nutritious bag lunch that includes the four food groups. Prepare the lunch.

2. List all the foods you ate last weekend. Did you meet the requirements of *Canada's Food Guide to Healthy Eating*? Make a list of healthy food changes and alternatives.

3. Prepare a nutritious breakfast for yourself that can be eaten "on the run." Include three food groups.

4. Prepare a poster depicting foods for one day's meals for yourself following *Canada's Food Guide to Healthy Eating*.

5. Plan a day's meals for yourself based on one of the methods described in this chapter.

## ☀ APPLY YOUR KNOWLEDGE

1. Change the given menus in a, b, and c to
   - Meet the nutritional requirements for a 15-year-old male.
   - Be varied in colour, texture, flavour, shape, and temperature.

   a.         Roast Chicken Breast
   Mashed Potatoes    Creamed Cauliflower
   Apple Sauce

   b.         Deep-Fried Shrimp
   Fried Onion Rings
   French Fries
   Apple Pie

   c.         Tacos
   Chili
   Gingerbread
   Cola

2. You are responsible for preparing lunch for your 12-year-old brother and 7-year-old sister. He dislikes vegetables, and she is a "picky" eater but loves finger foods. Plan a bag lunch menu that will accommodate both siblings.

3. Lien is an active gymnast trying to maintain her current body mass, but she loves to snack. Suggest snacks and snacking strategies for Lien.

4. With a partner, design and prepare a dinner menu using at least four of the French terms given at the end of the chapter. Add pictures of food from magazines to make the menu attractive.

# Unit Overview

## ☀ REVIEW YOUR KNOWLEDGE

1. As a class, brainstorm a list of special occasions celebrated throughout the year.
2. List five major factors to consider when combining foods for a meal.
3. Name six reasons for eating.
4. What is the body's reaction to eating a highly sweetened product such as a doughnut and coffee for breakfast?
5. Briefly describe two of the aspects that are part of achieving wellness.
6. In small groups, collect and mount photographs from newspapers and magazines that show the ways in which food affects people's lives. Include photographs from your community, Canada, and around the world.
7. What guidelines should be followed in preparing packed lunches for children?
8. Explain the difference between snacking and grazing.

## ☀ EXTEND YOUR KNOWLEDGE

1. As a class, plan a food drive to support a local food bank. Put the plan into action and donate the food.
2. Prepare a cookbook of cultural and favourite foods of your class. Sell the book as a school fund-raising project.
3. Research menus from countries other than France for their food terminology. Prepare a poster for each country with the accompanying food terms, for example,

   *Germany*

   en roulade          in a roll
4. As a class, survey the school cafeteria for foods displayed and commonly sold. Determine foods that are high in fat, sugar, and salt. Prepare a list of alternative nutritional foods that would be enjoyed by classmates.
5. Interview the school caterer, a snack vending machine owner, or a restaurant manager to learn the various aspects of the person's career. Discuss how the person tries to meet the nutritional needs of his or her particular clientele.

# Food Management

You have taken only one small step when you have decided what food choices to make for a family. Now the food needs to be prepared. Chapter 3 discusses such considerations as equipment in kitchens, how to manage space and energy, safety, and how to follow recipes.

Do you really need a pasta maker? How do you put out an oven fire? What does "fold" mean in a recipe? If you do not have chocolate squares can you substitute chocolate chips? Information in Chapter 3 will help you get the food to the table successfully, easily, and safely.

Chapter 4 will help you make smart shopping choices. What does the information on food labels mean? Should you shop at the corner store or the supermarket? Do you need a freezer for food storage or will the freezing compartment in your refrigerator be adequate? How can you keep food from going bad until you are ready to prepare it? Chapter 4 will answer your questions about food purchasing and storage.

Chapter 5 discusses table setting and service of food. Table manners are also included in this chapter because every culture has standards of behaviour at the table. The enjoyment of food can be spoiled if those sharing the food are not thoughtful of others while they eat.

# Kitchen Basics

## MAJOR KITCHEN APPLIANCES

The term major kitchen appliance refers to the principal appliances used in a modern kitchen, whether they are electric, gas, or propane. Appliances include a range or oven and cook top, refrigerator, freezer, and dishwasher. No doubt you will have a kitchen complete with appliances for your first cooking experiences. Because there are many different features on each appliance, the cook's first task is to master the use and care of the appliances available. Manuals that come with appliances are the best source for that information; they should be kept nearby for easy reference.

A person faced with purchasing a major appliance should invest time as well as money. Take the time to research the available brands, their features, and the advantages and disadvantages of each *before* spending the money. Be very clear about what special features are important to your needs.

## SMALL APPLIANCES

Some serious thought and a small amount of money can make a cooking area very efficient. Experienced cooks agree that of the available small electric appliances, the most versatile are a microwave oven, toaster oven, mixer, food processor, electric fry pan, and slow-cooker. A kitchen with major appliances is always more convenient by their addition. Even in a living space with only a sink and a small refrigerator, a person can prepare reasonable meals using only these appliances.

**Microwave Oven** ◆ Many people find microwave ovens convenient because they cook foods faster than conventional ovens. They are

Teens often prefer the convenience of a microwave oven over a conventional oven. How often do you use a microwave?

also easier to clean. Microwave ovens are useful for reheating foods and are especially good for cooking vegetables and fish. However, not all foods cook well in microwave ovens. For best results, read the instruction manual and the manufacturer's recipe book.

Toaster ovens are energy efficient for cooking many kinds of foods. Name five foods that you might cook in a toaster oven.

**Toaster Oven** ◆ A toaster oven does the job of a simple toaster, but can broil as well as bake small amounts of food. When cooking for one person, or cooking in a space without an oven, this appliance is especially useful. It also uses less energy than a conventional oven.

An electric fry pan has many uses, including frying, sautéing, simmering, panbroiling, stir-frying, and even roasting.

**Electric Fry Pan** ◆ In a living space without a range or cook top, an electric fry pan is indispensable. The electric fry pan's uniform heat is controlled by a thermostat. It can be used to fry, sauté, simmer, and panbroil. Turned low and with a high lid, it can also be used for roasting a large piece of meat or baking a dessert.

**Mixer** ◆ An assortment of simple hand-held and more sophisticated standing models of mixers is available. Portable, hand models are stored easily and perform a variety of lightweight mixing, blending, whipping, and beating jobs. A stand mixer is needed for mixing heavier combinations of ingredients, such as cookie dough, pastry, bread, and large volume recipes. Some brands have attachments, such as a blender, grinder, and slicer/grater. Stand mixers have powerful motors for heavy use and are more expensive than hand mixers. Many kitchens contain both. ◆

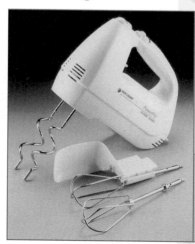

A hand mixer is a popular small appliance. Have you used one, or the larger stand mixer?

Food processors are popular in kitchens because of the wide variety of jobs they can perform.

**Food Processor** • A food processor is a machine that does most mixing, blending, grinding, cutting, slicing, chopping, grating, kneading, puréeing, or juicing jobs. There are full-size and compact models. Look for a powerful motor that will hold up under constant heavy use. This appliance is very useful for people who prepare a wide variety of homemade foods.

**Slow-Cooker** • Sometimes referred to as a "crock-pot," a slow-cooker is especially useful for students and working people. Raw foods with seasonings placed in the cooker early in the morning and turned to low heat will be a welcome hot meal by the end of the day. Most meals normally cooked in a pot can be created, including stew, roast, soup and variations, such as baked beans, chili,

Taking the time in the morning to put food in a slow-cooker means a hot meal waiting at home for you at the end of your day.

spaghetti sauce, curried foods, and fricassée. Because the meal can be left simmering in the pot, it is ideal for busy families when members eat at different times.

## KITCHEN EQUIPMENT AND TOOLS

Such a variety of cooking tools are now available that even a person very experienced in the kitchen will be surprised by the range of choices. The following are considered the basics.

**Knives** • In a well-designed knife the blade extends into the handle by at least half a handle length and is held in place by at least two rivets. The purchaser must decide what kind of steel blade he or she wants. Is it more important to have a sharp knife that can be sharpened easily or a knife that stays shiny and does not stain or rust when left wet? Stainless steel always looks nice but may not stay sharp. The steel used in a true chef's knife makes it expensive, but when properly cared for, it will last a lifetime. Visit a store that specializes in knives to see a full range and learn more about each kind. Then buy the best you can afford.

Cookware • A good pot has smooth flat sides and a flat bottom that fits one of the two sizes of stove elements. The pot and handle should be well balanced, and the pot should not tip over when the lid is removed. Lids should fit snugly, and handles should be strong and fit the hand comfortably. Check that handles and knobs are securely attached, usually with heavy screws and washers.

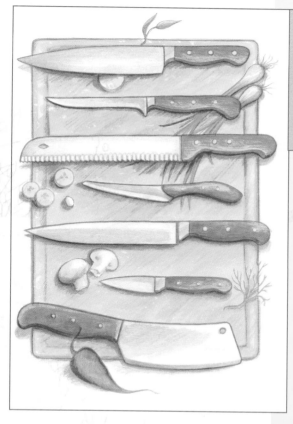

From top to bottom are: a chef's knife; a boning knife; a bread knife; a utility knife; a carving knife; a paring knife; and a butcher knife. Try to name a use for each.

The material used in manufacturing saucepans, skillets, and other cooking pots is important. Each has characteristics that influence heat conduction and ease of care and cleaning. Aluminum and iron are the best heat conductors. Stainless steel used alone will "spot burn" where the heat concentrates, but it heats more evenly if there is a bottom surface, or core, of a better conducting material.

Metals are combined to take advantage of the specific qualities of each. Aluminum is a highly satisfactory heat conductor that pits and stains. Stainless steel is easy to keep clean and shiny but is an uneven conductor of heat. A combination of these two metals produces a pan that has an aluminum exterior and stainless steel interior. It conducts heat well yet is easy to keep clean.

Within practical weight limits, the thicker the metal used the better the container. Cast metal is superior to pressed metal because there are

These are a few of the sizes available in one design of cookware.

no seams and pans can be sturdily constructed. Heavier cookware is more durable, the bottom does not warp, and heat is evenly distributed. Glass and ceramic materials chip easily, but they hold heat well. Be sure to reduce cooking temperatures by 10°C to 15°C when using them. Porcelain, heat-proof glass, and enamelware have become more popular with improved technology that reduces chipping, breaking, and spot burning.

Non-stick interior surfaces have been much improved over earlier coating formulas. The surface is now fused into the metal and is popular in fry pans, muffin pans, cookie sheets, and some saucepans. Fat is not required to prevent food from sticking to these surfaces, so they are very convenient for low-fat cooking. Utensils used for turning and stirring food on non-stick surfaces should not be of metal. Gentle treatment is recommended at clean-up time, and abrasive cleansers should not be used.

Bakeware ◆ Bakeware includes pans for cookies, cakes, muffins, pies, breads, and an assortment of specialty pans. What you need will depend on how much and what kind of baking you will do. The amount of baking time required for browning will depend on the pan used. For example, new, shiny pans will not brown, or burn, the product as quickly as a darker material. In fact, an older pan darkened by built-up food layers may tend to burn the product easily, unless the temperature or time is reduced. This is because shiny pans reflect the heat, while dark pans absorb the heat. Glass and ceramic pans are highly heat absorbent and will require a reduced oven temperature of at least 10°C.

Baking pans and cooking dishes used in a microwave oven need to be chosen carefully because most microwave ovens are damaged when metal is used. Most glass, ceramic, china, or pottery utensils without metal trim or metal glazing are suitable. Paper and plastic also work well for heating some foods. The shape of the pan or bowl may be important to the way the food cooks. Most recipes will give details.

Small Tools ◆ Some kitchens have many more graters, sifters, strainers, spoons, spatulas, tongs, and assorted special use tools than will ever be needed. These kitchens would operate more efficiently if only frequently used pieces were allowed to take up valuable space.

Which of these small tools do you recognize? Try to name them all.

A general guide for choosing tools is to buy for a specific purpose. Examine the individual pieces carefully for weakness of construction and presence of flaws to determine if they will be durable. Look for solidly secured handles and avoid materials, such as plastic, that melt when exposed to heat.

# KITCHEN MANAGEMENT

Management in the kitchen refers to how equipment and supplies are arranged for storage and how people use equipment, energy, and their own bodies to achieve the best results, in the least time, with the least effort. It applies to the kitchen you use at school, home, or work. This section has been arranged around these topics:

- Equipment Storage
- Body Mechanics
- Timesaving Work Methods
- Energy Conservation

**Equipment Storage** ◆ Even a well-equipped kitchen may not be efficient if its storage space is used poorly. When moving into a new home, there is a tendency to put away utensils and small appliances quickly, so that the counters are clear and the room looks tidy.

If you are not satisfied with the way your kitchen works, it may be because equipment and food items are not well placed. Begin by removing the contents from cupboards and drawers. Arrange items slowly with careful consideration of the reason for that particular placement. Be aware of the activities that will take place in the kitchen and where a worker will stand to accomplish each.

Some of these decisions are personal and may depend on your preference. You may prefer to wash dishes from right to left. If there is a dishwasher, then the decision of whether you work from right to left or left to right and where you

Where are the work centres in this kitchen? What would you place in the closed cupboards?

store items is more determined by where the dirty dishes will be stacked when they come from the table. If there is a view, or a television, or someone to talk to, you may want to do certain kitchen chores facing in that direction. As much as possible, place the equipment and supplies needed for each work centre (clean-up, baking, cooking, and food storage) in, or close to, that centre. Here are the generally accepted principles of good placement.

1. The most important principle is to locate articles at the *point of first use*. Placing articles where they will be needed, instead of where they have always been or where there is space, will save effort and time. Place the paring knives, vegetable peeler, colander, and electric kettle near the sink where they will be used with water. In the same way, plastic containers used to store food in the refrigerator might be located beside the refrigerator.

> Where would you store items in your cupboard to take advantage of the principles of good placement?

2. Locate articles within *sight* and *reach*. Place frequently used articles within your range of vision as you stand where you work and look up, down, and sideways, moving your head only slightly. Using large drawers for storing saucepans and food packages is another improvement. Seldom used articles can be stored where bending or reaching from a stool or ladder will be required. Done ruthlessly, this process may remove some bulky items from the kitchen altogether and free up valuable space.

3. Place items used most frequently within *elbow pivot range*. Imagine your hand and lower arm moving in a circle while your elbow is bent at your side. Items most often used should be within this circle. Items used less often can be placed within the *full arm pivot range*. This is the curve made by the sweep of your hands when your arms are out straight.

4. Consider how *heavy* the item is. Place heavier pieces within the curve made by the elbow pivot and lighter articles within a full arm's reach. Reaching out to lift heavy items can result in breakage, spills, and injuries.

## Body Mechanics •
Good lifting habits established early in life will serve you well over the years. They will protect you from injuries not only in the home but also in the workplace. A common-sense approach to using your body will reduce the chances of fatigue and contribute to effective work

methods. By using the principles of science you will be making body mechanics work for you.

1. Protect the natural spring of the spinal column. The backbone is shaped like an elongated S with individual bones, called vertebrae, surrounding and protecting an essential part of the nervous system, the spinal cord. Between each vertebrae is a disk of connective tissue that cushions each joint. Disks can be damaged by habitually doing work that is too heavy, working with the spinal column in a bent or twisted position, or lifting heavy objects with stretched or tense back muscles. One simple way to minimize heavy lifting is to avoid putting heavy weights on the floor. Place the load on a chair or counter instead.

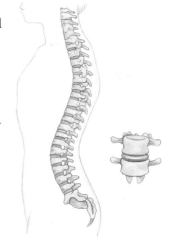

Disks of the spinal column protect your spinal cord, an essential part of your nervous system.

2. Keep the natural balance of your body. As long as your head, chest, and hip sections are in natural balance, one rests on the other with little muscular strain. When one of these major parts is out of line, as happens when you stand stooped, muscles, ligaments, and tendons need to work harder to hold the parts together. When a work surface is too low, the natural tendency is to bend to the work. Although tiring, it is far better to bend your knees than to work with your back out of line.

Bending at the knees when lifting is one way to keep the natural balance of your body while working. What other ways can you think of?

3. Take advantage of **leverage** and the force of gravity. Any tool used to pry off a lid is a kind of lever, and it makes the job easier than using the force of your hand alone. Here are some suggestions for protecting the body during heavy work that are based on the principle of leverage.

- Carry heavy items close to your body. This requires less force and applies less strain on the muscles and joints. The weight of a tray you carry is much like the weight at the other end of a seesaw.

Is this girl carrying the tray properly?

Compare the feeling of the weight of a tray carried close to you with the feeling when you carry it with your arms extended. It is easier to lift from a height that is near to the height of your elbow than from one that is higher or lower. Experiment carrying a heavy plastic bag of groceries at different heights.

- Push or grasp heavy weights near the centre of the heaviest part. For example, when moving a refrigerator from its position on the wall, place hands near the centre, not at the top.

- Use the large, strong muscles of the legs to move heavy objects. When you use the arms only, too much of the effect of the force is borne by the small muscles and ligaments in the lower back, which are not designed to withstand strong forces.

- Keep the body in its natural balance while you lift. When you pick up a heavy item such as a bag of groceries held close to the body, its weight is added to your own which tends to pull your natural balance out of line.

Timesaving Work Methods • Some people seem to know intuitively how to use timesaving work habits; others need to make a special effort to do so. Although in the home this is not always important, in a work setting it becomes essential to achieve efficient production. Here are the main principles to save work time.

1. *Omit* unnecessary tasks and motions. First review all phases of the job; then decide where steps may be simplified. For example, use a tray to carry dishes to and from the table, use a hot water rinse allowing dishes to air dry, or serve food in the dish it was cooked in.

2. Make use of *rhythm* in the kind and order of motions you do repeatedly. A skilled worker will have developed a system and will move from step to step smoothly by knowing the task from beginning to end. Valuable time and energy can be saved by doing this.

3. *Plan* to avoid undoing and redoing steps. By developing a good work method, later motions will not ruin the work of earlier ones. (When beating egg whites, your beater must be clean to get full volume. If you beat the egg whites first, then use the beater for beating yolks and other ingredients, you will save extra washing.) Sometimes rearranging equipment and food items as described in Equipment Storage on pages 65–66 may help.

Energy Conservation • Appliances, whether electrical, propane, or natural gas, use energy. This section deals with the conservation of that energy. Appliance manuals usually include suggestions for conserving energy. Some examples of energy conservation are:

- Prepare a large recipe and divide for future use.

- When using the oven to cook part of the meal, use it to cook other foods at the same time.

- Use ovenproof glass, ceramic, or earthenware dishes for oven cooking. Because these materials absorb and hold heat better than metal dishes, you can reduce the oven temperature by 10°C to 15°C.

- Do not extend preheating time of a conventional oven. Sometimes preheating is unnecessary. Turn the oven off for the last few minutes of cooking or baking time.

- To conserve electrical energy:
  * Use a microwave instead of a conventional oven.
  * Turn the burner off for the last few minutes of cooking.
  * Use a small electric kettle or the microwave to boil water rather than turning on a burner.
  * Use saucepans that have good heat conduction properties. See pages 63–64.
  * Use small appliances instead of large whenever possible. For example, instead of heating the oven to cook a small portion, use a toaster oven.
  * Avoid opening the oven door frequently to check on food being cooked. This allows heat to escape.

## SAFETY IN THE KITCHEN

Safety is essential whether in a commercial kitchen or at home. Care for details that seem small and even unimportant will go a long way toward preventing accidents. The other aspect of safety is knowing what to do if an accident does happen. Knowing general safety guidelines and basic first-aid procedures helps to reduce personal injury. Other preventive steps will help minimize equipment damage. Both personal injury and equipment damage are costly to an employer.

## General Safety Guidelines

1. Move in an unhurried, orderly way.

2. Keep kitchen traffic paths clear at all times and minimize clutter on counter tops.

3. Keep kitchen doors and drawers closed.

4. Keep pot handles turned to the back or to a protected side of the cook top.

5. Turn off burners and unplug appliances when not in use.

6. Check the safety of equipment. Never use pots with weakened or loose handles.

7. Keep kitchen poisons labelled clearly and out of reach of children.

## Preventing Fires

- Keep paper away from the cooking surface. Do not wear loose clothing that may come in contact with flame or burner.

- Never leave fat unattended when heating it or cooking with it. Control temperatures carefully. Smoke rising from fat means it is too hot. Keep small children away.

- Repair loose electrical connections and frayed or broken cords or plugs.

- To use a small electrical appliance, first plug the electrical cord into the appliance, then into the wall outlet. Always remove plug from the wall **before** disconnecting the cord from the appliance.

Different kinds of fires require slightly different approaches. If a fire does occur, general advice is to turn off the heat and cut off the air supply. Keep a small kitchen fire extinguisher nearby at all times. There are four kinds of fires that are a danger in a kitchen.

- Paper, fabric fires — Dowse with water or use an asbestos blanket to stamp out flames.

- Fat, oil fires — **Never use water**! It spreads the flames, which may ignite something else. Use baking soda, salt, or a chemical extinguisher to smother flames. Direct the fire extinguisher toward the base of the fire.

- Oven fire — *Never open oven door*! An opened oven door will let in oxygen, and the fire will gain intensity. Leave oven door closed and turn off the oven control.
- Electrical fire — Use a chemical extinguisher directed at the base of the fire.

## Preventing Burns

- Use adequate heat protection when handling hot containers. Potholders should be well padded and dry so the heat does not penetrate and form steam. Oven mitts are recommended when using an oven. A dish towel or apron is not adequate protection as it may touch a hot element and catch fire.
- Release steam from pots by lifting lid away from your body. Drain foods cooked in boiling water by pouring away from you, using both hands protected by potholders or oven mitts. Remove lids or plastic wrap from microwave dishes carefully so that steam does not hit your face or hands.

- When placing foods in a hot oven or testing or removing foods, open oven door completely and pull out oven rack to prevent your arms from touching the sides of the oven.

> If you do not protect yourself when releasing steam from a pot, you can burn yourself badly.

## Preventing Falls

- Wipe spills on the floor immediately to prevent falls. Moisture can be extremely slippery, especially if not expected.
- Use a kitchen ladder or well-balanced step stool to reach high storage areas.

## Preventing Cuts

- Store all sharp or pointed tools in specially designed holders or containers, near where they will be used.
- Never place sharp knives in the sink until they are to be to washed. Then wash individually, remove immediately from water, and dry carefully. Do not place sharp knives in the dishwasher. The heat of the dishwasher will destroy the **temper** (ability to keep a sharp edge) of the knife.

- Keep knives well sharpened so that you do not need to press hard when cutting.

- Learn how to use knives correctly, and use the right kind for the job. Cut with blade pointing away from you; carry with blade turned downward; pass with the handle to receiver.

# FIRST AID

## General First-Aid Principles in the Kitchen

1. Know the principles of first aid.

2. Post telephone numbers of a hospital, poison control centre, and fire department beside the phone.

3. Before beginning any treatment, be sure that there is no further danger to yourself or the victim.

4. Call the doctor if you are unsure about the seriousness of a burn, cut, or other problem.

5. Keep a small first-aid box in the kitchen.

## Treatment for Bleeding

- Cover with sterile or clean cloth.

- Apply direct pressure.

- If no dressing is available, apply firm pressure with your clean, bare hand directly over the wound.

- Continue pressure until bleeding stops. (This may take 15 - 20 minutes.)

- Help the victim to lie down and elevate the bleeding part unless a bone is broken.

- When broken bone, glass, or other object protrudes through skin, do not remove the embedded object. Instead, apply pressure close to the wound but not directly on the broken bone or object. Place sterile dressing around area covering wound. Maintain pressure without moving object while obtaining medical assistance.

## Treatment for Burns and Scalds

- Cool affected part by placing under cold, running water; then apply ice to relieve pain.

- Remove rings and bracelets before the affected part starts to swell.

- Cover with clean cloth and secure lightly with a bandage.

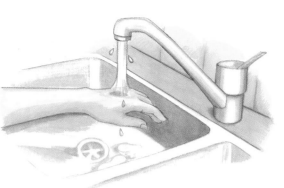

- To prevent infection, do not touch, or breathe, or cough on the burn. Do not open blisters.

- Never tear away clothing stuck to the burn as this could cause more damage.

- Never apply medications, ointments, or greasy substances, such as butter, to burn areas. This can make further treatment more painful.

- Obtain medical treatment for deep burns and scalds of areas larger than the size of a quarter.

If you burn your hand, immediately put it under cold running water. What other treatment should you give to burns?

## Treatment for Poisoning

- Call the poison control centre. The telephone number is usually in the front of the telephone book with other emergency numbers.

- Identify the kind of poison and its container. If required, call an ambulance and send the container and the remaining contents with victim.

- If the swallowed substance was non-corrosive and the poison control centre advises, induce vomiting after giving milk or water (adult: 1–2 cups, child: 1/2–1 cup). If the victim is unconscious, ***do not*** induce vomiting.

- If the substance swallowed was corrosive, ***do not*** induce vomiting. Give milk or water. Position the victim on his or her stomach with head to the side while waiting for help to arrive.

- For poisons that have contacted skin or eyes, flood area with cold running water for at least 15 minutes. Flush eyes gently as indicated on page 75.

## Treatment for Choking

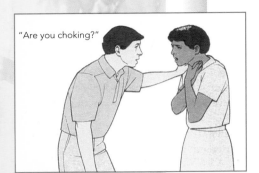

- Determine if the person is choking.
  - * Ask, "Are you choking?"

If the person is *not* choking
  - * Encourage the person to continue coughing.
  - * Continue to monitor the situation.

If the person *is* choking
- Shout for help.
  - * Summon someone who can help.
- Give abdominal thrusts
  - * Wrap your arms around the person's waist.
  - * Make a fist.
  - * Place thumb side of fist against middle of casualty's abdomen just above navel and well below lower tip of breastbone.
  - * Grasp fist with your other hand.
  - * Press fist into person's abdomen with a quick upward thrust.
  - * Each thrust should be a separate and distinct attempt to dislodge the object.

- Repeat abdominal thrusts until:
  - * Object is coughed up.
  - * Person starts to breathe or cough forcefully.
  - * Person becomes unconscious.

- If person becomes unconscious:
  - * If not already done, call Emergency Medical Services.
  - * Do a finger sweep.
  - * Attempt to ventilate if breaths do not go in.
  - * Give five abdominal thrusts.
  - * Repeat these three steps until effective or EMS or other trained person takes over.

NOTE
• • • • • •

Everyone should learn how to perform these steps for choking. Abdominal thrusts may cause injury if not done properly. Contact your local branch of The Canadian Red Cross Society for information on this and other first-aid techniques.

SOURCE: The Canadian Red Cross Society

## Treatment for Eye Injuries

- For all serious eye injuries, call the ambulance.

- For chemicals in the eye, wash eye immediately with large amounts of cold, running water for at least 15 minutes.

- If a foreign body gets in the eye, ***never*** rub the eye and ***do not*** try to remove the embedded material. Cover both eyes lightly with bandages. Contact the doctor.

# MEASURES

There are two kinds of measures, one for dry substances and another for liquids. **Liquid ingredients** are most accurately measured in a clear utensil having graduated marks on the side. Usually they are made of heat-proof glass. The top edge is curved into a pour spout, with the highest measurement well below the rim so that liquids will not spill. These are not suitable for measuring dry ingredients accurately.

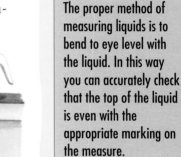

Liquid measures are available in 250 mL, 500 mL, and 1000 mL (l L) sizes with graduated marks of 25 mL or 50 mL, depending on the total volume of the measure. The measure should be filled to the appropriate mark while it *stands on a flat surface*, not held in the hand. A cook checks the level by bending until the eyes are level with the measurement line indicated in the recipe. To be accurate, the top of the liquid being measured should be even with the appropriate marking.

**Dry ingredients** are best measured using a standard set of dry measures. These measures have the full amount right at the rim for easy levelling. The measure should first be filled to overflowing and then levelled off with a straight-edged spatula or knife.

Sets of large dry measures come in 250 mL, 125 mL, and 50 mL. The smaller dry measures come in five sizes, usually attached by a ring, of 25 mL, 15 mL, 5 mL, 2 mL, and 1 mL. These are the only true metric measures.

The proper method of measuring liquids is to bend to eye level with the liquid. In this way you can accurately check that the top of the liquid is even with the appropriate marking on the measure.

A large set of dry measures contains 250 mL, 125 mL, and 50 mL. The smaller set contains 25 mL, 15 mL, 5 mL, 2 mL, and 1 mL.

Some suppliers have attempted to combine metric and Imperial volumes in one set of measures. These are inaccurate. For example, a dry measure may be labelled 1/4 cup and 50 mL. However, the 1/4 cup is actually equivalent to 60 mL and thus cannot be used to accurately measure 50 mL of dry ingredients. Generally, metric volume is about 10 percent more than the closest Imperial measure.

## MEASURING

Accurate measuring is very important to achieving a quality cooked or baked product, particularly fine cakes and special desserts. For quick breads such as biscuits, muffins, and pancakes, amounts can be approximated. Beginners are well advised to use accurate measurements until they learn where approximate measures will not jeopardize good results, such as in stews or salads. A more experienced cook knows this from years of practice.

In a commercial kitchen, accurate measurement is extremely important to maintain cost and quality control. An inferior quality product or unexplained increased costs will soon have an employer checking for the reason.

Measuring Flour • Improved milling techniques of recent years gives accuracy without sifting, for most recipes. Cake flour, however, tends to pack easily and when used for special desserts will require sifting. When a recipe calls for sifted flour, sift before measuring. For most recipes however, stirring the flour in its container before transferring to the dry measure is adequate. Fill the dry measure to overflowing and level with a straight-edged utensil.

Measuring Sugar • Granulated sugar is measured like flour, using a dry measure. When special recipes ask for sifted icing sugar, sift before measuring.

Brown sugar should be packed lightly in the dry measure before levelling off. If properly done, the sugar will hold its shape when turned out of the measure.

Measuring Oil • Oil is measured the same way as other liquids, using a liquid measure.

 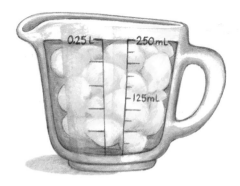

To measure 125 mL firm fat, place 125 mL water in a liquid measure. Add the fat in pieces until the water level rises to the 250 mL mark.

Measuring Shortening, Lard, Margarine, and Butter • Several methods can be used, depending on the kind and amount to be measured. Soft fats can be measured in dry measures. Press the fat into the measure to remove any air bubbles, then level off with a straight-edged utensil.

Firm fats can be measured by water displacement. Use a liquid measure a size larger than the amount to be measured. Place water in the measure to make up the difference between the fat required and the top level. Add pieces of the fat until the water rises to the top level without allowing any fat to rise above the water surface.

An approximate measurement of firm fats can be done by cutting a slice from the block, if the package has graduated marks for doing so. A 454-g block contains approximately 500 mL, and small wrapped table portions of margarine are about 125 mL.

## USING RECIPES

Recipes are written in many different formats. Some give detailed step-by-step instructions. Others merely list the ingredients and leave the method of combining them to the skill and interpretation of the cook. Beginners in food preparation are well advised to make use of well-tested recipes — from an instructor, a good recipe book, or a family favourite when you can receive help from home.

Developing an organized routine to any work in the kitchen is important for success. This is why it is important to follow a step-by-step routine with any recipe.

# Carrot Raisin Cake

## Standard Format

This format is most often used because it is easy to follow and takes the least space. Cooks can determine easily if all ingredients are on hand. Ingredients are listed in the order they are used and the step-by-step method of combining them follows.

| | | | | |
|---|---|---|---|---|
| 625 mL | whole-wheat flour | | 4 | eggs |
| 5 mL | baking powder | | 125 mL | sugar |
| 5 mL | baking soda | | 125 mL | vegetable oil |
| 5 mL | salt | | 625 mL | shredded carrots |
| 10 mL | cinnamon | | 250 mL | raisins |
| 5 mL | cloves | | 125 mL | finely chopped nuts |
| 5 mL | nutmeg | | | |

1. Stir measured dry ingredients together.
2. Beat eggs with sugar in a large bowl until fluffy.
3. Gradually beat oil into egg mixture.
4. Add dry ingredients to wet ingredients.
5. Stir in carrots, raisins, and nuts.
6. Pour into a greased 22-cm round cake pan or a bundt pan.
7. Bake at 180°C for one hour or until cake tests done.

## Active Format

This step-by-step format is popular and easy to follow, but it takes more space. Checking, at a glance, for the necessary ingredients is not as convenient.

*Measure and stir together:*

| | |
|---|---|
| 625 mL | whole-wheat flour |
| 5 mL | baking powder |
| 5 mL | baking soda |
| 5 mL | salt |
| 10 mL | cinnamon |
| 5 mL | cloves |
| 5 mL | nutmeg |

*If you are lazy and dump everything together, they won't come out as well as if you add one thing at a time. It's like everything else; no shortcuts without compromising quality.*
LIONEL POILÂNE

*In a large bowl, beat together:*

  4       eggs
125 mL    sugar

*Gradually beat in:*
125 mL    vegetable oil

*Add prepared dry ingredients to wet ingredients.*

*Stir in:*

625 mL    shredded carrots
250 mL    raisins
125 mL    finely chopped nuts

Pour batter into greased 22-cm round cake pan or a bundt pan. Bake at 180°C for one hour or until cake tests done.

### Narrative Format

Narrative format is written in paragraph form giving the ingredients along with the method of combining them. It works well for short recipes with few ingredients. This recipe would be very hard to follow using this format.

Measure and stir together 625 mL whole-wheat flour, 5 mL baking powder, 5 mL baking soda, 5 mL salt, 10 mL cinnamon, 5 mL cloves, and 5 mL nutmeg. In a large bowl beat together 4 eggs and 125 mL sugar. Gradually beat in 125 mL vegetable oil. Add prepared dry ingredients to wet ingredients. Stir in 625 mL shredded carrots, 250 mL raisins, and 125 mL finely chopped nuts. Pour batter into greased 22-cm round cake pan or a bundt pan. Bake at 180°C for one hour or until cake tests done.

# OVEN COOKING

**Conventional Oven (Radiant Heat)** ◆ In a conventional oven, the source of heat is an electric element or gas flame. When an electric oven is preheating, both the lower and upper elements are working. Once the desired temperature is reached, the upper element automatically shuts off, and a constant temperature is maintained with the lower element. If a pan of food is placed inside the oven before the oven reaches the set temperature, the top may burn. For broiling, the upper element only is turned on.

Place pans in the centre of the oven to allow an even distribution of heat. When the oven is crowded with food, the heat is unable to circulate properly and food will cook unevenly. Food closest to the heat source may burn. These principles apply to electric and gas ovens.

### Convection Oven ✦ 
In a **convection oven**, hot air circulates constantly heating the food and eventually cooking it. A true convection oven has no element or flame inside the oven. Air is heated behind the oven space and driven into the oven by a powerful fan. This means that the oven can be smaller and all the space can be filled to capacity. The oven needs to be preheated if the food requires a constant temperature, but if food is placed inside before the correct temperature is reached it will not burn. A convection oven cooks faster than a conventional oven but not as fast as a microwave oven.

### Microwave Oven ✦ 
Food in a microwave oven cooks when energy waves, called **microwaves**, make the food molecules move against each other and the sides of the container. The device that converts electricity into microwave energy in a microwave oven is the **magnetron**. The more powerful models cook faster than less powerful ones, but they all require less electrical power than other ovens. Generally, a microwave oven cooks in one-quarter the time of a conventional oven. However, it is impossible to estimate a time conversion accurately because, unlike a conventional oven, the greater the mass of food being cooked the longer the time required to cook it. A microwave requires no preheating. In fact, it should never be operated without food or liquid in it because doing so damages the magnetron. Damage also results when metal is used inside the oven. Covers and containers of plastic, paper, wood, and pottery and dishes especially formulated for microwave use are recommended.

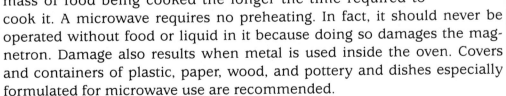

### Combinations ✦ 
Various combinations of these three types of ovens are now available. Be sure to read instructions carefully for the oven you are using. Directions for preheating, pan placement, type of containers, and timing will differ according to the heating program and features that you want to access.

Preparing to Cook ♦ The general steps to follow when preparing any recipe that requires oven cooking are outlined for you here.

1. **Adjust Oven Racks**

   The rack on which the pan or dish is to be placed should usually be in the centre of the oven for even cooking. Breads and cakes that will rise to a large volume, such as chiffon cake or yeast bread, should be placed on a lower rack so the product will bake evenly on all sides. In a true convection oven, there are no elements to worry about. The convection oven can be filled to capacity and still cook evenly. This makes it very popular in commercial kitchens.

2. **Preheat Oven**

   A convection or radiant oven should be turned on for some time prior to placing the food in it. This allows the oven to preheat, so that the product can be cooked at a constant temperature and timing can be estimated accurately. Some foods, such as a covered casseroles or slow-cooking, covered meat mixtures, can be placed into an unheated oven.

3. **Prepare the Pan**

   The recipe will usually specify the pan size and how to prepare it. If the recommended preparation involves coating the pan to prevent sticking, the following will help.

   - Butter and margarine brown rapidly at most oven temperatures. Using them for greasing may give an undesirable darkened crust or burned flavour. If a pale colour is wanted for the cooked food, use oil, shortening, lard, or one of the many spray coatings that prevent sticking.

   - A pan coated with a non-stick surface may not need to be greased. It will depend on the ingredients used in the recipe, particularly on the amount of fat.

   - Paper liners may be used instead of greasing pans for cupcakes or muffins. The paper may be hard to remove if the recipe is low in fat. An oil spray is a low-fat alternative to paper liners. Take care not to inhale the spray.

   - Pans for delicate butter cakes need to be greased and dusted with flour or the bottom lined with waxed paper.

   - Pans for foam cakes (angel food, sponge) are never greased and should be spotlessly clean so that the batter can stick as it rises up the sides of the pan. The pan is prepared by simply rinsing, then inverting it, until time to use.

*Pat-a-cake, pat-a-cake, baker's man,
Bake me a cake as fast as you can;
Pat it and prick it, and mark it with a B,
Put it in the oven for Baby and me.*
NURSERY RHYME

4. Assemble and Measure Ingredients

Gather all ingredients together before you begin to combine them. Correctly measured ingredients are an important factor to a successful product. Preparation time will also be reduced when you are more organized.

- At this time any missing ingredient can be obtained or a substitution made. If the recipe is for a flour mixture, correct substitution may be especially important. See substitution chart, page 87.

- Some flour mixtures lose part of their **leavening** power when allowed to stand. For example, beaten egg whites lose air and baking powder releases its carbon dioxide quickly. Muffin batter, especially, should be combined quickly and baked as soon as possible.

- Certain ingredients give better results when they are at room temperature. For example, solid fats combine with sugar more readily; egg whites will beat to a greater volume.

5. Combine the Ingredients

There are many different ways to combine ingredients. It is important to understand what the recipe means when it tells you to stir, beat, whip, fold, cream, or blend a mixture. These terms refer to the way ingredients are combined and the speed or intensity at which this is done. Use of the wrong procedure will affect the product. Here are some of the best known methods of combining and a description of each.

Stirring

- **Stirring** means to mix with a utensil. The basic stirring device is a wooden or stainless steel spoon, but a whisk, fork, spatula, or other similar utensil may be used. Stirring is used to combine liquids or to mix dry ingredients, separately or together, before the two mixtures are combined. It is also done to prevent separation of combined materials waiting to be used and to prevent sticking and burning during cooking.

- **Beating** involves the vigorous action needed to combine materials that tend to separate, to distribute air through the mixture, or to simply do the job in less time. It may be done with a spoon, fork, whisk, rotary beater, or hand mixer. Clearing the sides of the bowl regularly with a scraper or spatula is important.

- **Whipping** means to beat rapidly to incorporate air and expand ingredients, as in egg whites and whipped cream. A whisk, rotary beater, or hand-held or stand mixer is necessary for whipping.

- **Folding** means to gently combine two or more mixtures with a vertical motion, using a spoon or rubber spatula. A good technique is to tip the bowl slightly, holding it with one hand while folding with the other. Put the utensil through the mixture to the bottom of the bowl, pull it across and up to the top. At the end of the stroke raise the spatula and bring it back to the beginning just above the surface. Rotate the bowl slightly with each stroke.

  Folding is a technique used to combine ingredients such as beaten egg white or whipped cream with various batters or dry ingredients such as flour or sugar. Correctly done, the ingredients being combined may have some streakiness or other evidence of incomplete blending. Thorough or vigorous stirring will result in unwanted loss of air and a poor product.

Beating

Whipping

Folding

• **Creaming** involves mashing, stirring, or beating a solid fat (shortening, butter, margarine) so that it softens, absorbs air, and turns into a smooth mixture. One way to cream is to press the fat repeatedly against the sides and bottom of a bowl with the back of a spoon using a sliding motion. This process softens the fat by heat of friction, breaking down the fat structure, and mixing in air. Creaming is done frequently with an electric mixer at low speed. Batter needs to be removed often from the beater blades with a table knife or spatula as creaming continues. This ensures that all ingredients are combined fully.

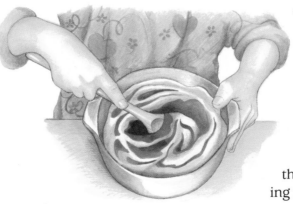

Creaming prepares the solid fat to mix more easily and completely with other ingredients, particularly sugar, which is added a little at a time as the creaming process continues. Simply warming the fat does not give the same results. Creaming is essential to obtaining a light batter with thoroughly dissolved sugar particles.

• **Blending** means to mix very thoroughly. It usually refers to combining ingredients that do not dissolve readily in each other. The process of blending until the two substances are completely into one another may take seconds or minutes, depending on the combination and on the mixing method. Any tool from a spoon to an electric blender can be used.

6. Place Into the Pan

Try to distribute the mixture evenly in the pan or on the pan so that uniform cooking can take place. As you place the mixture into the pan, avoid cleaning the spatula or spoon on the side of the pan. Wipe up any drips or spatters that fall where they are not intended. Clean-up is much more difficult once foods are burned on the pan.

- Push thick batters evenly up the sides and in the corners of the pan to produce a more level surface on the baked product.
- Fill cupcake pans only half or two-thirds full to allow room for expansion.
- Leave enough space between cookies to allow for expansion during baking.
- Allow room for yeast bread dough to double in bulk.
- Allow room for a casserole to bubble.

7. Cook

Cooking or baking times indicated in recipes are estimates and often include a range for suggested cooking times. Times will vary according to pan size, volume, altitude, temperature accuracy, and type of oven being used. Convection ovens cook faster than conventional ovens; microwave ovens cook much more quickly than either.

Check part way through the cooking time to be sure all is proceeding well. Do another test near the end of the estimated time to see if cooking has been completed. A good guide is to check when 80 percent of the total time has elapsed. In other words, if estimated time is 30 minutes, check when the recipe has been cooking for 24 minutes.

For delicate mixtures, such as soufflés or specialty cakes, maintaining a constant oven temperature is important to cooking time and product results, so if the oven must be opened it needs to be closed quickly. Most recipes will state how to know when a product is done. For those that do not, the following may help.

- Cakes will be golden browned and begin to pull away from the sides of the pan when done. A toothpick inserted near the centre will come out clean without dough sticking to it. A finger touched on top will not leave an imprint, the cake will spring back instead. Cupcakes and muffins can be tested in much the same way.

- Cookies will be browned and nearly firm in the centre. The more sugar used, the more quickly they will brown or burn.

- Bread loaves will be raised, gently browned, and will make a hollow sound when removed from the pan and tapped on the bottom.

- Casseroles and other mixtures containing liquid will be bubbling hot, and the individual ingredients will be cooked sufficiently to be eaten.

- Roast meat and poultry will have reached the correct internal temperature as shown on a meat thermometer. Cooked fish will flake easily.

> *The cook was a good cook, as cooks go; and as cooks go she went.*
> SAKI

**8. Serve or Cool**

Protect the surface under the hot pan with a hot pad or cooling rack.

- Some flour mixtures like muffins are at their best when served hot from the oven, others need to be cooled carefully to keep desired quality characteristics. Some may require further attention such as a glaze or frosting.

- Meat and other main dish foods should be served as soon as possible. The trick is to keep them hot and at optimum flavour and consistency until the remainder of the meal is ready to be eaten. Carefully estimating the time required to prepare other foods will keep the holding time of any hot food to a minimum.

- Allowing a cake to sit for 10 minutes before removing it from the pan allows steam to form at the bottom of the pan, which helps loosen the cake. Use a table knife or spatula to loosen the edges.

- Remove cookies to a cooling rack immediately or they may stick to the pan.

A good chef is not afraid to experiment with recipes. Have you ever adapted a recipe? What changes did you make?

## ADAPTING RECIPES

This section is included to help the cook decide what to do in a variety of circumstances:

- Healthier eating habits are desired.
- Dietary restrictions, such as low-sugar or low-fat, require recipe adaptations.
- The recipe makes more or less than the amount needed.
- Certain ingredients are not available or on hand.

The best cooks are adapting recipes constantly. This adds their own touch to the product. Let your common sense guide you when experimenting. The product may be different from the original recipe, but it may even be better and it will be yours. As you become more familiar with cooking, you will become more comfortable with adapting recipes.

For cooks wanting to improve the healthfulness of their baked products some guidelines are provided in

# Food Substitutions and Equivalents

## For Baking

| | |
|---|---|
| 5 mL baking powder | 2 mL baking soda plus 3 mL cream of tartar |
| 250 mL cake flour | 250 mL all-purpose flour less 25 mL (10%) |
| 250 mL sugar | 250 mL honey or syrup plus 2 mL baking soda with 50 mL less liquid |
| 250 mL sugar | 250 mL molasses plus 2 mL baking soda and omit baking powder |
| 250 mL honey | 250 mL molasses |
| 250 mL sour milk *or* 250 mL buttermilk | 15 mL vinegar or 15 mL lemon juice plus sweet milk to total 250 mL |
| 250 mL sweet milk | 250 mL sour milk *or* buttermilk plus 2 mL baking soda with 5 mL less baking powder |
| 250 mL whole milk | 250 mL skim milk *or* reconstituted powdered non-fat milk plus 7 mL additional fat, *or* 125 mL evaporated milk plus 125 mL water |
| 250 mL butter | 250 mL margarine |
| 250 mL butter or margarine | 250 mL vegetable oil less 25 mL (10%) |
| 1 square chocolate (30 g) | 45 mL cocoa plus 15 mL fat |
| 1 whole egg | 2 egg yolks plus 15 mL water plus 2 mL baking powder |

## For Thickening

| | |
|---|---|
| 15 mL flour | 7 mL cornstarch *or* 7 mL potato starch *or* 7 mL arrowroot *or* 10 mL quick-cooking tapioca |

## In Cooking

| | |
|---|---|
| 250 mL uncooked rice | 750 mL cooked rice |
| 250 mL macaroni | 500 mL cooked macaroni |
| half white onion | 5 mL onion salt and decrease salt by 2 mL |
| 1 medium white onion | 5 mL onion powder |
| 1 average garlic clove | 1 mL garlic powder *or* 3 mL garlic salt and decrease salt by 1 mL |
| 15 mL fresh horseradish | 30 mL prepared horseradish |
| 15 mL ginger root | 1 mL powdered ginger |
| 5 mL dried herb | 15 mL fresh, chopped herb |
| 1 lemon | 30–50 mL lemon juice *or* 10 mL lemon rind |
| 30 mL lemon juice | 15 mL vinegar |
| 1 medium orange | 100–125 mL orange juice *or* 30–50 mL orange rind |

SOURCE: Adapted from *Management and Foods*

the following pages to help reduce fat, sugar, and salt while increasing the use of whole grains. Knowing the function of an ingredient in a recipe will tell you whether or not a variation can be made and by how much. As a general principle, the finer the baked product, as in a fine-grained cake, the less easily substitutions can be made. That means that muffins and cookies are adapted most easily without failure. A chart giving the most frequently used substitutions and equivalents tells you what to use when an ingredient is missing. See page 87, Food Substitutions and Equivalents.

Other substitutions are a matter of common sense. If a recipe calls for chicken legs, you can usually substitute the same amount of chicken breasts. Or you can likely substitute pork for chicken. Once you are familiar with herbs and spices, you can substitute or add different ones. If you do not have cream on hand, use milk, but do not expect the result to be as rich. Do not be afraid to experiment.

Increasing Whole Grains ◆ There are many ways to introduce whole grains into a recipe. One is adding cereal, such as rolled oats, bran, or wheat germ, to a drop cookie recipe or to a meat or fish loaf. Whole-wheat flour can be substituted in a recipe calling for all-purpose white flour but with varying degrees of success. For example, whole-wheat flour makes a less satisfactory pastry or layer cake. Whole-wheat flour has less **gluten**, the protein that forms the structure in the product. A light textured bread is not possible, but as long as expectations are adapted, the resulting product can be perfectly acceptable. Many people prefer it. Whole-wheat flour makes good muffins, biscuits, pancakes, and cookies.

Decreasing Fat ◆ Fat is present in recipes for a number of reasons. In keeping with recommendations of health care professionals and *Canada's Food Guide to Healthy Eating*, we should reduce our intake of fat, including fat in baked products. Many cooks have experimented with their favourite recipes and discovered that an acceptable product results even with a drastic reduction of fat. Similarly, the type of baking fat can be changed with little trouble.

The main thing to keep in mind when making changes is to know the function of fat in the particular recipe. For example, in a pastry recipe the fat is important to the tenderness and flakiness of the product. Therefore, it is difficult to obtain a satisfactory product by reducing the total fat, although some variation in the kind of fat is possible. Margarine or shortening can be used instead of lard. Oil could be used but the method must be changed. In a muffin recipe it may be acceptable to cut the fat content by as much as a half. In any recipe that calls for fat to be melted, vegetable oil can be substituted successfully.

Decreasing Sugar • In most recipes sugar is present to give a sweet flavour. The amount can be reduced to your taste without difficulty. Other sweeteners, such as honey and molasses, can be used instead, but each form of sugar gives its own distinctive flavour. Most people agree that honey is sweeter than sugar so from a flavour standpoint it is more acceptable to use less honey than sugar.

Sugar used in baked products also helps browning. It **caramelizes**, when exposed to oven heat giving the product a golden brown colour that is considered desirable. If a pale colour is acceptable, then sugar can usually be reduced considerably. Try eliminating 20 percent to 25 percent and evaluate the resulting product. Always note changes made to the original recipe and the result, so that future use will be successful. However, it is unwise to reduce the amount of sugar by much in yeast breads since sugar is necessary for the yeast to grow.

Many commercial bakeries have reduced the amount of fat in their muffins. Try a taste test of a regular muffin and a lower-fat muffin to see if you can tell the difference.

Decreasing Salt • Eating foods containing less salt is a dietary restriction for some people and a general guideline for most Canadians striving for healthy food habits. The person responsible for meal preparation has considerable control over the salt content of the food. Individuals are then responsible for whether or not they add salt at the table during mealtime. You might try removing the salt shaker from the table.

As the cook you can easily decide to reduce salt in most recipes and eliminate it in many cases. Here again the decision of what to do is based on knowing the role of salt in a given recipe. When salt is used principally to enhance the flavour, the gradual reduction of the amount used is usually accepted easily by family members. For example, salt can be eliminated easily from recipes containing other seasonings and herbs. In boiled potatoes, however, it may be better to reduce the amount more gradually. In yeast bread recipes salt controls and slows the growth of the yeast and is important in attaining a quality product.

A conscious decision to use fewer foods containing a high-salt level is an option for the cook and for the food shopper. Processed meats, ham, canned meats, soups, and meal mixtures are especially high in salt and could either not be bought at all or be bought less often. Other processed foods tend to have high-salt levels. This is another reason to read labels carefully.

### Increasing or Decreasing Recipe Size

• Many recipes can be altered easily by dividing the recipe in half or by doubling the number of servings. Mixtures, such as salads, fruit puddings, casseroles, stews, and vegetable dishes, can be made easily in smaller or larger amounts. If you want larger amounts, multiply the recipe by the number required. A larger container will be needed, and if oven cooking is required, it will usually take longer to cook. For baked products, such as bread and muffins, pans will be the same size but more will be needed. Recipes for most baked products can be doubled successfully.

For smaller amounts, the recipe can be divided to produce the desired yield. If the recipe yields six servings and you want only two servings, then one-third of the quantity of each ingredient is needed. Because the quantity is smaller, the food can be put in a smaller container and it will cook more quickly. Some recipes cannot be adapted in this way, however. Baked products generally depend on exact amounts of each ingredient in relation to each other and unless it can be cut in half or thirds exactly, it is best not to make a smaller amount. How can you measure one-third of an egg? A better solution is to make the full recipe and then freeze for future use the portion that cannot be used immediately.

Be aware that the original recipe may not state the number of servings accurately. Unless you have made the full recipe at least once and carefully used portions of a size the recipe suggests, unexpected problems may develop. For example, you may spoon out larger mounds of cookie dough than the author of the recipe intended. The result will be fewer and slightly larger cookies. If your intent was to have one for each person at a large gathering or catered event, this variation may be critical. If the cookies are being made for children at home, the resulting larger cookies will be appreciated, but the children will have fewer of them.

Preparing food for a large family may involve doubling or even tripling a recipe. How might a recipe size be adapted for your family?

Consideration must also be given to the appetites of family members. If everyone likes stew and all members are hungry, the estimated number of servings indicated by the recipe may not be appropriate for the group you are serving. Serving sizes are average, but your idea of average and that of the recipe author may be quite different.

## Adjusting for High Altitudes • 

Recipes are developed for locations at low elevation. Consequently, ingredients and temperatures need to be adjusted for cooking and baking in mountainous areas. Roasting procedures do not differ from those at sea level. However, processes that involve liquid do because the boiling point of water gets lower the higher up you go. Depending on your location, you may need to increase the amount of liquid in your baking. You may also need to reduce the amount of baking powder and baking soda. For very high elevations (2100 m), sugar needs to be reduced and flour increased. If you live in a mountainous part of Canada, ask your teacher or consult a good cookbook for information about the quantities involved.

Oven temperatures may also need to be increased. For every increase of 1500 m altitude, increase baking temperatures by 6°C to 9°C. On the other hand, deep-frying should be done at a lower temperature. Since the boiling point is lower at high altitudes, candies, jams, and jellies will cook faster and must be watched carefully. Remember, too, that altitude will affect the accuracy of the gauge on a pressure cooker.

## KEY TERMS

Use the words listed below to complete the following statements in your notebook.

broil
cream
cost control
conductor
body mechanics

water displacement
aeration
quality control
sift
point of first use

1. A dark metal pan is a better _____ of heat than a shiny pan.

2. To save time and energy and prevent injury, use good _____.

3. If items are stored at _____ you will be more efficient.

4. To cook food using only the top element of an electric oven, set the oven to _____.

5. To accurately measure solid fat use the _____ method of measuring.

6. To dissolve sugar when making cookies _____ the fat and sugar together.

7. In a bakery _____ and _____ are important if repeat customers are wanted.

8. When egg whites are beaten _____ occurs.

9. To combine dry ingredients thoroughly _____ together.

## FOCUS YOUR KNOWLEDGE

1. List items that you have used under the headings kitchen appliances and kitchen equipment. Be prepared to share with your classmates the advantages of using each item.

2. Briefly describe how food cooks in a convection oven, a conventional (radiant) oven, and a microwave oven.

3. If you could choose only 10 hand tools for your kitchen which ones would you choose? Justify your answer.

4. Find five recipes where you think accurate measuring is important. Find five recipes where accuracy is not as important for good results.

5. Prepare a chart of safety rules for the classroom.

6. Develop a list of time- and energy-saving techniques to use when preparing a recipe of your choice. Share your techniques with your classmates.

7. Find a recipe for a simple casserole and describe ways the recipe could be adapted.

## ☀ DEMONSTRATE YOUR KNOWLEDGE

1. Measure flour before and after sifting. Note any difference in the amounts.

2. Measure solid fat using the water displacement method. Explain the principle behind what you are doing to a partner.

3. Select a method of combining ingredients and demonstrate to the class how you would perform the action. Include an explanation for your choice of equipment for that method.

4. Demonstrate how to carry a heavy tray without straining your back. Have a partner evaluate your performance.

5. Role play first-aid procedures for
   a. a cut finger.
   b. a burn on an arm.
   c. poison having been swallowed.
   d. a splash of a chemical in the eye.

## ☀ APPLY YOUR KNOWLEDGE

1. Determine the composition of a variety of cooking pots and pans. Prepare an organizer of the advantages and disadvantages of each. Include stainless steel, aluminum, aluminum with a non-stick coating on the inside surface, copper, tin, glass, cast iron, and enamel.

2. Using the information in this chapter rate your kitchen at home for efficiency. What improvements would you make?

3. Using the text's information on body mechanics, evaluate a classmate as she or he prepares a recipe.

4. Compare three different recipe formats for the same type of recipe. Which format is easiest to follow? Justify your choice.

5. Take a recipe for six and calculate how to adapt it to make two servings. Adapt the same recipe to make eight servings.

# Buying and Storing Food

## BUYING FOOD

The person responsible for buying food for the household shares in the responsibility for the health of its members. The best general advice available is *Canada's Food Guide to Healthy Eating*.

The purpose of *Canada's Food Guide to Healthy Eating* is to promote and maintain health among well people and to reduce the risk of nutrition-related diseases. It provides important messages about the kinds of foods to choose to achieve optimum health.

Foods that are not part of the four food groups, such as butter, margarine, oils, salad dressing, sugar, sweets, high-fat and/or high-salt snack foods, beverages, herbs, spices, and condiments are called Other Foods. They add to our enjoyment of healthy eating, but those that are high in fat, salt, and kilojoules should be used in moderation.

## Shopping Guidelines

- Plan meals as outlined on page 27.
- Review the foods needed by members of your household according to *Canada's Food Guide to Healthy Eating*.
- Make a list that includes a variety of foods from each of the four food groups.
- Before you leave home, review newspaper advertisements and weekly flyers. Check prices for featured items in the stores available to you and decide where you will shop. Some experienced shoppers go to several stores to take advantage of their special prices. However, the cost of travelling between stores, both in time and dollars, needs to be balanced with the savings achieved.
- You may want to eat before you go shopping. It will help reduce impulse buying that happens more often when you are hungry.
- Once inside the store, select foods from along the outside walls first. There you will find each of the food groups represented: Grain Products (bread), Vegetables and Fruit, Milk Products, Meat and Alternatives.

Busy shoppers find this a good way to be sure they get the most important foods on their list in the quickest possible time. Moving up and down the aisles takes much longer and may encourage more impulse buying. It is also where the more costly and less nutritious temptations are located.

- Consider buying staple foods from the bulk foods area. The price is usually less, and you can select only the amount you need.

- Consider choosing no-name or generic products that are packaged for sale in certain stores. The store you shop at may also have its own less expensive brand.

- Consider the value of using coupons. Using a coupon for a product that you want to buy saves money. On the other hand, using a coupon for a product that is not on your list may not be wise.

- Be aware of the psychology used in grocery stores to arrange products and create displays. Unless you are very determined to buy only what is on your list, it will be hard to resist other items.

Generic products are a good money-saving choice. What kinds of generic products have you tried?

## Shopping Tips by Food Group

### Grain Products

- Emphasize whole grains as you choose a variety of breads and grain products.

- Look for bread that has whole-wheat flour as the first ingredient. Unbleached flour or wheat flour is still white flour.

- Choose cooking cereals that are whole grain, such as rolled oats, any multigrain cereal, barley, kasha, or cracked wheat.

- Choose high-fibre cereals with greater than 4 g of fibre per serving. Boost the fibre content of regular cereals by adding high-fibre cereals.

If you were choosing whole-grain breads, which of these would you choose? Clockwise from top to bottom are: long loaves of French and Italian bread; round French bread; and Russian black bread.

- Choose low-sugar cereals. Read the ingredient list — sucrose, glucose, fructose, and honey are all sugars, and they should not be found as one of the first three ingredients. Aim for no more than 8 g of sugar per serving, the equivalent of 10 mL.

- Be selective. Most purchased muffins, granola, and granola bars have a high-sugar and fat content. Read labels carefully, or try making your own granola instead.

- Choose converted rice and brown rice which are more nutritious than plain white rice or instant rice. Avoid packaged mixes of rice or pasta. They are usually high in fat and salt and always more expensive than making your own mixture.

- Look for whole-wheat crackers and crispbreads, melba toast and rice cakes. Cut down on grain products containing saturated fat, such as hydrogenated vegetable shortening, coconut oil, or palm oil.

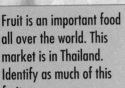

Fruit is an important food all over the world. This market is in Thailand. Identify as much of this fruit as you can.

### Vegetables and Fruit

- Fresh, local produce is a better nutrient buy than produce that travels long distances. Fewer nutrients are lost when the time from field to store is shorter. Produce picked when fully ripened is more flavourful than produce ripened while stored.

- When vegetables and fruit are not in season or not available, choose frozen ones. Because some vitamins and minerals are destroyed in the canning process and often sugar and salt are added, choose canned vegetables and fruit less often than fresh or frozen.

- Plain frozen vegetables and fruit are a better buy than packages with additional ingredients since the addition of sauces adds fat, empty kilojoules, and cost.

- Choose whole fruit instead of juice for maximum nutrients including the natural fibre.

- Buy fresh juice, frozen juice, or juice from concentrate. Products labelled "Cocktail," "Drink," "Beverage," "Punch," and "Nectar" are mostly sugar and water.

## Milk Products

- Choose skim or fat reduced (1% or 2%) milk and milk products. Check the expiry date.

- Increase calcium content by adding skim milk powder to foods such as hot cereal, ground meat, and sauces.

- Choose plain skim milk yogurt to mix with with fresh or frozen fruit instead of buying premixed combinations. Read fruit yogurt labels for added sugar and percentage fat content.

- If you are lactose intolerant, you can buy lactase enzyme drops or caplets to add to regular milk.

- Choose low-fat yogurt or low-fat sour cream as a substitute for mayonnaise or sour cream in dressings, dips, and baked products and use as an accompaniment or garnish.

- Choose lower-fat cheeses. Check the label for the fat content. Combine these with aged cheddar cheese in recipes to reduce fat but keep a strong flavour.

Milk products include milk, cheese, ice cream, yogurt, butter, and cream. Which milk products do you choose most often?

## Meat and Alternatives

- Keep in mind that an average serving of raw, boneless meat is 100 g, about the size of a deck of cards.

- Buy according to the number of servings per kilogram, rather than the cost per kilogram only. Consider the amount of fat and bone that will not be part of the cooked serving. For example, a round steak that serves six people may cost more per kilogram than a similar size chuck steak that will not serve as many people because it contains bone and fat.

- Choose meats with little **marbling**, identified by white streaks of fat in the red part of the meat.

- Choose the leanest sliced deli meats, such as roast beef, turkey, ham, and pastrami.

- Most fish is very lean. Good sources of omega-3 fatty acids, identified as a "good" form of fat, are found in tuna, salmon, mackerel, herring, and rainbow trout.

- Fresh shellfish prices vary by season and area. Compare carefully. Look for good values in frozen and canned shellfish.

Atlantic salmon is one good source of omega-3 fatty acids.

Beans can be a healthy meat alternative. Name the different kinds of beans you have tried.

- Choose meat alternatives regularly with two meatless meals per week as a guideline.
- Eggs provide valuable nutrients. Most people benefit from eating them in moderation (3 - 5 eggs per week) without any harmful rise in blood cholesterol. If blood cholesterol needs to be considered, try substituting two egg whites for a whole egg or use an egg substitute.
- Choose tofu as a substitute for meat in casseroles and stir-fries. There are a variety of tofu products, such as patties, wieners, and cheeses.
- Choose dried or canned beans depending, on your time and budget.
- Choose beans and lentils to use as filler in ground beef recipes like meat loaf and meat patties.
- Read peanut butter labels carefully to find brands without added fat and sugar.

*Fats and Oils* ◆ Although this is not one of the four major food groups in *Canada's Food Guide to Healthy Eating*, fats are the most concentrated source of kilojoules in the diet and a principal concern of health professionals. Canadians typically get 40 percent or more of their food energy from fat. Because of the number of diseases and other health issues associated with fat intake, dietitians recommend that people aim to have no more than 30 percent of their kilojoules from fat. Dietitians and nutritionists suggest the fat added to foods be limited to 30 mL per day. This includes butter, margarine, mayonnaise, and all oils, salad dressings, gravies, and rich sauces.

- Choose canola and soybean oils. They contain omega-3 fats which may reduce the risk of heart disease and cancer.
- Read labels carefully and look for soft tub margarines with a liquid vegetable oil listed as the first ingredient. Examples of vegetable oils are canola, soybean, olive, sunflower, corn, or safflower.
- Choose a margarine that has at least 6 g of **polyunsaturates** and **monounsaturates** per serving listed on the label.

### REMINDER
- Choose a *variety* of foods from each group every day.
- Emphasize whole-grain and enriched products.
- Select lower-fat foods.
- Choose lower-fat milk products.
- Choose leaner meats, poultry, and fish, as well as dried peas, beans, and lentils.
- Eat dark green and orange vegetables and orange fruit often.

**9 8**

- Choose margarines with the *least* amount of **saturated** and **hydrogenated** fats. Hydrogenation of polyunsaturated oil makes it saturated, with the same tendency to raise blood cholesterol as any naturally saturated fat from animals.

- Look carefully at label claims or advertisements of "cholesterol free." Cholesterol is found only in animal products, and, therefore, all vegetable oils are naturally free of cholesterol, but they are not fat free.

- To reduce the fat in your diet from salad dressings, try "fat-free" dressings or make your own from a low-fat recipe. Try mixing low-fat yogurt with these for a new flavour and reduced fat content.

- Choose light mayonnaise.

- Try light or diet margarines. They contain half the fat and kilojoules of regular margarine achieved by whipping and the addition of water. Diet margarines do not work as well in cooking and baking, however.

## FOOD GRADING

In Canada, agricultural products are graded and inspected to the benefit of everyone. Grading ensures that producers and processors are paid according to the quality of their production. Consumers obtain quality products that are nutritious, wholesome, and safe to eat. They are assured also that labels on the food accurately list the contents.

Grades are established and composition standards set by Agriculture Canada for a wide variety of foods: dairy products, eggs, meat, poultry, vegetables and fruit, honey, and maple syrup. Inspection of produce occurs at the time of production, packing, and distribution. Agriculture Canada inspectors also check all registered warehouses and packing plants to ensure that sanitary requirements are met for construction and operation. Many provinces have additional legislation similar to federal grading regulations, and they appoint Agriculture Canada inspectors to enforce them.

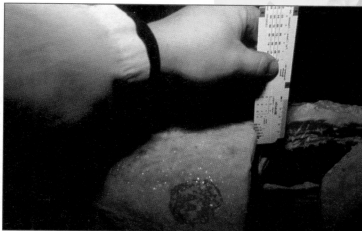

Beef is one category of Canadian food that is graded.

The handling and sale of food in retail stores is inspected by Consumer and Corporate Affairs. Checking for incorrect or deceptive labelling is also their responsibility. Labelling requirements are established by the Food and Drug Act and Consumer Packaging and Labelling Act.

The Meat Inspection Act controls inspection of meat and meat products. Federal veterinarians examine the animals before and after slaughter to ensure wholesomeness. All processing operations are regulated and inspected to meet rigid sanitary requirements. Federally approved meat and meat products are stamped or labelled with the round "Canada" meat inspection mark.

There are standards that apply to foods shipped from one province to another as well as to imports or exports. The word "Canada" on a product means that the food meets the quality standards of the "Canada" grade. Imported fresh vegetables and fruit may use this grade mark but must also be marked with the country of origin. For example, a product graded "Canada No.1, product of U.S.A.," was imported from the United States but meets the Canadian standard. Imported processed vegetables and fruit cannot be labelled this way when sold in the original containers.

Every graded food product has quality standards for the established grade designations. Specific grades, as they relate to the food under discussion, are noted in Unit 3 Chapters 6 to 10.

## FOOD LABELLING

Labels, which help consumers make their purchases, are regulated by the Consumer Packaging and Labelling Act. Every label on food sold in Canada must include the same standard information:

- Common name of the food.
- Quantity, stated by weight or volume, of the contents only.
- Name and address of manufacturer or distributor.
- Complete statement of ingredients, listed in decreasing order of proportion.

If the product is graded, the grade name must appear on the principal display panel.

Labels must list all food ingredients, seasonings, flavourings, vitamins, minerals, and additives that have been used. Nutrition labelling is voluntary in Canada, but for companies that choose to include it, there are guidelines. Health and Welfare Canada has identified a core list of standard nutrition labelling. It requires values per serving of:

- Energy
- Protein
- Fat
- Carbohydrate

Nutrition labelling can help consumers make sensible food choices, if they have an understanding about nutrition and healthy eating.

The amounts of vitamins and minerals are expressed as a percentage of the **Recommended Daily Intake** or RDI. It serves as a uniform standard to help consumers more easily compare the nutrient values of foods. The RDI is not intended to indicate actual needs of individuals. It was established as a reference standard for labelling purposes only. It is intended to give consumers an idea of the nutritional contribution that a food can be expected to make in their daily meals. Any nutrient claim must identify the serving size and its content.

Many companies are choosing to provide nutrition labelling on food packages, such as cereals or frozen dinners, in response to consumer interest. Good labels will provide a full nutritional profile, not just the values for the core list. Many of the ready-to-eat cereals and some whole-grain bread products are the best labelled foods to date.

## What Label Terms Mean ♦ *Nutrition Information* is the heading used for detailed nutrition facts about a product. The nutrients are always listed in the same order to make it easier to scan a label for information. Some food packages list only a few facts under Nutrition Information. Others, such as the example shown, provide more details. Once a label like this is understood it will be possible to easily pick out key pieces of information from almost any label.

*Serving size* indicates the size of a serving for which the Nutrition Information is given. If you eat more or less than this amount, the food energy and content of other nutrients, like fat and sodium, increase or decrease as well. When food is packaged as a single serving, the Nutrition Information is given for the single-serving portion.

Find the following information on this food label: Nutrition Information; serving size; energy; fat; carbohydrate; sodium; potassium; ingredients.

*Energy* is the kilojoules (kJ) or calories per serving.

*Fat* indicates the total amount of fat in one serving of the food expressed in grams. Sometimes the label also gives the content of various kinds of fat (polyunsaturates, monounsaturates, saturates, cholesterol). However, the most useful information is the grams of total fat.

*Carbohydrate* includes the content of sugars, starch, and fibre. The example shows a complete breakdown of carbohydrates. Sometimes information is given for only one type of carbohydrate.

*Sodium* is the measure of the amount of salt in one serving of the food.

*Potassium* is the measure of potassium in a serving of the food.

*Percentage Recommended Daily Intake* is the way information on vitamins and minerals is listed.

Read Labels With Caution ◆ A few nutrients like sodium and potassium must always be reported together on the label. Others, however, can be listed alone. Manufacturers need not report all Nutrition Information. They can highlight a positive feature, such as fibre content, but choose not to mention a high-fat content. An example: A package of crackers may highlight the product's fibre content but not mention a high-fat content. *Tip*: A good food choice is not determined by any one nutrient.

Nutrition Information is based on the foods as sold. Consumers must also consider what may be added before the item is eaten. For example, a cake mix sold as "cholesterol free" may be mixed with eggs and oil before baking and have an icing added afterward. These additions are neither cholesterol free nor low in fat.

Reporting Nutrition Information on a per serving basis can be impractical. For purposes of nutrition labelling, a serving of potato chips is 40 g. However, even the smallest bag of potato chips weighs 60 g. Rarely does a person eat less than the amount in a small bag of chips.

Nutrition claims must be accurate but can be misleading. Claims such as "low in fat," "high in dietary fibre," and "cholesterol free" must always be supported with facts about the amount of a nutrient in a serving of the food.

Nutrient claims have required limitations based on the Recommended Daily Intake for that nutrient:

• Source of — at least 5 percent

• High source of — at least 15 percent

  * For vitamin C — at least 30 percent

• Excellent source of — at least 25 percent

  * For vitamin C — at least 50 percent

A claim for any nutrient means that one serving supplies at least 5 percent of the RDI for that nutrient.

Products can be light in texture, taste, and colour as well as in energy (kilojoules) and fat. If the claim is made in reference to food energy, look for the fine print to see how much lower in food energy or fat it is. A product can be light in texture or taste but not reduced in fat or kilojoules at all.

A claim of "cholesterol free" or "no cholesterol" does not mean the food is low in fat. Only foods that have an animal source contain cholesterol. Foods made from vegetable sources such as vegetable oil can be very high in fat but contain no cholesterol.

A "fat profile" must be displayed in packaging or advertising claims related to cholesterol or a specific kind of fat. The profile includes information on:

- Total fat
- Polyunsaturated fat
- Monounsaturated fat
- Saturated fat
- Cholesterol

As useful as the complete fat profile may sometimes be, the total amount of fat is still the key factor to consider in overall healthy eating.

A nutrition claim of "50 percent less salt" means the product is *lower* in salt but not necessarily low in salt. Even a salt-reduced food can contain a lot of salt and be a high source of sodium. Because a claim for salt is made, the amount of sodium must be given. Read the labels carefully.

# FOOD ADDITIVES

Adding substances to keep food longer or improve the flavour has a long history in Canada. Early explorers carried meat packed in salt to preserve it. The use of spices to make the flavour more appealing or to hide the flavour of overripe or spoiled foods was a practice in early kitchens.

**Food additives** are substances that, when used in food, become part of it or affect its characteristics. As defined by Health and Welfare Canada under the Food and Drug Act, food additives do not include food ingredients (such as salt, sugar, or starch), vitamins, minerals, amino acids, spices, seasonings, and flavourings.

The use of food additives accounts for much of the variety in our food supply. Without them many food products could not be sold in their present form, and those that are available would be more expensive.

## CAREER SKETCH

WHEN ASKED what he was going to do with his life, Doug Bradshaw decided he might as well do something that he liked. He chose photography. During high school he set up a darkroom in his basement and developed his own black and white and colour photographs. With the ability to see almost immediately what he had captured on film, he began to explore his "school-world" through the lens of a camera.

Doug Bradshaw, food photographer

He pursued this career path and graduated from the Photography program at Sheridan College. Bradshaw began his career by assisting another photographer for one year, at no pay, to learn in a busy studio. He then freelanced for four years doing travel photography. This involved flying to various locations to "capture the flavour of the destinations." Back into studio work he photographed everything from large appliances to microchips. Gradually he moved into food photography and has specialized in this area for the past ten years. Among his major international clients are Campbell's Soups, Loblaws, Nestlés, and Pillsbury.

One of the things Doug Bradshaw likes most about food photography is working with highly talented people as a team during the photo shoot. From the client to the art director to the photographer's representative to the food and prop stylists to the assistants, everyone brings talent to the shoot.

Photographing food can involve as little as a couple of hours to take one photograph. Or it might take as long as three days or more. The process begins when the client needs to have a photograph made. An art director or designer helps the client decide what is needed for the photograph and how it would best be laid out. After the client approves the layout, the art director must then decide which photographer would be best for the job. The art director may call on a number of photographer representatives to submit photographers' portfolios. The art director and the representatives will talk about such things as pricing, schedules, and deadlines.

Once these aspects are agreed upon, the food stylist and prop stylist are brought into the project. They are given the information needed to bring whatever food or props are necessary. During the shoot a "stand-in" (a roughly put-together example of the product) is used to set up the lighting and technical aspects to get an idea of the image. At this point the client usually arrives and may suggest changes. Once everyone is in agreement with the look of the photograph, the real product is substituted for the stand-in as quickly as possible. Timing is crucial. The object is to capture the food at its peak, and some foods, such as ice cream, fade quickly. As Bradshaw states, "This kind of work is fragile. There are a couple of minutes when the food looks 'perfect,' then it's over." This is one of the challenges of food photography that he finds exciting.

Bradshaw compares food photography to performance art. The photograph is almost always different from his first concept. It evolves and takes on a life of its own. "There is nothing worse than being predictable. The work should always be fresh to yourself." Bradshaw always tries to find new ways to design and present his photographs. His aim is to make each photograph new, different, interesting.

Bradshaw has the following advice for students interested in this career: "Hang around a studio that specializes in food photography and is run by a very good photographer. Learn all that you can by the knowledge passed down. Food photography cannot be 'taught' to any great extent; it has to be learned by being around it, and by doing it."

According to regulation, food additives must meet one or more of these functions:

- Maintain nutritional quality of the food.
- Improve storage quality of the food.
- Make the food more attractive, but not in a deceptive way.
- Aid in food processing.

The Health Protection Branch of Health and Welfare Canada monitors and controls the use of food additives. Decisions are made as to what additives can be used, in what foods, for what purpose, and in what amount. Each decision is based on guidelines that have been firmly established.

Additives extend the storage life and make transportation possible over great distances for a wide assortment

The Health Protection Branch of Health and Welfare Canada carefully tests food additives.

of foods. This contributes to the variety of our food supply. The following list outlines some of the functions that food additives play in the Canadian food supply. Some of the functions listed do not fall under the strict federal definition. There are many additives not mentioned here.

## Functions of Some Permitted Food Additives

1. Additional Nutrients — Some nutrients are added to improve food value. Examples are vitamin D to milk, iodine to salt, iron and B vitamins to grain products, and vitamin C to fruit drinks. These are regulated by the Food and Drug Act and are not actually considered food additives.

2. Preservation — Preservatives reduce or eliminate food spoilage. Allowed preservatives are used to maintain the appearance, wholesomeness, and flavour of food, and play an important role in reducing food waste. Preservatives allow foods to be transported over vast distances and stored for extended periods of time before being consumed safely. Some prevent the formation of moulds, such as sodium diacetate in bread. Others are added to fatty foods, such as cooking oil and potato chips, to prevent rancidity or to fruit to keep them from darkening (butylated hydroxytoluene or BHT). Read more about food spoilage and food preservation on pages 111–116.

3. Colour Improvement — To make food more appetizing, artificial colouring is often added to replace colour lost during processing or to make a food substitute look more like the original, such as the addition of carotene to butter and cheese. Colouring agents are permitted in products like frozen and gelatin desserts, puddings, soft drinks, and margarine. Bleaching (chlorine) and maturing agents speed up the whitening of freshly milled flour making it possible to have a high quality flour quickly and consistently.

4. Flavour Enhancement — Flavouring agents added to some foods improve the natural flavour, making it tastier. Non-nutritive sweeteners are used to sweeten dietetic foods without contributing calories. Citric acid intensifies fruit flavour.

5. Maintain Texture — Texture modifying agents improve and control the desirable consistency of foods whether crunchy, smooth, chewy, or otherwise. Three main categories are allowed:

   • **Thickeners** regulate the consistency of foods such as jams and jellies and thicken others such as ice cream.

   • **Emulsifiers** permit tiny globules of one liquid to be dispersed in another, such as oil in vinegar for salad dressing. They also improve the volume, uniformity, and fineness of grain in bread and rolls.

- **Stabilizers** keep particles from separating from a mixture and settling to the bottom, such as chocolate in chocolate milk. They also prevent formation of ice crystals in frozen desserts (mono and diglycerides in ice cream).

6. Leavening — Yeast, baking powder, and baking soda are widely used in baked goods as leavening agents. They react chemically, releasing carbon dioxide into the product to give a light texture.

7. pH Adjustment — The acidity or alkalinity of foods is controlled by pH-adjusting agents. They are most often used for technological purposes during food manufacturing (sodium bicarbonate in baking powder).

8. Prevention of Caking — Anti-caking agents are used in many dry and powdered mixtures to keep them free running (magnesium carbonate in icing sugar).

## FOOD STORAGE

Nature has its own way of preserving some foods. Fruits like apples have skins to protect them from bacteria penetration. Grain seeds are dried thoroughly during ripening which makes them more resistant to spoilage and ensures the next grain crop. Other foods require more attention in their storage.

In the early years when every family was also a food-producing unit, root vegetables like beets and turnips were stored in a cold, dark place called a "root cellar" or "root house" to extend their storage life. Traditionally, fish fillets and thin strips of meat were placed in the sun and air to dry for later use. Alternatively, game meat and fish were buried deep under the snow in a simple version of a home freezer. The forerunner of the refrigerator was an ice-box, which held large blocks of ice that provided cooling for as long as the ice lasted.

Today there are a variety of techniques to hold food from season to season. Some of these methods allow food to be transported from places of abundant production to places of little or no production. This equalizes supplies in all parts of the country at all times of the year and provides a wider variety of foods at moderate cost.

Poorly stored food loses flavour and nutrient value and perishes rapidly. Most unrefrigerated foods keep best in a cool, dry place. If storage space of this kind is limited, buy these foods in smaller quantities.

This stone root cellar was built in the early 1920s in Calgary, Alberta.

## Refrigerator Storage

| Food | How to Cover | Approximate Time Limit | Comments |
|------|--------------|------------------------|----------|
| Milk, cream | Tightly | 7 days | Reseal tightly after each use. |
| Butter, margarine | Tightly | 2 weeks | Will absorb unwanted odours. Rancidity causes disagreeable flavours. |
| Eggs, in shell | Loosely | Several weeks | Moisture evaporates through the shell if air is dry or warm. Deteriorates quickly at room temperature. |
| Egg yolks | Tightly | 2–3 days | Cover with water to store. |
| Egg whites | Tightly | 1 week | |
| Cheeses<br>Unripened:<br>Soft and semi-soft varieties | Loosely | 3 days | Use promptly before quality is lost. Spoilage begins quickly. |
| Ripened:<br>Hard,<br>Very hard | Tightly | Several weeks | These keep well when not exposed to the air. Keep in original wrapper; after opening cover with foil, airtight wax paper, or plastic film wrap. |
| Process spreads | Tightly | Several weeks | Keep in jars. |
| Meats<br>Small cuts,<br>organ meats | Loosely | 2 days | Remove original wrapping. Cover loosely to permit some evaporation and drying of surface to discourage bacterial growth. For pork cuts, storage time is somewhat shorter. |
| Large cuts, beef, lamb, veal | Loosely | 1 week | |
| Cold cuts | Loosely | 6 days | Leave in original wrapper. |
| Ground meat | Loosely | 1–2 days | |
| Cured meat | Loosely | 7–10 days | |
| Fish | Tightly | 1–2 days | Use promptly. Fish spoils quickly. |
| Poultry, fresh | Loosely | 2–3 days | Same as meat. Remove giblets. |
| Poultry, cooked | Tightly | 2–4 days | Remove any stuffing and store separately. |

| | | | |
|---|---|---|---|
| Fresh fruits:<br>Citrus juices | Tightly | 2–3 days | Deterioration in flavour starts after 24 hours. |
| Berries | Uncovered; spread out | 2 days | Deteriorate rapidly. Do not wash or stem. |
| Apples | Uncovered | 3 weeks (keep dry) | Some varieties of apples may be kept for months. Keep in perforated plastic bags or vegetable crispers. |
| Pears and peaches | Uncovered | 3 weeks | Protect from bruises. |
| Citrus fruits | Uncovered | 5 weeks | Keep in damp air. |
| Melons | Uncovered | 1 week | Keep dry. |
| Vegetables<br>Leaf:<br>lettuce, spinach, cabbage | Loosely | 5 days | Protect against moisture loss to prevent wilting. Use plastic bags or a food crisper. |
| Firm green:<br>cauliflower, broccoli, beans, celery | Loosely | 5–10 days | Use plastic bags or food crisper. |
| Root:<br>potatoes, carrots, turnip | Uncovered | Several months | Keep cool or store bagged in refrigerator. |
| Nut meats | Very tightly | 6 months | Rancidity of oil in nuts caused by air and warm atmosphere makes flavour disagreeable. |
| Salad oils and dressing after opening | Tightly, using original cover | Several months | Rancidity caused by air and too high temperature. Disagreeable flavours result from rancidity. Wiping off of bottle or jar opening after each use is a good practice. |
| Desserts such as milk puddings, custard pies, eclairs, cream puffs | Loosely | 1 day | Desserts made of milk and cream should be eaten very soon after preparation. Spoilage is rapid. |
| Fresh herbs | Tightly | 3 weeks | Wash and drain and put in plastic bags. |

SOURCE: Adapted, from *Management and Foods*

## Freezer Storage

| | Frozen Food | Optimum Time at –20°C |
|---|---|---|
| Meat | Beef — roasts, steaks | 8–10 months |
| | Lamb — roasts, chops | 6–8 months |
| | Veal — roasts, chops | 8–12 months |
| | Pork — roasts, chops | 3–6 months |
| | Ground meat | 2–4 months |
| | Cured and smoked meats | 1–2 months |
| | Cooked beef, pork, veal | 2–3 months |
| | Cooked ham | 1–2 months |
| Poultry | Uncooked — whole | 6–9 months |
| | — pieces | 3–4 months |
| | Cooked — sliced, cubed, in broth/gravy | 2–3 months |
| | Dressing — packaged separately | 1 month |
| Game | Game animals | 8–10 months |
| | Game birds | 6–9 months |
| Prepared meals | Casseroles | 1–2 months |
| | Stew, meat pie, TV dinner | 1–2 months |
| | Baked beans, chili, spaghetti sauce | 3–4 months |
| | Soups | 2 months |
| | Sauce, gravy, broth | 1 month |
| Fish | Oily fish — salmon, trout, mackerel | 1–2 months |
| | Lean fish — halibut, sole, cod | 4–6 months |
| Shellfish | Shrimp, oysters, clams | 1–3 months |
| | Lobster, crab | 1–2 months |
| Baked goods | Breads — quick breads | 2–3 months |
| | — yeast breads and rolls | 1–2 months |
| | Cakes — plain and iced | 4–6 months |
| | — fruit cake | 12 months |
| | Cookies | 9–12 months |
| | Cream puffs and eclairs | 1 months |
| | Pies — baked fruit, mince | 3–6 months |
| | Sausage rolls | 2–4 months |
| Fruit | All kinds | 9–12 months |
| Vegetables | All kinds | 9–12 months |
| | Onions | 2 months |
| | Potatoes | 1 month |
| Jam | Jams, jelly, marmalade | 12 months |

SOURCE: Adapted from *Management and Foods*

Packaged foods, such as flours, cereals, crackers, and mixes, need tightly sealed containers to avoid absorbing or losing moisture or becoming infested by insects. Foods containing fat, such as nuts, coconut, and cookies, do not keep well at room temperature. They can be stored in the refrigerator or freezer. Baked goods should be separated into crisp and moist types and stored in separate tins in a cool place.

Good storage techniques save money. Poor storage results in loss of nutrients and wasted foods. Many foods are now required to have a "best before" date stamped clearly on them. Note the date stamp when you buy the food and use it before the date expires. If a food is spoiled when you bring it home, return it to the store for exchange or refund.

Frozen foods can sometimes be refrozen safely. The following are general guidelines:

- Any frozen food that is completely thawed and held at room temperature for an unkown period of time should be discarded.

- The general rule, "Do not refreeze," appears on most commercially frozen food packages. This is the best advice since the safety of the food may be affected if refrozen.

- Refreezing foods always causes some deterioration in texture, flavour, and colour. When in doubt, do not refreeze.

- Take special care with vacuum-packaged foods. Any vacuum-packaged food that has been improperly thawed should be discarded.

The charts on pages 108–110 provide guides for refrigerating perishables at 2°C to 7°C and freezing foods at –20°C.

# FOOD SPOILAGE

All food preservation methods attempt to stabilize the condition of the food and prevent it from spoiling. To understand the principles of food preservation it is helpful to understand why food spoils. Food deteriorates as a result of one or more of these conditions:

- Enzymes within the living cells.
- Microorganisms (moulds, yeast, bacteria).
- Oxidation of the food.

### 1. Enzymes

**Enzymes** are chemical substances produced within the living tissues of all plants and animals. They speed the changes that eventually occur within plant and animal tissue cells. In vegetables and fruit, enzymes are responsible for normal ripening or maturing; in meat their activity breaks down muscle tissue making it more tender.

Enzymes are inactivated easily by the simple application of heat. This happens during **blanching**, sterilizing, or cooking. Refrigeration or freezing inhibits enzyme activity, but the enzymes themselves are not destroyed. Whenever warmer temperatures are again reached, the normal ripening process continues.

2. Microorganisms

**Microorganisms** are always present in the soil, air, and water. They include many varieties and strains of moulds, yeast, and bacteria. Some are perfectly harmless, some are hazardous, and some are extremely useful in food and medicine production.

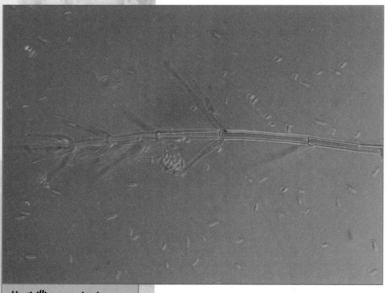

*Verticillium* species is a common general spoilage organism. This one came off a mouldy banana peel. The structures shown are the magnified spore-producing cells and the spores.

**Moulds** are distributed widely in nature and are familiar to everyone because of their visibility on the surface of spoiled food. Mould found growing on canned food means the jar was not sealed properly and the food is not safe to eat.

Moulds feed on sugar, starch, and protein foods and reproduce by means of creating **spores** that scatter easily in the air. Moulds and their spores are destroyed easily by heating food to boiling temperature and holding it there for a few minutes. This is the method used in a boiling water canner.

**Yeasts** are naturally all around us in the environment but are easily controlled in canning. For optimum growth, yeasts require food (sugar), warmth (25°C is optimum), and moisture. They reduce the sugar to alcohol and produce carbon dioxide gas. Spoilage is recognized easily by the bubbles the gas produces. Able to grow readily without oxygen in the presence of acids, yeasts are destroyed by heating the food for a short time to boiling temperature (100°C). They are destroyed when bread bakes or jam is cooked.

$$\text{YEAST + SUGAR} \xrightarrow[\text{moisture}]{\text{warmth}} CO_2 + H_2O + \text{ALCOHOL}$$

**Bacteria** are the most dangerous type of microorganisms because they are the most difficult to destroy. (See Food-Borne Illness, pages 116–119.) Refrigerator temperatures allow growth of some bacteria, and certain bacteria even grow without oxygen present.

Bacteria multiply by cell division under ideal conditions. They can be destroyed by applying boiling temperatures for a suitable period of time. However when the environment becomes more unfavourable, many bacteria, like yeasts and moulds, produce spores which are so highly resistant to heat that they are able to survive until conditions again become favourable. In addition, some bacteria produce deadly **toxins**, tasteless and odourless substances that cause no visible changes in the appearance of the food but are life threatening when eaten.

This means that during home canning, if the jar of food does not receive sufficient heat, the spores may survive. Then later, during storage, they may grow in the sealed jar and cause botulism, a very dangerous kind of food spoilage from the toxins produced. Time and temperature of processing have a direct relationship, and the natural acid in fruits slows bacterial growth. This is the reason why all non-acid foods such as meat and vegetables must be processed only in a pressure canner following directions exactly.

## 3. Oxidation

**Oxidation** refers to the exposure of a food to oxygen in the air. In vegetables and fruit this occurs in combination with enzyme action, resulting in a brown discolouration of the surface. A noticeable change in the texture, usually softening of the food, also occurs. The exposure of food to air causes dehydration and contributes to loss of vitamin content, particularly vitamin C. Several compounds have been developed that prevent discolouration of light-coloured fruits during canning and freezing. They can be found in the home preservation section of the supermarket.

# FOOD PRESERVATION METHODS

The methods used to stop or slow the decomposition of food are derived from the factors described above that cause food spoilage. Very often two or more methods are used together to ensure success. For example, canned fruit is exposed to a high temperature and then is stored in an air-tight vacuum-sealed container to prevent later contamination. Depending on the concentration used, added sugar may or may not have a preservative effect. **Freeze drying** involves subjecting the food to both low temperature and drying conditions.

### 1. Low Temperature

Reduced temperatures inhibit the activities of both enzymes and microorganisms. It is wise to remember that freezing does not destroy all the microorganisms present in food, it only slows growth. Similarly, enzyme activity is slowed but the maturing process resumes when temperatures are warm enough.

### 2. High Temperature

Canning involves heating containers of food to temperatures high enough to destroy microorganisms and enzymes. This process also drives air out of the container. As the container cools, the airtight seal keeps both air and microorganisms from reentering the container. Blanching of vegetables and fruit involves a heat treatment with boiling water or steam which halts the surface enzymes and other spoilage agents until another preservation method, such as freezing, can be completed.

**Sterilization** is application of sufficient heat to destroy both enzymes and microorganisms, including spores, present in the food or on the utensils to be used. This is the principle applied in home canning.

**Pasteurization** refers to the application of slightly less heat than would cause sterilization with the result that some other means of preservation must also be used. For example, pasteurized milk needs refrigeration to control the growth of undestroyed spoilage agents. Pasteurized fruit juices have a high acidity making them unsuitable for the growth of any remaining spoilage agents.

A boiling water canner is often used to preserve fruit and jams.

### 3. Removing Moisture

**Sun drying**, one of the oldest methods of food preservation, has been used to extend the storage of dates, figs, raisins, apricots, sliced apples, fish, and meat. In situations where sun drying is not a reliable method (unsuitable climate or more speed required), forced air is used widely. The same principle is used in home food dryers. A greater variety of vegetables and fruit can be dried this way and requires less time.

Liquid foods, such as milk, eggs, and coffee, are dehydrated by **spray drying**. This involves spraying the liquid into a heated cylinder. When the resulting particles are later clustered by moistening and further drying, called **instantizing**, the powdered dried food will disperse in water more readily. This is the method used to make dried skim milk.

## 4. Excluding Air

The exclusion of air from a food is important to its stability because it prevents oxidation. Vacuum-packaged foods are an application of this principle. Properly processed canned foods have a vacuum seal. Wax prevents contact with air in jams, jellies, some pickles, and the surface of certain cheeses.

## 5. Irradiation

Food **irradiation** involves exposing packaged or bulk food to one of three types of ionizing energy: gamma rays, machine-generated electrons, or X-rays. This is done in a special room or chamber for a specified amount of time. The most common procedure is treatment of the food with cobalt 60 gamma rays in an irradiator. Cobalt 60's gamma energy can penetrate food and cause small molecular changes, just like other cooking or preservation methods, such as canning or freezing. Unlike chemical treatments, the energy passes through the food but leaves no residue. Irradiation works by disrupting the organic process that leads to food decay. Bacteria, yeasts, and moulds are broken down and parasites, insects, or their eggs and larvae are either killed or made sterile.

Worldwide standards for irradiation have been established by a United Nations group. In Canada, potatoes, onions, wheat, flour, and spices were the first foods to be approved for irradiation. Irradiation holds great promise in controlling food-borne diseases, such as salmonella food poisoning. It can extend the shelf life of many foods relatively inexpensively instead of using fumigants and chemicals that may leave residues. Properly done and correctly stored, irradiated foods will retain more of their original texture, flavour, and nutrient value than foods exposed to heat for preservation.

## 6. Adding Preservatives

Wood smoke has long been used as a preserving method. Some spices assist in preservation, but the most common preserving substances used at home are sugar, salt, and vinegar. These are used commercially as well. An assortment of other preservatives are available for use by food companies, provided they meet the guidelines established by Health Protection Branch of Health and Welfare Canada. See Food Additives on page 103.

The concentration of the preservative determines the chemical reaction that takes place and whether or not any additional methods of preservation need to be used. For example, sugar in jam is sufficiently concentrated to destroy the microorganisms present. Further contamination by airborne yeasts and moulds is prevented by careful sealing. The

*Peter Piper picked a peck of pickled pepper; A peck of pickled pepper Peter Piper picked; If Peter Piper picked a peck of pickled pepper, Where's the peck of pickled pepper Peter Piper picked?*
NURSERY RHYME

115

less concentrated sugar solutions used for preserving fruit will improve flavour, colour, and texture but do not have an appreciable effect in preserving the food. In canning, adequate processing and a vacuum seal are more important than the sugar used.

The oldest methods of preserving foods — salting, smoking, pickling, and sun drying — are still being used today. But many other methods have been developed to enable foods to hold their flavour and quality during long periods of storage and transportation.

## FOOD POISONING

Food-borne illness, or food poisoning, affects thousands of Canadians each year and costs millions of dollars in health care and lost wages. The symptoms of food poisoning range from mild nausea and discomfort to violent cramps, vomiting, and diarrhea. Occasionally death results.

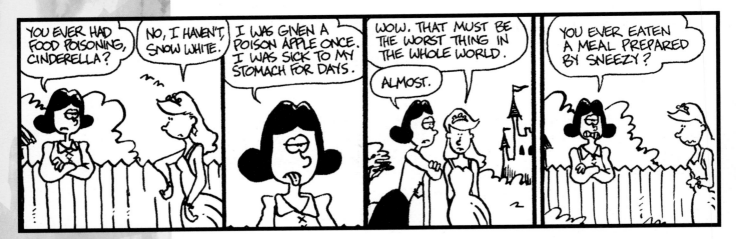

Most food poisoning is caused by bacteria. Bacteria in our environment are generally harmless or even beneficial, but a few strains can cause mild to serious illness. The bacteria causing food-borne illnesses can be divided into two categories:

- Infectious bacteria cause illness when they enter the digestive system in contaminated food. Under ideal conditions the organisms multiply rapidly, which explains the immediate nature of the illness. Most infectious organisms that cause food poisoning are controlled by adequate cooking and refrigeration.

- Toxin-producing food organisms are dangerous. The toxins that they make in response to conditions restricting their growth are poisonous to humans.

The organism itself is quite harmless when eaten in moderate amounts, but some of the toxins produced are not destroyed by extended periods at high temperature. Examples are **staphylococcal food poisoning**, commonly called staph, and **botulism**. These are potentially the most serious bacterial infections. For this reason certain foods at higher risk like non-acid vegetables, meat, and fish require pressure canning for long-term preservation.

There are a variety of other causes of food-borne illnesses:

1. Contamination by coughing or sneezing of food handlers. Colds, flu, and diphtheria can be transmitted this way.

2. Diseases and germs are carried by rats, mice, roaches, and flies. Foods left uncovered can be contaminated by these creatures.

3. Contaminated water transmits some diseases, such as dysentery and typhoid fever, when it is used for drinking or washing vegetables or fruit that are eaten raw. When travelling in some countries, it is advisable to peel or cook vegetables and fruit that may have been in contact with contaminated water.

4. Animal parasites or "worms" sometimes cause diseases. The most familiar of these is the larvae of a parasite called *Trichinella spiralis* that can cause a disease known as **trichinosis** in humans. Because it has been found in pigs, fresh pork should be cooked until the internal temperature reaches 85°C.

5. **Paralytic shellfish poisoning**, known as "Red Tide," is caused by an organism that washes into shellfish beds occasionally during July and August. Shellfish that feed on the organism are unsafe to eat. The organism contains a substance that is very toxic to humans, and because of the chemical nature of the toxin, ***no amount of cooking will make such shellfish fit to eat***. During May through October, local ocean fisheries officers monitor shellfish conditions and post warnings.

6. Certain chemicals can be harmful to humans; some people are more sensitive than others. There is a wide variety of opinion about illness perceived to be caused by pesticides and insecticides and other environmental factors.

## Controlling Food–Borne Illnesses • Carefully controlled temperatures and sanitary food handling practices are the most important safeguards against food-borne illnesses. Bacteria that cause food-borne illnesses are everywhere — in the house, on raw foods, on counter tops, and on the hands, nose, and hair. For them to produce illness, bacteria must be given

NOTE
• • • • • •

In order to minimize the incidence of food spoilage or contamination, any person handling or preparing food must follow good sanitary practices. Personal cleanliness, frequent washing of hands with soap and hot water, and thorough washing of equipment and work surfaces are essential.

Sanitary food handling practices are vital in food production to avoid food-borne illnesses. What sanitary practices do you see here?

the opportunity to multiply to large numbers. They grow very rapidly and within a few hours will reach dangerous levels given the right food (milk, meat, eggs) and optimum temperatures. Danger Zone is 4°C to 60°C.

This temperature guide describes conditions that will successfully control food-borne illnesses.

| Temperature Guide | |
|---|---|
| Home canning | 115°C to 137°C |
| Cooking | 75°C |
| Warm holding | 60°C |
| DANGER ZONE | 4°C to 60°C |
| Refrigeration | 2°C to 5°C |
| Frozen storage | −15°C to −20°C |

## To Prevent Food Poisoning

1. Keep everything in the kitchen clean.
2. Buy food in clean stores only.
3. Avoid handling food if you have an infected cut, a cold, or a cough.
4. After shopping, place frozen foods immediately into the freezer until needed. The freezer compartment of a refrigerator will not hold the temperature as low as a separate freezer unit will. Therefore, optimum storage times will be shorter in a refrigerator freezer.
5. Frozen foods that are completely thawed or have been held at refrigerator temperature more than one or two days should not be refrozen. Do not buy frozen foods that have partially or completely thawed. Avoid buying frozen foods that have large ice crystals. This means the food may have been stored at an unsafe temperature.
6. Keep hot food hot (60°C or higher) and cold food cold (4°C or lower). Ready-to-eat prepared foods should be bought piping hot and kept hot until serving time, or refrigerated immediately. An example is barbecued chicken.
7. Do not prepare foods to be served cold (sandwiches, salads, a buffet foods) more than four hours beforehand, unless the foods are refrigerated until serving.
8. Refrigerate leftover cooked foods within an hour and keep refrigerated until serving or reheating. Store cooked poultry and dressing separately.

9. All protein foods, such as meat, poultry, fish, gravy, milk products, salads with dressing, especially potato or pasta salad, are an ideal growth medium for bacteria and require refrigeration.

10. Vacuum-packed meat is perishable and requires refrigeration. Check the expiry date stamped on the package.

11. Heat precooked, commercially frozen foods for the time and temperature recommended on the labels.

12. When home canning non-acid foods, such as meat, fish, meat–vegetable mixtures, soups, and vegetables, always use a pressure canner with an accurate gauge. Follow the instructions for processing carefully.

13. Never taste foods that have a suspicious or bad smell, an off-colour, mould, cloudiness, or noticeable bubbles. Especially do not taste food from bulging or leaking cans, or cans whose contents spurt or bubble forth. Dented cans are safe if there is no evidence of bulging or leaking. "When in doubt, throw it out" is a good rule to follow.

A roast turkey may be too large to eat completely at one meal. Any leftovers must be refrigerated properly to enjoy later.

## ☀ KEY TERMS

Use the words listed below to complete the following statements in your notebook.

| | |
|---|---|
| rancid | danger zone |
| enzymes | sterilized |
| contaminated | bacteria |
| botulism | toxins |
| dysentry | spores |

1. Some _____ are harmless, some are useful in food production, and some are very hazardous.

2. When food is _____ harmful microorganisms are destroyed.

3. Foods kept next to cleaning supplies could be _____.

4. Some bacteria produce _____ in the body that cause food-borne illnesses.

5. _____ cause food to ripen.

6. High-fat foods will go _____ if not stored properly.

7. Hot foods should be kept hot and cold foods cold otherwise they are in the _____.

8. A bulging can of mushrooms might cause _____ if the mushrooms are eaten.

9. When dirty water is used in food preparation there is a danger of _____.

10. _____ produced by bacteria and moulds can lie dormant until ideal growing conditions return.

## ☀ FOCUS YOUR KNOWLEDGE

1. Compare a variety of products labelled light. Determine what this term means.

2. What would you do with a food that has mould on the surface? Give reasons for your answer.

3. Explain what spores are and how they survive.

4. How does freezing a food affect enzymes or microorganisms?

5. List each of the preservation methods and give an example of a food preserved by each method. Give reasons for matching each food to the method of preserving.

6. Prepare an organizer showing the causes of food spoilage and foods that could be affected by each spoilage agent.

7. Briefly describe how to keep food free from food-borne illnesses.

## ☀ DEMONSTRATE YOUR KNOWLEDGE

1. Prepare recipes using tofu and have a buffet to sample the products made. Be prepared to evaluate the recipes prepared.

2. Observe what happens to an uncovered glass of milk for six days in the refrigerator. Describe how milk should be stored and give reasons for your answers.

3. Experiment with yeast by providing warmth, sugar, and moisture in varying amounts. Based on your results, describe the ideal conditions for yeast to grow.

4. Select a food that has nutrition labelling and interpret the label for your classmates.

## ☀ APPLY YOUR KNOWLEDGE

1. Read cereal labels and identify three cereals that have more than 4 g of fibre and less than 8 g of sugar per serving.

2. Consult a reliable reference to find out how to freeze or can a fruit. Prepare a chart of the necessary steps.

3. Leave a piece of cut vegetable or fruit covered lightly at room temperature for 24 hours. Record the appearance, colour, and texture at the beginning and at the end of the 24 hours. Describe what has happened to the vegetable or fruit. See your science teacher to determine how to set up an experiment accurately.

4. Locate an article on food-borne illness. Summarize the article and report what you learned to your classmates.

5. Visit a grocery store and chart where milk, fruit, and meat are kept. Give reasons for the placement of these foods.

6. Develop criteria of what ingredients are most important in a fruit beverage. Read labels from a variety of fruit beverages. Based on your criteria, determine which is the best nutritional buy.

# Serving and Eating Food

An important aspect of the enjoyment of food is the way it is presented. At home or in commercial establishments, food is served in a variety of ways. Food service also varies within cultures and individual lifestyles. Other related information is found in Chapter 2, Eating Out.

## TABLE MANNERS

In days past most families gathered around the dining table every night to share food and discuss the events of the day. During mealtime children learned social skills and good table manners, as well as the art of conversation, which includes the important aspect of listening. Some families still maintain the family dinner hour. They believe it is important and are able to organize their schedules to accommodate it. Other families are simply unable to follow this pattern, and children must learn about table manners in other ways.

All good manners are based on consideration for others. This is no less important at mealtime. The main reason for learning table manners is to allow you to be comfortable in any situation. Table manners need to be practised just as you would practise to perfect any skill. Given enough experience, you will instinctively know what to do without needing to make any additional effort trying to remember what it was that you learned. There are many good references in any library that will supplement what is provided here.

There is one place where good table manners may be especially important, and most young people do not think of it until they find themselves in the situation. Many employers making a final selection for a position purposefully place prospective employees in a social setting to watch how they respond. The test might be as simple as serving coffee to the candidate during or after the interview. It might be more complicated, like inviting him or her to a reception or dinner.

In this way employers can learn a lot about how a candidate could function in business settings involving other people. Someone with relaxed and acceptable table manners will be able to direct his or her attention to what is being said, rather than worrying about using correct utensils while eating.

FOCUS ON

- the practice of good table manners
- the correct way to serve and eat specific foods
- general guidelines for table etiquette
- principles of table setting
- variations of table service
- the visual aspects of food presentation

For the most part, table manners also have a practical aspect having to do with neatness, cleanliness, and noiselessness when eating. Over the ages table manners have evolved in keeping with the conditions of the times. Originally, people ate with their hands. With the discovery of metals, knives came into use. Each person owned a knife, which was carried for many uses besides eating. Eventually every individual had a set of eating utensils, including a cup and plate.

The development of eating customs of various ethnic groups is an interesting study. Many recent immigrant families have distinctive ways of serving and eating their meals. In fact, some of the practices mentioned here may be quite the opposite to what is acceptable in some other cultures. It would be impossible to include all the alternatives. Try to think of some as you read this section.

Some families mix traditional habits with those used by people they know. When visiting people of a different culture, the same principle of consideration for others that is the basis of all good manners is a safe guide. You will manage to fit in and act appropriately if you follow these guidelines:

• Be alert to the differences and adapt what you do.

• Watch what the host or others do and follow their lead.

Your general behaviour while at the table or when eating says a lot about you to those in your company and can provide a good or bad impression. Here are some general guidelines:

• Wait until everyone is at the table before being seated. There will be a signal from the host or the head of the household. Women are usually expected to be seated first, assisted with their chairs by the server or the male nearest them. Younger people assist older people.

• Avoid placing large objects on the table. Handbags and briefcases may be placed on the floor or hung on the back of the chair. Leave room for the server to move freely. Very small handbags may go in your lap or on the table if there is room.

• As soon as you are seated, put your napkin in your lap. Open it out to full size unless it is very large, then it may be left folded in half. The napkin remains on your lap throughout the meal. In rare instances the server of a specialty restaurant may place it under your chin if you will be eating ribs, spaghetti, or lobster. If you leave the table for any reason, the

Good table manners are important whether in a family, business, or social setting, at home or in a restaurant.

napkin should be placed on your chair. Only at the end of the meal should you leave it on the table.

- While waiting to be served, keep your hands in your lap.
- Keep the elbows off the table until the end of the meal.

  - Add to the conversation. Show interest. Ask questions. This is your contribution to the pleasant experience the meal is intended to be.
  - Wait for the host to indicate it is time to begin eating. If you are the host, you are expected to be the first to start.
  - Take or accept, a bit of everything the host has prepared unless, of course, you are allergic to it. It is a courtesy to the cook to taste it all.
- Ask for the item to be passed to you rather than reach across the table. You may help yourself to food that is closest to you. When passing salt and pepper, pass them together, even if only one was requested.
- When serving yourself, take only the amount you can eat. Be considerate of others by noting how many people are eating and by taking no more than your share.
- If you wish a second helping, wait until it has been offered to you. When your plate needs to be passed, make sure your knife and fork are placed firmly on the plate.
- If you finish eating before the others, wait patiently and continue to make polite conversation as appropriate.
- If you are the host it is considered polite to delay finishing your meal until your guests have done so.
- Eating utensils are correctly placed on the table in such a way that, for a meal with several courses, a person can begin from the outside and work toward the centre of the place setting. An exception is chopsticks, which are placed above the plate. A spoon and/or fork found at the top of the place setting is intended to be used for the dessert course. If in doubt watch the utensils that the host uses.

## Appetizers

- When sauce is served for chips, vegetables, nachos, or other appetizers, a portion of the sauce should be spooned onto your plate for dipping. *Do not* dip your food into the main serving bowl, unless plates are not provided.

- Seafood cocktail is eaten with a tiny fork placed on the outside of the table setting or on the cocktail serving plate. Use a teaspoon for fruit cocktail.
- Place the fork or spoon on the plate when you are finished before it is removed from the table and taken to the kitchen.

## Bread and Butter

- Take butter from the butter dish with the butter knife provided and place it on your bread-and-butter plate or, if the meal is a buffet, on your dinner plate. When small pieces of butter are served in a dish, a tiny serving fork is usually supplied.
- Break off a bite-sized piece of bread or roll and spread butter on it as you are ready to eat it.

## Soup ◆ It is difficult to eat soup quietly and neatly. Hold the spoon between thumb and forefinger as you would a fork, not the way you would hold a toothbrush.

- Dip the spoon into the bowl moving the outside edge of the spoon away from you. Lift the spoon to your mouth and sip *quietly* from the side of the spoon, not the tip.
- If the soup is too hot, you may fan it gently with your spoon or simply wait for it to cool. *Never* blow on it.
- Raise the spoon to your mouth rather than bending to get your mouth down to the bowl. This applies to eating any food. The arm you are eating with should not be touching the table.
- Place the spoon on the side of the plate when you are finished. Leaving a spoon in a bowl or cup can be a hazard when the table is being cleared.

## Salad ◆ When salad is served with the main course, it is usually eaten with the dinner fork. If the salad is served separately before the entrée, a salad fork will be provided. Look for it at the outside of the setting on the left. A small fork placed next to the plate may be intended for dessert, not for the salad. When salad is served after the entrée, the server will check that you have a fork or provide one.

- Large pieces of lettuce sometimes present a problem. You may cut them one at a time with a knife or form them with the knife and fork into a roll before placing them into your mouth.

> *Beautiful soup! Who cares for fish, game, or any other dish? Who would not give all else for two pennyworth only of beautiful soup?*
> LEWIS CARROLL

- When you have finished, leave the cutlery across the salad plate, on an angle known as the five o'clock position, with the fork beside the knife and tines facing down.

Entrée • **Entrée** is another word for the main course. If you are right-handed, the knife should be held in your right hand and the fork in the left hand. If you are left-handed, the reverse is correct. Called the "Continental style," this method may not be comfortable to you at first. The alternative, used for a less formal meal, is to cut a portion of meat or other firm food, then lay the knife on the side of the plate, and transfer the fork to the dominant hand to eat. It is considered impolite to cut all of your food at once.

STANLEY FROZE, UNSURE OF WHICH FORK TO USE.

- When cutting food, hold the fork and knife close together to prevent food from being pushed off the plate.

- Cut, do not tear, food into pieces that are small enough to fit neatly into your mouth.

- Be considerate of people sitting beside you and keep your elbows close to you.

- Take small bites and eat slowly with your mouth closed. Avoid talking with food in your mouth.

- Eating spaghetti politely can be a real challenge. First lift a few strands of spaghetti from the plate with your fork. Then, while holding the points pressed against a large spoon held in your other hand, wrap the strands around the fork tines. This forms a ball that can be placed into your mouth quietly and neatly.

- Wait until you have swallowed the food in your mouth before taking a sip of beverage. Avoid slurping liquids. Beverages in bottles or cans should be poured into a glass before drinking. It is not considered good manners to drink directly from the container or to bring one to the table.

- *Never* leave your knife and fork propped on the sides of the plate like oars in a rowboat. *Never* place the knife between the tines of the fork. Place your eating utensils to give the correct signal to the server:

  * Knife and fork crossed on the plate — "I am taking a pause in my eating."

  * Knife and fork placed on the plate in the five o'clock position with fork tines turned down — "I am finished, please remove my plate."

- Leave your plate where it is. Do not push it away from you or pass or stack it with others. Under cramped conditions, a server may ask you to pass items, or you may offer to help at home or at a friend's home.

Dessert • Use the dessert spoon or fork provided. It should be the only utensil left at your place, unless a beverage spoon has been included. Sometimes the dessert spoon is provided at the time the dessert is served.

## End of the Meal

- A finger bowl is a small bowl containing water sometimes with a piece of lemon. If one is offered, dip one hand at a time, swish gently, and dry on the napkin.

- The host will signal the end of the meal by placing his or her napkin on the table or asking if people would like to move from the table. Do not get up until your host rises. If you are the host, be sensitive to the hour. Make it possible for guests to leave when they would like.

- Lay your napkin loosely at the left side of your plate when you leave the table.

- Whether the meal took place in a home or a restaurant, the host should be thanked. In some more formal circumstances, a telephone call or note of thanks is a welcomed, polite gesture.

*The others had already started eating. No one spoke and for a long time the only sounds were those of violent mastication and heavy breathing, as if the meal were a tedious chore.*
NEIL BISSOONDATH

## CAREER SKETCH

Rebecca Dawson, chef

**R**EBECCA DAWSON was born in Vancouver in 1959. One of the main reasons she was drawn to a career in foods was "that feeding people can be a very positive act. Using quality ingredients, cooking them with care, and serving them creatively can be a very challenging and rewarding career."

Dawson was educated in foods and design, graduating in Home Economics at the University of British Columbia. A French culinary program at Vancouver's Dubrulle French Culinary School followed. She worked in various restaurants and quickly became responsible for the kitchen. At age 28, Dawson was chef at The Raintree Restaurant with a total of 20 staff.

Dawson gained much public notice while working at The Raintree. She was featured in various publications for her "simple and hearty approach to regional cooking." *Chatelaine* described her as using "a signature northwest cuisine based on friendly, almost homey, dishes seething with freshness." Local seafood and produce were main ingredients in Dawson's cooking.

At age 31 she returned to Dubrulle French Culinary School as Chef Instructor to teach cooking. Later she ventured to France and Italy and worked in twelve different restaurants to observe and learn. A career highlight for Dawson was giving a cooking demonstration at Ottawa's food and wine festival. She was the only female West Coast representative.

Dawson says, "Cooking can be extremely rewarding. As in many careers there are demanding hours, stress, and competition. A chef needs to be physically fit, current, a manager, an accountant, and particularly aware that the quality of the raw ingredient is all very important to the final result."

Cooking is a creative, positive experience to Dawson. She is interested in the many facets of the restaurant business—following trends, using quality products, creating new dishes. "A chef uses all the senses—sight, smell, taste, hearing, and touch," states Dawson. She feels that it is her responsibility as a chef to educate the customer to healthier eating. She is looking forward to opening a small restaurant in the south of France.

## General Guidelines

- Uncertain what to do? — Watch your host and follow his or her lead.

- Need to cough, sneeze, or blow your nose? — Do it as discreetly as possible. Turn your head from the table and cover your mouth with a napkin or your hand. Blow gently. If coughing persists, leave the table.

- Something stuck in your teeth? — Excuse yourself and go to the bathroom to take care of it.

- Wearing lipstick? — Blot it before going to the table so as not to leave stains on the napkin or glass. Reapply lipstick in the powder room at the end of the meal.

- Wearing a hat? — Males should remove them upon entering a restaurant and before coming to the table in a home.

- Wearing a dental appliance? — Remove privately before you come to the table and replace it discreetly afterward. Do not place it on the table.

- Meal has fish bones, seeds, pits? — Remove small articles discreetly from your mouth with index finger and thumb and put them on the edge of your plate.

# TABLE SETTING

Think of a place setting as a blueprint for what will be eaten. While standing at one place at the table, imagine how the person will hold the utensils. The knife will be in the right hand, fork in the left, spoon in the right hand. Then place the pieces of cutlery that way: knife and spoon(s) to the right of the plate and fork(s) on the left. The exceptions are the seafood cocktail fork, if needed, which is placed to the right of the soup spoon, and the dessert fork and spoon, which are sometimes put across the top.

Remember to place the utensils in the order that they will be used, working from the outside of the setting toward the plate or centre of the place setting. A table properly set in this way provides information on what foods or courses might be served.

Glasses for beverages go on the right and slightly above the plate. Beverage cups are placed to the right of the plate

Whether for casual or more formal meals, there are certain time-honoured positions for table setting.

beyond the cutlery and, if space is limited, slightly above the plate and to the right of any glasses. The bread-and-butter plate goes to the left of the plate beyond the outside fork. A bread knife, if used, may be laid across the top of the bread-and-butter plate or just outside the dinner knife.

Napkins may be placed on the plate, to the left of the plate or on the bread-and-butter plate. Although some informal restaurants do so, cutlery should not be placed on the napkin. It needs to be readily accessible at the very beginning of the meal.

# SERVING FOOD

Many people today have very busy schedules and often tend to eat on the run. Food might be prepared using a minimum amount of time or, alternatively, previously prepared or purchased food may be reheated in the microwave. Family members might eat alone or in front of the television. All these situations affect how the food will be served. How is food served in your family? Foods are also served in many different ways in commercial eating establishments. Several of them are discussed here.

## Table Service

As with table manners and table setting, there are a few principles that guide how food is to be served at the table. The main object should be to present it in such a way that those eating will appreciate it most. This means that food should be at the correct temperature and be arranged attractively. These suggestions apply whether the serving is being done at home or at a restaurant.

The server should move in a calm, routine manner around the table. Individual servings should be placed in front of the guest or patron with the right hand from behind her or his right side. Plates are removed in the same way, from the same side.

Beverages should also be served from the right, with the right hand. Water may be poured in that manner, as well. Greater care should be taken when serving hot beverages to prevent scalding. Remove the cup on its saucer, pour, and then return the cup and saucer to the table. Whenever you need to pass your cup, either as a guest or server, remember to pass the saucer as well, so that any drips are caught.

## Cafeteria or Self-Service

In order to maintain freshness and quality of their foods, self-service estab-lishments need to separate cold and hot items. While standing in line you will find that foods requiring refrigeration will usually be the first items you see. These are frequently attractive desserts that tempt hungry patrons before they have decided on the main part of the meal. Next may be other tempting foods, such as appetizers, salads, and breads, so that they too are already on the tray when the main course is selected. This arrangement results in opportunities for customers to select more items than they might normally eat, increasing sales.

Soup is usually the first hot food to be displayed. Next comes what-ever is being served as the hot main course, with accompanying vegetables and sauces. The bever-age station is found near the end of the presentation. Placed here, hot beverages will not have time to become cooled before consump-tion. The cashier is positioned at the end. Usually cutlery and condi-ments are available either beyond or to the side of the cashier, but not in a place that will slow down peo-ple who are ready to pay for their meals.

Customers often serve their own beverages in cafeterias. Name five kinds of beverages you might find in a cafeteria.

## Buffet Service

• Buffet service means that dishes of prepared foods are placed on a table separate from the one where people sit to eat. Individuals then select the foods they want and in desired portions. Sometimes cutlery is also picked up by the guests; other times tables are set with utensils for the guests to use. At home, buffet service is suitable for an informal meal or a very elegant dinner party.

Whether at home or in a commercial establishment, buffet service is the easiest way to serve large groups. You may be served this way at a banquet, especially if the organizing group, the customer, wants to keep costs down. Fewer staff members are needed to put out the food dishes and tables can be cleared all at once, which also saves staff time.

## Fast-Food Outlets

The main characteristic of food service in a fast-food outlet as its name implies, is that it takes very little time. Customers state the foods they want, pay for them, and wait a short time for them to be ready. Often at least part of the food is precooked or ready to serve. Food is provided in paper, plastic, or foil packaging, and utensils are also disposable. Condiments are often available for customers to select for themselves.

# PRESENTATION

As discussed under Menu Planning, pages 30–33 the appearance of food on the plate is very important to its appeal to the eater. Restaurant personnel use this knowledge to advantage when they arrange foods on a plate. Workers in commercial kitchens are instructed to exercise care in serving and arranging foods so that customers have a good visual first impression of the meal. Some of this effect is achieved by the desirable appearance of the foods themselves. An additional technique is the attractive use of **garnishes**. A garnish is an edible item added to a food that improves its appearance. Some of them are very simple to use. For example, chopped parsley on boiled potatoes, paprika on poached eggs, radish slices in green salads. Others may take a little more time and effort to prepare.

What garnishes have been used to make these turkey thighs look more attractive?

## KEY TERMS

Use the words listed below to complete the following statements in your notebook.

buffet service          cutlery
table manners          place setting
table service          finger bowl
continental            garnish
entrée

1. _____ are based on consideration for others.

2. _____ is another name for the main course of food.

3. To use a _____, dip one hand at a time, swish, and dry on a napkin.

4. In _____ dishes of prepared foods are placed on a table separate from the table where people are eating.

5. A _____ is an edible item added to food to enhance its appearance.

6. Holding the knife in the right hand and the fork in the left to eat is called the _____ style.

7. The pieces of tableware needed by one person to eat a meal is called a _____.

8. An important principle of _____ is presenting food at the correct temperature and arranged attractively.

9. Knives, spoons, and forks are pieces of _____ .

## FOCUS YOUR KNOWLEDGE

1. Explain briefly why table manners are important. Include the following aspects:
   a. in a family setting
   b. in a business setting
   c. with friends

2. What should you do if you are unsure how to eat a certain food?

3. List the general guidelines for considerate behaviour at the dinner table.

4. Explain briefly correct procedures for eating the following:
   a. appetizers
   b. bread and butter
   c. soup
   d. salad

5. What is buffet service? When is buffet service most suitable to use?

6. Describe how and why garnishes are used in food service.

## ☀ DEMONSTRATE YOUR KNOWLEDGE

1. Role play a formal dinner situation in which a future employer is interviewing a prospective employee.

2. Prepare an individual place setting for the following menus:

   a.
   Seafood Cocktail
   Roast Beef
   Baked Potato
   Peas    Carrots
   Apple Pie
   Water    Coffee

   b.
   Lasagne
   Garlic Bread
   Tossed Salad
   Fresh Fruit Cup
   Milk    Tea

   c.    Cream of Broccoli Soup
   Rolls    Butter
   Baked Chicken
   Caesar Salad
   Wild Rice    Carrot Nuggets
   Trifle
   Coffee    Water

3. Demonstrate to a partner the correct procedures for the following:
   a. Eating spaghetti.
   b. How to place the knife and fork at the end of a meal.
   c. How to hold a soup spoon.

4. Demonstrate how you would handle each of the following situations:
   a. The salmon steak you are eating has a large bone that you would like to remove from your mouth.

   b. In the middle of dinner you suddenly develop hiccups.
   c. You feel full, but there is still food on your plate.

## ☀ APPLY YOUR KNOWLEDGE

1. Write a menu for a pasta dinner that includes a salad, bread, dessert, and a beverage. Draw a diagram of each place setting you would have for a family of four.

2. Brainstorm with a partner topics for conversation that might be appropriate at mealtime. Are there any topics that would be wise to avoid? Give reasons for your answers.

3. Plan menus and table settings for the following occasions:
   a. A sixth birthday party for six children.
   b. Pizza party for ten 13-year-olds.
   c. Mother's Day brunch for a family of four.
   d. Buffet dinner for twelve people.

4. Using the school or local library, research the table manners of one particular ethnic group. Decide on points of comparison, then compare them with table manners in Canada.

5. Observe the effect that colour has in enhancing the presentation of table settings. Prepare different coloured "placemats" of construction paper and set an individual place setting using the various colours. Note the colours that you found most pleasing.

# Unit Overview

## ☀ REVIEW YOUR KNOWLEDGE

1. Discuss with a partner how the planning and organization of a kitchen can result in greater efficiency and save time.

2. Choose a favourite recipe and list five ways that it could be adapted.

3. From a nutrition label, identify the largest quantity ingredient and all types of fat and sugar. Compare the label with one for a similar product. Which product provides more nutrition?

4. Name the causes of food-borne illnesses.

5. Prepare a list of *do's* and *do not's* for table manners in the food lab or classroom.

6. Explain the differences in service at a fast-food restaurant, continental restaurant, and cafeteria.

## ☀ EXTEND YOUR KNOWLEDGE

1. In small groups, prepare a short video demonstrating the following techniques:
   a. Measuring 250 mL milk.
   b. Measuring 125 mL margarine.
   c. Measuring 375 mL cake flour, sifted.
   d. Preparing a cake pan for an angel cake.
   e. Separating an egg.

2. In small groups, visit different food stores to determine the services each provides. Include a corner grocery store, a supermarket, and a bulk food store. Prepare a report on the advantages and disadvantages of each store to the customer.

3. Arrange a class visit to a restaurant specializing in international foods. Observe the menu, table setting, table appointments, and service provided. Prepare a report of your observations.

4. In groups of four, arrange a simulation of various physical disabilities in the laboratory. One person at a time should:
   a. Wear a blindfold.
   b. Use a wheelchair.
   c. Use crutches.
   d. Wear oiled rubber gloves.
   Try such activities as opening a cupboard door, stirring a saucepan on a stove, and cleaning vegetables. Discuss how you felt during the experience.

5. Contact your local or provincial department of health to research the major occurrences of botulism or another food-borne illness in your community. Ask the contact person to identify the contaminated food and food handling practices that caused the bacteria to develop.

6. Research a career in food service. Consider positions such as maître d'hôtel, host, server, chef, and caterer. What interests you about these careers? What disadvantages do you foresee?

# UNIT 3

# Food Preparation

Is a tomato a fruit or a vegetable? Why is brown rice a more nutritious food than polished white rice? Can you make a sauce in the microwave oven? Chapters 6–10 explore the many different foods available to us and ways to prepare them.

Each chapter in this unit deals with a specific food group from *Canada's Food Guide to Healthy Eating*. You will learn about the different products made from grain, such as cereal, pasta, and bread. You will explore vegetables and fruit, then milk and its products. The Meat and Alternatives chapter covers many topics, including poultry, fish and shellfish, eggs, legumes, and tofu. Finally you will learn about the Other Foods category from which the foods should be eaten in moderation.

Foods within the same food group often share the same nutritive value and even methods of preparation and cooking. Understanding the basics about food preparation helps you make appropriate choices and enjoy the food. You will also have less waste and more variety in meals.

# Grain Products

## GRAINS

Since ancient peoples first discovered that the kernels of grain on the top of some grasses were good to eat, grains have been an important food source. The significance of grains was underlined early by the belief that protection of grain was in the care of the goddess Ceres, from which the name cereal is derived. Other reports in history refer to grain being kept safe by wise women of the church. By entrusting seeds to an important person, there was little chance the seeds would be eaten for food during times of famine.

A kind of bread was first formed when people learned to pound the grain between stones. They mixed the coarse powder with water into a mash, which was then dried in the sun or baked on heated stones. In many countries bread made from wheat is referred to as the *staff of life*. Wheat provides nourishment for more nations of the world than any other food. Rice is second in importance overall as it is used widely in countries with very large populations, such as India, China, and Japan.

FOCUS ON
- the different types of grains
- the kinds of cereals and how to cook them
- the types of rice and how to cook them
- how to successfully cook pasta
- types of flour used in baking
- the role of ingredients in flour mixtures
- the classification of flour mixtures
- the basic steps in making pancakes, muffins, and biscuits

Most bread is made from wheat. What is your favourite kind of bread?

Kinds of Grains • Flour made from *wheat* is important because it has the highest percentage of protein of all the grains. Wheat protein, called gluten, is the substance that forms the framework of baked products. The climate of much of the Western world is well-suited to growing wheat, an important crop of the Prairie provinces of Canada.

*Oats* rank second to wheat in Canada as a cereal grain produced mainly to make breakfast cereals. Sometimes these are used as ingredients in baked products and desserts. Oat cereals are rich in nutrients because the whole grain is used after the outer husk has been removed. See diagram, page 140.

*Corn* is used extensively as a cereal, but with production limited in Canada, most of our corn is imported. Products made from the corn grain are breakfast cereals, cornstarch, corn oil, and corn syrup. *Grits*, made from hulled and ground white corn, are popular in the southern United States. *Hominy* is the grains of white corn with only the bran and germ removed.

*Rice* is important in many forms. Most rice is used as a main course food, but it is also made into breakfast cereal. Those with wheat allergies find rice flour a satisfactory replacement for products made with wheat flour. Milling removes the bran to give polished rice. The length of the grain is related to the length of the growing period and the amount of irrigation. See pages 143–146 for more information on rice.

*Rye* is mainly used to make flour for bread. When it is the only flour used, the resulting loaf is almost black and very heavy. This is a popular bread served in Russia, Germany, Poland, and Scandinavian countries. The protein of rye flour is not as strong as that in wheat flour and the bread will not rise. To make the loaf lighter, more porous, and a paler colour, wheat flour is combined with rye flour.

## Examples of Foods in the Grain Products Group

### One Serving

| | |
|---|---|
| Cooked cereal | 175 mL |
| Ready-to-eat cereal | 175 mL (30 g) |
| Bread | 1 slice (25 g) |
| Muffin, roll | one small (40 g) |
| Corn tortilla, chapati, roti | one (15 cm diameter) |
| Graham wafers | 4 (20 g) |
| Soda biscuits | 6 (20 g) |
| Holland rusks | 1 1/2 (20 g) |

### Two Servings

| | |
|---|---|
| Pasta, cooked | 250 mL |
| Rice, cooked | 250 mL |
| Hamburger bun, hot dog bun, pita bread | one (60 g) |
| Bagel, English muffin, kaiser roll | one (50 g) |
| Baking powder biscuit, scone | one (5 cm diameter) |
| Pancake, waffle | one (10 cm diameter) |

*Bread deals with living things, with giving life, with growth, with the seed, the grain that nurtures. It is not coincidence that we say bread is the staff of life.*
LIONEL POILÂNE

### REMINDER

*Canada's Food Guide to Healthy Eating* Suggested Servings of Grain Products

Children
  5–12 servings
Youths (10–16 years)
  5–12 servings
Adults
  5–12 servings

*Barley* is important for the flavour it imparts and its high mineral and low-fat content. In the form of pot barley, which is the whole grain, or pearl barley, the more refined cereal, it is used to thicken and flavour soups or as an ingredient in main dish mixtures. Malt is made from barley; it flavours malt syrups, malted milk, and breakfast cereals.

The main *buckwheat* product familiar to most of us is pancake flour. Some breakfast cereal contains buckwheat groats, which are coarsely ground buckwheat grains. *Kasha* is a traditional eastern European side dish that consists of coarsely ground buckwheat kernels with the bran removed.

**Structure and Nutritive Value of Grains** • **Bran** is the outer layer of the grain that remains after the protective **husk** has been removed. Bran is composed of cellulose with minerals, iron, and phosphorus to provide a rigid structure. Significant amounts of thiamin and also some riboflavin and niacin are found in bran. When the bran is removed during the refining processes the resulting product lacks these valuable nutrients.

The **germ** is the part of the grain from which the new plant grows. For this reason it is not surprising that it also has the greatest nutritive value. It is a rich source of the B vitamins, vitamin E, and iron. Because of the presence of fat it has poor keeping qualities.

The **endosperm** is the largest part of any cereal grain. Its natural value as seed for a new crop is to furnish nourishment to the developing plant. It contains mainly starch and some vegetable protein but is lacking in vitamins, minerals, and cellulose. When grain products are highly refined, such as in white flour and polished rice, the endosperm is the only part of the kernel used.

> Try examining a single grain under a microscope and see what parts you can identify.

BRAN
ENDOSPERM
HUSK
GERM

# CEREALS

**Kinds of Breakfast Cereals** • As the name implies, *whole-grain cereals* are made from the entire kernel of the cereal grain. They are preferable because they contain important amounts of B vitamins, iron, and phosphorus and provide an economical source of vegetable protein and starch.

*Refined cereals*, which are processed by intensive milling, contain mostly the starchy endosperm of grains. Enrichment, controlled by federal government regulations, adds vitamins and minerals to restore food value close to that of the whole grain.

*Ready-to-eat cereals* are produced from wheat, rice, oats, and corn. Processing converts the cereal grain to a flaked, shredded, puffed, or popped, essentially carbohydrate, food that has been precooked and usually presweetened. Most of the naturally occurring nutrients have been destroyed. Although an attempt is made to replace the loss by addition of B vitamins and iron, little of the important cellulose or trace elements remain.

*Baby cereals* have a fine texture that is specially suited to infants and others needing a near liquid diet. Vitamins and minerals are added and the cereal is precooked so that only liquid, usually milk, needs to be added before serving.

*Instant cereals*, like baby cereal, need only be mixed with hot milk or water before serving. They cost more and sometimes have a less desirable flavour than cooked cereal. Preparation time is the big saving.

*Quick-cooking cereals* require only a few minutes cooking time. They are made by finely cutting the cereal kernel. For example, quick-cooking rolled oats are cut into thinner flakes than regular rolled oats.

*Regular cereals*, sometimes referred to as "original," require the longest cooking time because they are the least processed. Only a few examples, including oatmeal, rolled oats, and cracked wheat, are still readily available in this form.

## Cooking Cereal

Because at least three-quarters of any cereal grain is starch, it is really the principles of starch cookery that are being discussed when we consider cereal cookery. The objectives for both are the same:

- Freedom from lumps
- Gelatinization of the starch
- Improved flavour
- Softened cellulose

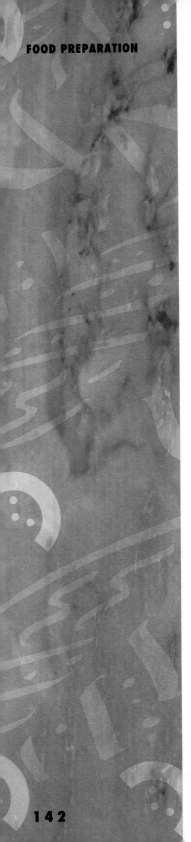

To simplify your understanding of cooking both breakfast cereals and other starch-thickened mixtures, such as sauces and gravies, they are discussed together here.

### Principles of Starch Cookery •

To prevent lumps from forming, stir the cereal slowly into rapidly boiling water and continue stirring until the water boils again. Lumps form because the outer surface of each cereal granule becomes sticky as soon as it contacts water. The stirring action prevents the granules from sticking together. The finer the cereal, the greater the tendency to form lumps.

Separating agents used to prevent sticking in some other starchy mixtures include:

- Cold liquid, in preparation of a flour–water slurry for gravy.
- Sugar, for sweet sauces in desserts, such as puddings.
- Melted fat, used in making gravy or a roux for white sauce.

As the starch cooks, the grains absorb liquid, swelling to many times their original size. This swelling of starch granules in hot liquid is called **gelatinization**. When the granules swell, they crowd each other and fill the space. This thickening occurs gradually as the mixture becomes fully heated, and it can be observed.

In the case of breakfast cereals, as the cereal grains absorb water the cereal increases in bulk. The heat converts absorbed water to steam, which bursts the granules and releases the soluble starch inside. Some cereals, such as cream of wheat, absorb more water than others. Various cereal grains require different amounts of water to achieve the right consistency.

Flavour is generally improved with extended cooking of cereal, flour, or cornstarch. Since the flavour of cereal is quite bland, a good texture is important to making it palatable. Using the right proportion of water to cereal and cooking thoroughly help. Adding a small amount of salt also brings out flavour.

Flavouring extracts are added last to prevent their evaporation during cooking. Any acid ingredient, such as lemon juice to pudding or tomatoes to a soup or sauce, must be added when the cooking is completed and the desired thickening is achieved. If added too soon, the product will not thicken properly.

All starch is more digestible after cooking. Cooked starch is about 90 percent digestible, while uncooked starch is only about 50 percent digestible. This is because softened starch granules are more accessible to the enzymes of the human digestive tract that help in the digestive process.

Since there are so many different varieties of cereals available, some of which have been precooked, the best advice is to follow the directions on the cereal package. Sometimes a slightly longer cooking time than recommended improves the flavour.

## Qualities of Well-cooked Cereal

- Smooth, uniform texture with flowing consistency and no lumps.
- Thoroughly cooked with a nutlike flavour and no taste of raw starch.
- Hot serving temperature.

# RICE

In world importance, rice is second only to wheat among the principal grains. In Asian countries and for many Asian-born Canadians it is a dietary mainstay. In other countries it is served most often as an accompaniment to protein foods or vegetables.

Like other cereal seeds, rice has a husk, or outer layer, that is not eaten. The husk and germ, from which the new plant will ultimately grow, contain most of the vitamins and the protein and fat. During milling, the husk and germ are normally removed, leaving only the endosperm, which is mostly starch. In countries using rice as the staple food, a thiamin deficiency disease called **beri-beri** is fairly common. Converted rice is prepared in a way that distributes thiamin throughout the grain.

Long-, medium-, and short-grain rice result from screening the cleaned rice kernels to separate them by size. Once milling removes the bran, the resulting polished rice is sold or altered further.

In some rice-producing areas of the world, three rice crops a year can be harvested. Because rice thrives in hot, moist conditions, Canada's climate is not suitable for rice production. However, Canada does have a very suitable climate for growing wild rice.

When you are choosing servings from Grain Products, remember the variety of rice available to you.

## Kinds of Rice
• *Brown rice* is an unpolished rice with only the hull and some of the bran removed. It is, therefore, the richest in vitamins and minerals. Cooked brown rice is light brown with kernels that

remain well-separated. With a nutlike flavour, it is well-suited for use in casseroles, main dishes, and special stuffings.

*White rice* is less flavourful and less nutritious than brown rice since it consists only of the starchy endosperm of the rice grain. Long-grain rice is the product of more irrigation and a longer growing period. It is light and fluffy when cooked. The grains separate and keep their individual shape well. This kind is useful in almost any rice dish or served alone. Medium- and short-grain varieties are tender and moist, and the grains tend to stick together. These are most often used in recipes requiring a tender, easily moulded rice, as in a dessert.

*Converted rice* is the result of a special milling process that conserves its nutritional value. The cleaned rice is first exposed to steam so that nutrients in the outer layers of husk, bran, and germ diffuse into the endosperm. After drying, the milling that follows does not remove the nutrients. Converted rice is more creamy in colour, more flavourful than other white rice, with each cooked grain separate. Sometimes called "special process rice" or "parboiled rice," it is suitable for most uses.

*Instant rice* is a rice that has been milled, completely cooked, and then dried. White coloured, it is very bland in flavour and can be somewhat soggy when served. Other names for instant rice are "precooked rice" and "five-minute rice." The main advantage and reason for its use is that it is ready to serve as soon as it has absorbed enough boiling liquid.

*Wild rice* is not a true rice. It is the seed of a water grass that grows naturally in shallow water along the edges of lakes and ponds in some regions of Manitoba and Ontario and around the Great Lakes. The ripened kernel is long and greenish black. Unless harvested as soon as it is ripe, the wild rice kernels will be lost in the water. Harvesting is done by hand from a boat, which makes the product very expensive. Limited supplies also contribute to the cost. Wild rice is usually served in small quantities as an accompaniment dish or mixed with brown or white rice in a casserole or stuffing. Its nutty flavour and firm texture are suited especially for serving with game, wildfowl, poultry, such as goose, duck, and, of course, chicken or turkey.

This nineteenth-century drawing illustrates Ojibwa women harvesting wild rice.

The Edward E. Ayer Collection, The Newberry Library

Cooking Rice ◆ When cooking rice the main consideration is to choose the correct rice for the intended use. Other considerations are nutritive value and desired characteristics of the cooked product. Each rice requires a different cooking time which must be considered in meal planning and preparation.

Package instructions are usually reliable to obtaining good cooked rice. However, even the most experienced cooks sometimes have difficulty. Experimenting with amounts of water to rice, the pot for cooking, and heat control are recommended. Once the desired results are achieved, note how you got them and use that combination next time. Here are some additional suggestions:

- Measure accurately. Rice swells when cooked:
  * 250 mL brown, white, or converted rice yields 750–1000 mL cooked rice.
  * 250 mL instant rice yields 500 mL cooked rice.
  * 250 mL wild rice yields 1000 mL cooked rice.

- A ratio of water to rice, for all except instant and wild rice, is 500 mL water for each 250 mL uncooked rice. For firmer rice with well-separated kernels try 250 mL rice to 400 mL water. For softer rice use more water.

- Use a heavy pot with a tight-fitting lid or a rice cooker.

- Cook with the lid tightly in place so that measured water will not be lost as steam. Do not peek during cooking time.

- Time rice carefully. A guideline is:
  * Brown rice — 45–50 minutes
  * Converted rice — 25–30 minutes
  * White rice — 15–20 minutes

- Rice can be cooked in the microwave oven, although it is one food that does not cook more quickly by this method. Follow package instructions.

- Do not stir rice after it boils because this breaks up the grains and makes the rice gummy.

- Cooked rice will feel tender when a single kernel is pressed between thumb and forefinger.

Rice can also be baked in the oven. The same proportions are used, providing the cover is tight. Baking temperature is about 180°C or less. *Rice pilaf* is a popular combination of rice or rices and liquid, such as broth or juice, with assorted chopped vegetables like onions, celery, peppers, and mushrooms. Pilaf is a suitable accompaniment to many main course

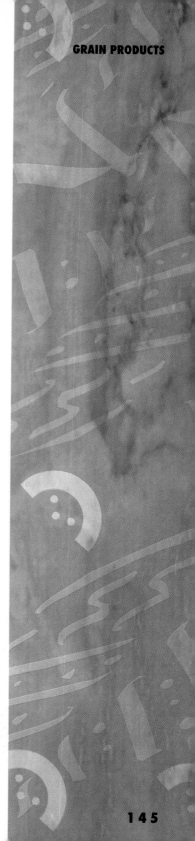

foods or, with the addition of seafood or poultry, it may be the main course. Because it can be held easily at the correct temperature, serving is simplified and last minute preparations are reduced.

Once cooked, rice can be kept hot in the cooking pot or placed in the serving dish in a warm, not hot, oven until served. Rice can be cooked ahead and reheated. Reheating can be done in a microwave oven or in a covered saucepan with a sprinkling of water. Leftover rice can be refrigerated for up to a week or frozen for up to six months.

## PASTA

The term **pasta** refers to all macaroni and noodle products. They are all made from the same basic formula of flour and water. Noodles also contain egg solids which contribute flavour, colour, and tenderness to the dough. Commercially made pasta uses flour made from durum wheat. This extremely hard spring wheat has a high gluten content to provide strength. Processed into semolina flour, durum wheat gives pasta a characteristic nutlike flavour and yellow colour that holds its shape and firm texture when cooked.

Pasta comes in over one hundred assorted shapes. Whatever the shape, the same procedure is followed for making it. The mixed dough is forced through special machines to produce the desired shape, then dried slowly in special dryers. Shapes are of four general types.

- Long, thin pasta — spaghetti, spaghettini, vermicelli
- Hollow pasta — elbow macaroni, rigatoni, penne
- Flat pasta — lasagna, flat or curly egg noodles
- Decorative pasta — shells, bows, alphabets, stars

Pasta comes in all shapes and sizes.

### Cooking Pasta

1. For every 225 g of pasta, use 2 L of water and 5 mL of salt or less. Bring the water and salt to a rolling boil. Add approximately 15 mL of vegetable oil to the water to soften the pasta and help prevent it from sticking together. Oil also reduces the chances of having the mixture boil over.

2. Add pasta gradually to the rapidly boiling water while stirring. *Do not allow the water to stop boiling*. Spaghetti ends are placed into the water and pushed down as the rods soften. Because wide noodles are easily broken they require careful handling.

3. Cook *uncovered* according to the time indicated on the package. If the pasta is to be combined with other foods and heated further, cooking should be reduced by one-third.

4. *Cook only until tender*. When tasted, pasta should be tender but still chewy. The Italian term, **al dente**, is used to describe the correct consistency. It means the pasta is tender yet chewy when tasted "under the tooth."

5. Once cooked, drain the pasta immediately in a large strainer. Transfer to a heated serving dish and serve immediately. Pasta that is going to be served in a sauce should never be rinsed in water. It will spoil the texture of the pasta and prevent the sauce from sticking. If the cooked pasta is to be used later in a salad, rinse under cold water and refrigerate.

## BREADS AND OTHER FLOUR MIXTURES

Try to determine which of these breads contain whole-wheat flour.

Kinds of Flour • *All-purpose flour*, sometimes called white flour, is made from the endosperm of hard spring wheat. It contains from 12 percent to 14 percent protein, known as gluten. When moistened, gluten gives the elasticity needed for bread to rise. All-purpose flour, as its name signifies, is suitable for most baking needs as well as for thickening liquids and coating foods.

By definition, *whole-wheat flour* contains at least 95 percent of the total weight of the wheat from which it is made. All the natural parts of the wheat kernel are utilized. Although having the bran and germ present means the total protein value is greater than that of all-purpose flour, whole-wheat flour produces a heavier product. This is because the bran particles cut the developing gluten strands when the dough is mixed. For lighter breads and quick breads some white flour is generally included to provide structure.

*Stone-ground flour* and *cracked-wheat flour* are made from whole-wheat kernels. Stone-ground

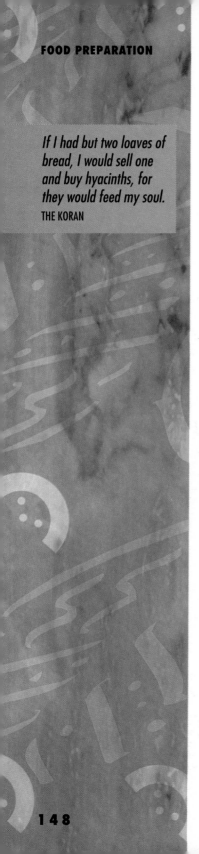

flour has a coarse texture that produces heavy bread. Cracked-wheat flour is made from cracked rather than ground kernels, producing a coarse flour that is usually mixed with white flour for baking.

*Bread flour* is milled from hard spring wheat and sold mainly to bakers. It makes excellent bread with bakery equipment but has too much gluten for home bread making except when homestyle bread makers are used.

*Cake and pastry flour* is a specialty flour milled from soft winter wheat. It is low in protein. Because it has been milled very finely, cake and pastry flour is smooth to touch and its high-starch content makes it pack easily. It produces a fine-grained, tender product when used for pastries and cakes, such as angel and sponge cakes, that are leavened by air. It is also used in a wide variety of delicate desserts and other specialty cakes. When it is necessary to substitute all-purpose flour for cake and pastry flour, use 10 percent less than the recipe requires.

*Graham flour* is white flour made from hard spring wheat with bran and other parts of the wheat kernel added. Used for making yeast breads and quick breads, the additions give it a brownish colour.

*Self-rising flour* is white flour that is premixed with salt and baking powder. It is more common in Great Britain, Australia, and some European countries than it is in Canada. If it is not available and a recipe asks for it, add the amount of baking powder and salt that would be used in similar recipes.

*Soy flour* lacks gluten so a baked product made from it will not raise and become as light as one made from wheat flour. *Rice flour* is a starchy powder lacking protein since it is made from rice. Both make delicate baked products but neither is suitable used alone to make bread. They are especially useful to people with wheat allergies.

*Rye flour* is dark-coloured, low-protein flour made from rye. It gives a distinctively strong, nutty flavour to bread.

*Cornmeal* is made from kernels of corn that have been coarsely ground and will not dissolve. As a flour, it is called *masa*. Cornmeal is used for corn bread, often called johnnycake, tortillas, tacos, and tortilla chips.

## Role of Ingredients in Flour Mixtures

*Flour* • Flour is the most important ingredient in any flour mixture since it creates the structure of the product once liquid is added. In the case of wheat flour, gluten is formed when flour and liquid are mixed. The strength of the elasticlike strands depends on the degree of mixing. Vigorous mixing or kneading produces stronger strands; gentle stirring or folding of the flour maintains a tender, delicate textured product. The recipe specifies the method required.

*Leavening Agents* ✦ A **leavening agent** is an ingredient or combination of ingredients that makes the flour mixture rise and become light and porous. The most common leavening agents are yeast, baking powder, baking soda, steam, and air.

*Yeast* is a single-celled microscopic plant that produces carbon dioxide as a by-product of its growth. It must have sugar, moisture, and the right temperature (25°C) to grow. Stored in a cool, dry place, yeast can be kept for long periods of time.

*Baking powder* is a commercially prepared leavener made from an acid compound, bicarbonate of soda, and starch, usually corn-starch. Once moistened it starts to work by releasing carbon dioxide.

There are two kinds of baking powders. Single-acting baking powder has one acid ingredient and begins to give off carbon dioxide as soon as liquid is added. Double-acting baking powder has two active acid ingredients. One acts as soon as liquid is added, the other has a delayed action and begins to form carbon dioxide only when the batter or dough is exposed to heat. It is the most popular kind.

Yeast is available in various forms suited to specific baking needs.

This action explains why baking powder needs to be stored in an air-tight container to keep it dry. It is important as well to cook batter as soon as liquid has been added so that none of the leavening effect will be lost.

For *baking soda* to act as a leavening agent, it is combined in the flour mixture with an acid substance, such as buttermilk, sour milk, sour cream, yogurt, vinegar, lemon juice, molasses, or an acidic fruit. These ingredients contribute a slightly sour flavour as well. To assure lightness, some recipes utilizing the baking soda action also call for baking powder.

*Steam* is produced from the liquid in the batter or dough when it is heated. This may happen whether an oven, a fry pan, or a deep-fryer is being used. Even a small amount of moisture in the mixture can produce considerable leavening action because the volume of water expands when it is converted to steam. A spectacular increase in volume is achieved when the batter for popovers, Yorkshire pudding, or cream puffs is baked. Steam is the only leavener for these mixtures. Water expands to 1600 times its own mass and causes the gluten strands to separate quickly with high heat to produce a hollow centre.

*Air* also contributes to the leavening of all batters and doughs. Its relative importance is determined by the amount and kind of mixing done, the thickness or thinness of the batter, other ingredients used, and length of time before baking. Air present in the batter will expand as it is heated and increase the volume of the product. Air is incorporated when the batter is beaten, when eggs are whipped, or when an ingredient, such as whipped cream or beaten egg whites, is gently added. The best example of the value of air as a leavener is in foam cakes, such as angel or sponge cakes. They rise to a great volume with the benefit of only air and steam as leaveners.

*Liquids* ◆ Liquids moisten flour and form the gluten strands. They also moisten chemical leaveners, such as baking powder and baking soda, so that carbon dioxide can be released. Liquid ingredients dissolve dry ingredients, such as sugar and salt, and contribute to the leavening action as steam during baking.

Many different liquids can be used in flour mixtures — water, juice, milk, sour milk, buttermilk, sour cream, and yogurt. Each contributes a characteristic flavour and texture to the product. Water and juice give a coarse texture; milk and dairy products give a finer texture and better flavour because of the additional protein and fat they contain.

*Fat* ◆ Whether butter, margarine, lard, vegetable shortening, or vegetable oil is used, fat has several important functions in the flour mixture. It makes the product tender by shortening the strands of gluten. Fat also increases the volume of the product and improves the keeping quality and flavour.

Yeast bread has very little fat. When it is kneaded the gluten strands become long and well developed. In contrast, pastry has a very high proportion of fat, which allows it to be rolled into a thin crust that is still tender in

Each ingredient plays a vital role in baking breads. Which ingredients could have been used to bake these breads?

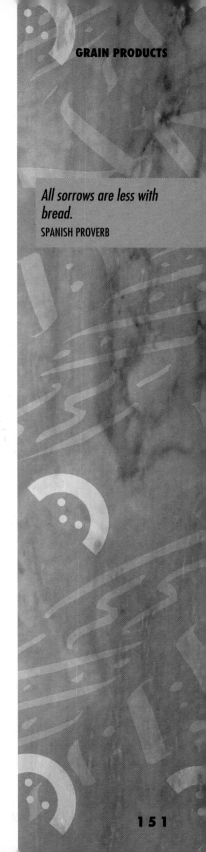

spite of being handled. Muffin batter and cake batter have similar ingredients in very different proportions. The greater amount of fat in "butter" cake makes it possible to mix and beat until all the ingredients are well combined. Muffin batter, on the other hand, needs to be gently stirred just until dry and liquid ingredients are fully combined. When overmixed the product becomes tough and full of large holes.

The type of fat used affects the colour of a product. Batters made with butter and margarine brown more easily than those made with vegetable oil, shortening, or lard. Flavour may also be affected by the kind of fat used. A recipe for shortbread can be made with butter or margarine but substituting lard or shortening would not be a good flavour alternative. However, substitution of shortening for butter or margarine in a chocolate cake recipe does not change the flavour noticeably.

*Sugar* ◆ Because sugar is sweet it naturally contributes to the flavour of flour mixtures. Each type of sweetener — brown or white sugar, molasses, honey — contributes a distinctive flavour. Sugar makes other contributions as well. When batter is heated the sugar in it caramelizes and causes browning to occur. The main difference between ingredients in a loaf of bread and a fruit loaf or muffins, aside from the leavener, is the sugar content. The loaf of bread is a light, golden colour; the fruit loaf is a much darker colour, or light brown. This same factor explains why a plain white cake browns more than biscuits or pie crust that contain no sugar.

Sugar attracts liquid in a batter, leaving less liquid available for gluten development. In this way a mixture containing sugar can be mixed thoroughly without unwanted toughening. Sugar increases the time it takes for the mixture to reach the temperature required to make the proteins firm. A longer baking time is thus needed before the structure is finally set. During this longer baking time more leavening takes place to make a lighter product.

*Eggs* ◆ Eggs can be used in several ways in flour mixtures. The contribution depends on the number and method used. When the whole egg is used, it contributes nutrients, colour, and flavour.

The protein of eggs contributes to the protein framework. When heat is applied, proteins coagulate, and the structure becomes fixed. For example, a single egg in a muffin recipe contributes little to its protein framework, while the higher number of eggs used to make a butter cake makes a significant contribution. In a sponge or angel cake, air is beaten into separated egg whites, which contributes to leavening as well as the protein structure. Usually pastry, biscuits, and yeast breads do not contain eggs.

*All sorrows are less with bread.*
SPANISH PROVERB

*Salt* • The presence of salt in any mixture improves the flavour of other ingredients present. Salt also helps to regulate the rate at which the yeast grows in a flour mixture leavened by yeast and gives it a more even texture.

## Classification of Flour Mixtures—Liquid to Dry Ingredients

• Flour mixtures are often classified according to their consistency resulting from the proportions of dry to liquid ingredients. During preparation, a batter can be beaten more or less vigorously, depending upon the proportion of ingredients used and especially the proportion of liquid to dry ingredients. The terms "pour" (thin) and "drop" (thick) describe the consistency of the mixture when poured or dropped onto the prepared pan.

Doughs are too thick to be beaten once the full amount of flour has been added. They must be kneaded or otherwise worked to properly combine the ingredients. Doughs are further classified as soft or stiff on the basis of the proportion of liquid to dry ingredients.

For a general guideline of the method used for preparing a flour mixture cooked by baking see pages 81–86, Preparing to Cook.

This is a bread dough that has already been kneaded and has been left to rise.

| Mixture | Liquid | Dry | Examples |
|---------|--------|-----|----------|
| Batters | | | |
| Thin (pour) | 1 part | 1 part | Pancake, waffle, popover, Yorkshire pudding |
| Thick (drop) | 1 part | 2 parts | Muffin, cake, coffee cake, gingerbread, cornbread, fruit loaf, drop biscuits |
| Doughs | | | |
| Soft | 1 part | 3 parts | Bread, biscuits, fritters, doughnuts, dumplings |
| Stiff | 1 part | 4 parts | Pastry, rolled cookies |

SOURCE: Adapted from *Management and Foods*

## Examples of Flour Mixtures

*Pancakes* ✦ The ingredients and mixing method for pancakes and muffins are the same, except that pancakes have more liquid which allows the batter to be poured. Fat used in a liquid form helps tenderize the product and prevent sticking to the pan. If there is enough fat in the batter the griddle may not need to be oiled. Sugar assists browning. Eggs improve nutritive value, flavour, and texture.

*Preparation and Cooking of Pancakes* ✦ Whether you are using a commercially prepared mix, your own basic mix, or a favourite recipe, this information applies:

- The griddle is ready if a drop of water bounces when dropped on the pan. Grease the griddle with oil or shortening, not butter or margarine, as both burn easily and darken the product. For even heat distribution the griddle should be heated slowly unless it is controlled by a thermostat.

- The thickness of the batter influences the resulting product and the way it is cooked. A thin batter makes a thin, crisp pancake that cooks quickly. It is ready to turn when the bubbles that form on the surface begin to break. Thicker batter does not form noticeable air bubbles on the surface and more care needs to be taken not to overcook. Turn pancakes only once during baking, otherwise they will become heavy.

- Pancakes are best served while very hot. Once cooled, pancakes are a good alternative to bread for lunch. Extra pancakes can be frozen for future use. Thaw by popping in the toaster at a darker than usual setting.

- Favourite toppings for serving include butter and maple or fruit syrup or honey. For a change and better nutrition try peanut butter, thawed orange juice concentrate, applesauce, fresh berries, or any other fresh or frozen fruit.

*Preparation and Baking of Muffins* ✦ The method used to combine muffin ingredients, called "muffin method," is used to make many other flour mixtures. Examples include waffles, popovers, Yorkshire pudding, quick cake, fruit and nut loaves, and fruit breads. Because the muffin method is basic to many other mixtures, all cooks will want to learn to use the method easily and well.

Although there are several variations in the order of combining ingredients in the muffin method, liquids and dry ingredients are always mixed separately first, then stirred together gently and quickly. Best results are achieved when milk or other liquid is added to well-beaten egg before the melted fat is added. Beating the egg first reduces mixing later, and the milk dilutes the egg so that the hot fat does not cook the egg beforehand. Using vegetable oil eliminates this concern. Some easy muffin recipes suggest combining liquids in a food blender.

Regardless of the recipe used or whether you are using a home or commercial mix, this additional information will be helpful for good results.

Remember to waste no time in getting the muffin batter into the pan and then into the oven.

- The critical step is combining the dry and liquid mixtures. All recipes advise gentle stirring, preferably with a fork or spatula, only until the dry ingredients are moistened. The batter can still be quite lumpy. Pour batters will not be lumpy. Overmixing produces muffins that have a smooth exterior surface, a peaked top, and tunnels inside.

- Dry and liquid ingredients should be combined quickly, with no delay in getting the mixture into the oven. This is why it is important to have the oven heated and pans prepared. Carbon dioxide gas produced by the baking powder is the main leavener and begins forming as soon as the baking powder comes in contact with liquid. Double-acting baking powder is recommended because it produces additional gas when heated in the oven.

- As with other baked products, preparation of pans is an important step for good results. Use vegetable shortening or oil to grease them as butter and margarine will cause additional browning and will eventually discolour the pans.

- Muffins are baked at temperatures in the high range, 190°C to 220°C, which quickly changes the moisture to steam. This expansion contributes to the leavening action. Muffins taste best when served hot and are served most often at a meal in place of bread. They are reheated easily in the oven or microwave. Favourite high-fat and sugar varieties are sometimes eaten hot or cold as snacks. They may better be considered a dessert item in *Canada's Food Guide to Healthy Eating* Other Foods category.

*Preparation and Baking of Biscuits* • Biscuit making demonstrates the technique of "cutting in" firm fat and working with a stiff dough. The skills required are similar to those needed to handle recipes like pastry and rolled cookies. Therefore, learning to make good biscuits is an important step in learning to make progressively more difficult mixtures.

The first step is to measure and mix together all the dry ingredients, usually flour, baking powder, salt, and sometimes sugar. Then cut in the cold fat — shortening, margarine, or butter — until the mixture resembles a coarse cereal. To cut in, use two table knives in a crisscross motion or a pastry blender. Whether you are using a commercial biscuit mix or your own recipe or mix, the following applies.

Biscuits are an example of a quick bread and are best served fresh from the oven while they are still hot.

- Once the flour–fat mixture is the appropriately texture, add the measured milk all at once. Mix with a table fork and avoid overstirring. Only about 30 strokes are necessary to thoroughly combine liquid and dry ingredients.

- The mixture will be stiff, and light kneading is required to ensure proper layering of fat and flour. Turn the mixture onto a lightly floured board and knead gently, taking care not to overwork the dough. Usually 10–15 strokes are sufficient.

- Roll or pat the dough on the lightly floured board to a thickness of 1.5 cm–2 cm. Rolling it too thin will result in flat, hard biscuits. Round shapes are cut with a floured biscuit cutter pressed straight down without twisting. It is best to make cuts close together so that there will be a minimum of scraps. Scraps should be combined, rerolled, and cut with minimal working of the dough and without adding more flour. Additional working of the dough beyond the original kneading will develop gluten further and toughen the product. One way to reduce manipulation is to simply cut the rolled dough into straight-sided pieces with a sharp knife.

- Drop biscuits are made by using enough milk to give a thick drop batter. This is spooned directly onto a greased baking pan. Made this way, the product has an irregular shape and crumbly texture.

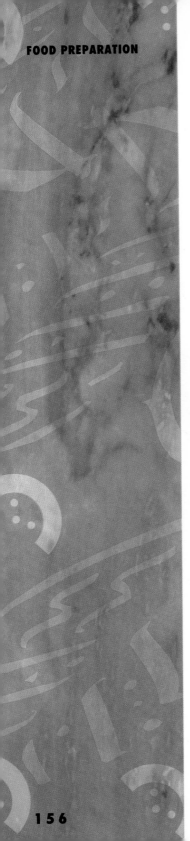

- Biscuits are baked in a hot oven, usually 220°C. This high temperature means that biscuits rise quickly to form flaky layers characteristic of a good product. Shiny pans will give the biscuits a desirable pale colour. Pans do not require greasing. Place biscuits on the pan with space between them so that heat can circulate freely. For biscuits with soft sides, place them close together or touching.

*Basic Mix* ◆ Cooks in the home and in commercial settings use a variety of mixes. This basic flour mixture recipe is one of many that you can make for your own use. It stores easily, is readily carried outdoors, and can be used in many ways, such as for biscuits, pancakes, or muffins. Experiment with it to see how many different possibilities you can develop.

## Basic Mix

| | |
|---|---|
| 1000 mL | all-purpose flour and 1500 mL whole-wheat flour or |
| 2250 mL | all-purpose flour |
| 75 mL | baking powder |
| 10 mL | salt |
| 500 mL | shortening |

1. Measure all dry ingredients into a very large bowl or container. A roasting pan, pot, or clean plastic bucket works well.
2. Cut shortening into dry ingredients until mixture resembles coarse oatmeal.
3. Store at room temperature in a covered container for up to six weeks. (A 4-L ice cream container is an ideal size.) For longer storage, place in the freezer.
4. To use, stir mix to reduce packing, spoon into a dry measure, and level with a knife or spatula. Add liquid and any other ingredients. Mix and cook as appropriate.

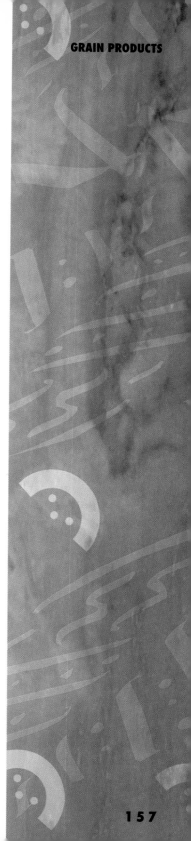

*Variations*

1. To get maximum economy and convenience, add 250 mL skim milk powder to the dry ingredients. Then when making up a recipe use water in place of milk. This variation of the mix is especially useful when fresh milk is not readily available, as when camping or boating.
2. For improved nutrient value, substitute 250 mL of wheat germ for 250 mL of the flour.
3. For better browning, add 25–50 mL sugar to the mixture. Alternatively, add sugar only to the recipes that need it, rather than to the mix.

## Recipes Using Basic Mix

*Basic Mix Biscuits*
500 mL basic mix

Yield: 10–12 biscuits
125 mL milk

*Basic Mix Pancakes*
500 mL basic mix
15 mL sugar

Yield: 12 pancakes (10–12 cm)
2 eggs
300 mL milk

*Basic Mix Muffins*
750 mL basic mix
50 mL sugar
5 mL grated lemon rind

Yield: 12 muffins
1 egg
250 mL milk
10 mL lemon juice

**FOOD PREPARATION**

 KEY TERMS

Use the words listed below to complete the following statements in your notebook.

| | |
|---|---|
| gluten | staff of life |
| leavening agent | kneading |
| batter | grains |
| dough | endosperm |
| pasta | al dente |

1. Nearly all cultures make some form of bread, which is why bread is called the _____.

2. Most flour mixtures have a _____, which causes them to rise.

3. A mixture that has as much liquid as flour is called a _____.

4. A mixture that is stiff enough to be worked with the hands is called a _____.

5. Wheat protein is also called _____.

6. The major part of all-purpose flour comes from the _____.

7. An Italian term used to describe properly cooked pasta is _____.

8. _____ is the term used to describe all macaroni and noodle products.

9. A process used to develop gluten is called _____.

10. _____ are the seeds produced by grasses.

FOCUS YOUR KNOWLEDGE

1. Name the types of grains.

2. Identify the foods you ate yesterday that you consider to be in the grains food group. Assess your accuracy against *Canada's Food Guide to Healthy Eating*.

3. Identify the nutrients found in grain and describe the function of these nutrients.

4. Name three foods made from each of the grains discussed.

5. List the different types of rice and suggest ways to include each in a meal.

6. List the types of leavening agents and find a recipe in which each is found.

7. Read four different recipes for flour mixtures and decide whether each is a batter or dough.

## ☀ DEMONSTRATE YOUR KNOWLEDGE

1. In small groups, design an experiment to show the action of a leavening agent. Conduct the experiment and record the results.

2. Prepare a variety of rices and serve them to a taste panel. Note the characteristics of each type of rice prepared. Chart the cooking time, colour, flavour, and texture of each rice.

3. Locate and prepare a recipe that uses the muffin method of mixing.

4. Locate and prepare a recipe that uses the biscuit method of mixing.

5. With a partner select and prepare a type of pasta. Organize a buffet to enjoy the pastas prepared by you and your classmates.

## ☀ APPLY YOUR KNOWLEDGE

1. Examine a cereal grain under a hand lens. Try to identify the parts shown on the diagram in this chapter.

2a. In small groups develop a score card (standard) for a baked product, such as muffins or biscuits. Standards are based on appearance, texture, and flavour.

b. Under these headings describe what a perfect product should be like.

3. Interview a person of another culture about the grain products he or she uses. Report your findings to the class.

4. Visit a store and list all the varieties of pasta available. Divide your list into the four basic types.

5. Create a list of recipes that could be made with the Basic Mix as their basis.

# Vegetables and Fruit

*Canada's Food Guide to Healthy Eating* combines vegetables and fruit in one food group and recommends 5–10 servings per day. Servings of these foods can be fresh, uncooked or cooked, or frozen, canned, dried, or as juice. No matter where they live most Canadians have a wide variety of vegetables and fruit available to them, and a healthy eating pattern will incorporate many different kinds of vegetables and fruit regularly.

## VEGETABLES AND SALADS

### Classification of Vegetables ◆
Vegetables can be classified in many different ways: by flavour, by colour, by the predominant nutrient provided, or by the part of the plant used. Here they have been grouped according to the part of the plant that is eaten. It may be helpful to think of these parts by listing them in the order in which they grow and mature.

Energy to nourish the growing plant is stored in the *tubers*. It is logical then that tubers contain carbohydrates and vitamins. These vegetables contain the most kilojoules. Examples are potatoes with vitamin C, and yams and sweet potatoes with the vitamin A that is associated with their yellow colour.

*Root vegetables* come from the part of the plant that grows below the ground. They contain fewer carbohydrates than tubers, mainly in the form of sugar. Common examples are turnips, carrots, parsnips, and beets.

*Bulb vegetables* have an intense flavour as their principal value. Think of examples like onions, garlic, and leeks.

Minerals and vitamins are transported through the *stem* or *stalk* to other parts of the plant. In addition to these nutrients, stalk vegetables, such as celery and asparagus, also contain fibre.

*Enjoy— Manitoba Vegetables*

These are some of the vegetables grown in Manitoba. What vegetables are grown in your province?

The *leaves* of any plant contain **chlorophyl**, the substance manufactured in plants, with the help of light, that gives the green colouring. Leaf vegetables are a good source of vitamins and minerals, but not carbohydrates. The darkest green leaves have the most vitamin A. Examples include spinach, vegetables of the cabbage family like Brussels sprouts, chard, and kale, and the many varieties of lettuce.

The *flower vegetables* are valued for their high vitamin and mineral content and low number of kilojoules. The name describes their appearance as seen in cauliflower, broccoli, and artichoke.

The *fruit* of the plant have distinctive flavours. Most have few carbohydrates but plenty of vitamins and minerals. Examples are tomatoes, eggplant, pumpkin, and squash and peppers of all kinds.

*Seed vegetables* are intended by nature to create and nourish a new plant. Therefore, they contain protein and carbohydrates as well as vitamins and minerals. Examples are corn, peas, and beans.

Some vegetables can be both root and leaf vegetables. Beets are roots, and beet tops are leaf vegetables. Can you think of any other vegetables that may have more than one classification?

Clockwise from the top left these are: cabbage; lettuce; pumpkin; broccoli; eggplant; cauliflower; potatoes; radishes, corn; onions; green beans; garlic; celery; carrots; tomatoes; green pepper.

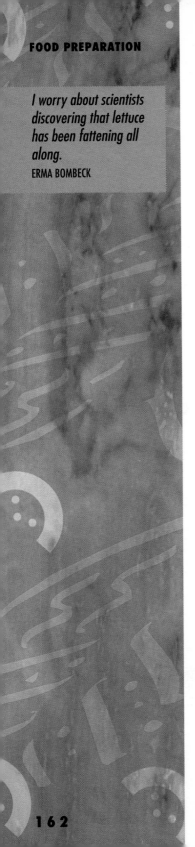

*I worry about scientists discovering that lettuce has been fattening all along.*
ERMA BOMBECK

Nutritive Value of Vegetables ◆ All fresh vegetables are valuable sources of nutrients, principally vitamins and minerals. Leafy green and bright orange ones are dependable sources of vitamin A. Vitamin C is present in vegetables of the cabbage family, tomatoes, and potatoes. Individual B vitamins are obtained in certain groups of vegetables. Iron and calcium are the most significant minerals. Leafy green vegetables are the best mineral contributor, although there are other specific vegetable sources.

Some vegetables also contain carbohydrates — sugar as in peas and sweet potatoes, and starch found in potatoes, corn, and beans. A few, like beans, peas, lentils, and soya beans, are important for the incomplete protein they supply. The plant structure of most vegetables means that they contain some fibre that will provide bulk and assist with elimination of body wastes. For further details on the nutritional value of vegetables see the nutrient chart on pages 314–315.

Choosing Fresh Vegetables ◆ Careful selection and appropriate storage of vegetables are the first steps in obtaining maximum food value from them. This is easier to do when vegetables are home grown. When vegetables are purchased the length of storage time and the storing conditions are unknown to you. They may be quite old. The best advice is to learn to recognize the characteristics of freshness in the vegetable you want and be prepared to substitute if the quality is unacceptable. Here are some key considerations.

- Buy only what you can use while it is still fresh.
- Buy what is in season. Improved refrigeration and transportation systems have extended availability. Nonetheless, there are periods for each vegetable when prices and quality are at their best. Root and tuber vegetables that keep well may be available year round.
- Cost should not be the primary consideration. Reduced prices for inferior or damaged produce will offer poor nutrient value and you may end up throwing it out. This is not value for your money. Learn to recognize blemishes, such as bruises or cuts, that do not affect food value or the cooked product and take advantage of the lower price.
- Choose on the basis of use for the vegetable. Sometimes smaller or uneven shapes are quite suitable and may even have better texture or food value. Carrots used in a stew, for example, need not be straight and

all the same size as they would be for a fresh vegetable tray. Decide if perfection is important for your use.

The accompanying chart will supplement these points.

## Buying, Preparing, and Serving Vegetables

| Vegetable | Desired Qualities | Preparing and Serving |
|---|---|---|
| Asparagus | Straight, tender, crisp, bright green stalks with tightly closed tips. Bunches having stalks of uniform size and thickness. | Wash. Break off base where it snaps easily. Steam, boil, microwave, or bake. Serve with sauce or butter and nuts. Eat young tips raw or with dip. |
| Beans — green and wax (yellow) | Young, crisp, tender, fairly straight beans free from blemishes. Beans of uniform size with well-formed seeds. | Remove ends and any strings. Leave whole, cut in 3-cm pieces, or French cut by cutting lengthwise in strips. Steam, boil, microwave, or bake. Serve with sauce or herb butter. |
| Bean sprouts | Tiny white shoots with pale green hoods; a crunchy texture. | Cook briefly to retain crunchiness. Add to omelettes, shellfish, salads, soups, and other vegetable dishes. |
| Beets | Clean, firm, smooth beets free from cracks or other blemishes. Beets of uniform size to cook together. | Wash without bruising skin. Boil with skins on leaving roots and part of stem attached. When cooked, skins and stem will slip off. Serve sliced, diced, in sweet-sour sauce or cold in vinegar. |
| Beet tops | Fresh crisp leaves. | Wash in lukewarm water, then cold water. Cut. Leave water on leaves for cooking. Steam, boil, or microwave. Cook only until limp. Use all the vegetable. Requires little cooking. Stir-fry or use in soups. |
| Bok choy | Long, smooth white stems and large dark green, crinkly leaves. | Use all the vegtable. Requires little cooking. Stir-fry or use in soups. |
| Broccoli | Tender, firm stalks with compact green heads. | Wash. Trim leaves and woody stems. Strip coarse outside of stalks. Cut lengthwise in several serving-size pieces. Steam, boil, or microwave. Serve plain or with sauce. Eat raw, plain, or with dip. |
| Brussels sprouts | Firm, compact heads with fresh green leaves. Sprouts of uniform size to cook together. | Trim stems and outer leaves. Make two crosswise cuts in base of large sprouts. Steam, boil, or microwave. |
| Cabbage — red, green, or savoy | Firm, compact heads with crisp green or red leaves. Savoy has distinct crinkly green leaves. | Wash. Trim outer leaves and stem. Cut in wedges (core attached), chunks, or shred. Steam, boil, or microwave. Serve raw in coleslaw or for contrast in green salad. Use for cabbage rolls, sauerkraut. |

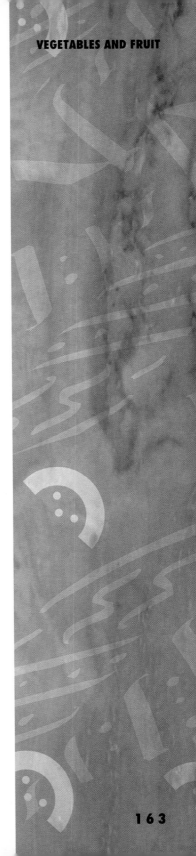

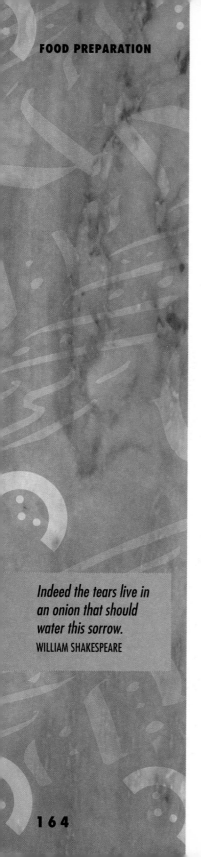

| Carrots | Bunched young carrots with fresh green tops. Packaged mature carrots firm, well-shaped, smooth, free from blemishes and green colour. | Brush or scrape young carrots; peel others. Leave small carrots whole; cut others in fingers, 2–3-cm chunks, or thin slices. Serve raw in sticks or grated in salads or slaw. Steam, boil, microwave, or bake. |
|---|---|---|
| Cauliflower | Firm, creamy-white, smooth, compact, and heavy head. | Wash. Trim outer leaves and stem. Leave whole, cutting out 3 cm of core or separate into florets. Serve raw, plain, or with dip. Add small pieces to salad. Steam, boil, microwave, bake. Good with sauce, such as cheese. |
| Celery | Crisp, fresh, green bunches with straight stalks free from blemishes. | Wash. Trim root and leaves. Separate stalks. Slice diagonally 0.5–1 cm thick. Eat pieces raw or in salads. Use in casseroles, stews, and soups. |
| Corn | Freshly picked with bright green husks tightly wrapped around well-filled ears. Creamy-yellow, plump kernels, not shrivelled or dry. | Remove husks and silk. Cut off most of stalk. Steam, boil, microwave and eat from cob with butter. Or cut off kernels to cream or use in soups and stews. |
| Eggplant | Well-shaped, firm, heavy with smooth, satiny, purple skin free from blemishes. | Wash, remove stem, and peel if desired. Slice 1–1.5 cm thick. Steam, pan fry, coat with batter or crumbs and deep-fry. Use in casserole mixtures, soups, or stews. |
| Fennel | Firm, crisp looking. | Trim and wash, then halve, quarter, or slice. Serve raw — plain or in a salad. Braise and add to casseroles. |
| Mushrooms | Fairly clean, white, and firm. Caps not opened fully. | Trim stalk. Slice lengthwise. Serve raw with dip or mixed in salad. Use cooked in casseroles, soups, stews, or sautéed alone. |
| Okra | Small, firm, green pods. | Cut off the stalk end. Good addition to vegetable stews, curries, and spiced rice dishes. |
| Onions | Firm onions with dry, brownish-yellow skins. Not sprouting. | Remove dry skin, root, and stem. Leave whole, halve, quarter, slice, or dice. Steam, boil, bake, microwave whole or use sliced or chopped in assorted mixtures. |
| Parsnips | Firm, straight, smooth parsnips free from blemishes. | Trim stem and root ends and peel. Leave small parsnips whole; cut others in fingers or thin slices. Boil, steam, bake, or use in stews or soups. |
| Peas | Freshly picked, crisp, bright green pods, well-filled but not bulging. | Shell pod peas. Trim ends of sugar peas and snow peas. Steam, boil, microwave, and serve plain or with herb butter sauce. Use snow peas in stir-fry recipes. |

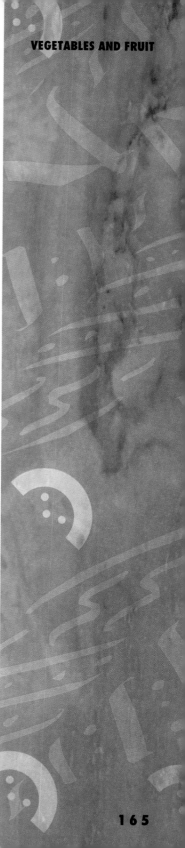

| | | |
|---|---|---|
| Peppers — green, red, yellow | Crisp, bright-coloured peppers with smooth skin. Symmetrical shape for stuffing. | Halve lengthwise. Remove stem, seeds, and membrane. Cut into chunks or strips to serve raw with dip or in salad. Chop or slice to use in casseroles and stew. Stuff halves with seasoned ground meat or rice and bake. |
| Potatoes | Fairly clean, well-shaped potatoes, relatively free from blemishes, and no green colour. Several varieties are available. | Scrub. Leave skins on or peel. Leave whole, halve, quarter, slice, or cut in fingers. Steam, boil, microwave, or bake. Serve plain or in sauce. Use in stews and soups. |
| Spinach | Fresh, clean, crisp green leaves. | Trim roots and heavy stems. Wash bulk in warm then cold water. Rinse packaged leaves. Leave a little water on leaves for cooking. Use raw in green salad. Steam, boil, microwave. Cook only until limp. |
| Squash — summer (vegetable marrow) and winter | Summer varieties — tender skin, free from soft spots, heavy for size. Winter varieties — hard shell, free from soft spots or damage. | Summer varieties — leave skin on; remove seeds if desired. Steam, boil, or bake. Winter varieties — leave skin on or peel; remove seeds. Halve, quarter, or cut in chunks. Steam or bake. Sprinkle with brown sugar and dot with butter. |
| Swiss chard | Fresh, crisp, green leaves. Crisp, fairly clean, light green stalks. Young chard for best flavour. | Remove outer, blemished leaves. Wash in lukewarm then cold water. Chop leaves coarsely. Cut firm ribs and stems in 3-cm pieces. Use raw in salad or slaw. Steam, boil, or microwave. Cook only until limp. |
| Tomatoes | Plump, firm tomatoes. Uniform red with firm skin. | Wash. Leave whole, halve, quarter, or slice. To peel dip in boiling water 30–60 seconds, cool briefly in cold water. Serve fresh in salad or sliced alone. Use in mixtures, such as stews, soups, and casseroles. |
| Turnips (white) Rutabagas (yellow) | Firm and heavy with few scars and roots. Fresh, crisp, green tops. | Peel whole, small, white, turnips. Slice, dice, or cut in fingers or chunks. Leave small turnips whole, if preferred. Steam, boil, microwave, or bake. Use in soups, stews, or other mixtures. |

SOURCE: Adapted from *Management and Foods*

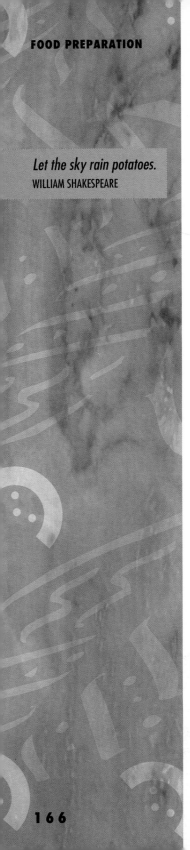

*Let the sky rain potatoes.*
WILLIAM SHAKESPEARE

## Storing Fresh Vegetables

- Tuber vegetables should be stored in a cool 10°C dark, airy place. They will keep for 4–9 months. The exception is new potatoes, which should be stored in the refrigerator and used within 1 week.
- Remove tops of root vegetables before storing in a cool, moist place or in the refrigerator. They will keep several weeks.
- Store bulb vegetables uncovered in a dry, airy place. Use within several weeks.
- Stalk vegetables should be put in a plastic bag and kept in the refrigerator. Use within the week.
- Store leaf vegetables in a plastic bag in the refrigerator and use within 1–2 days. Vegetables of the cabbage family will keep longer, but should be used within 2 weeks.
- Broccoli should be stored in a plastic bag in the refrigerator. Store cauliflower in the refrigerator with the outer leaves attached; cut a thin slice from the stalk. Other flower vegetables should be stored uncovered in the refrigerator. They should all be used within the week.
- Put peas and beans in a plastic bag; leave the husks on corn. Store all seed vegetables in the refrigerator. Corn and peas should be used the same day. Beans should be used within 5 days.
- Store mushrooms in a paper bag in the refrigerator. The paper absorbs any moisture given off by the mushrooms. Use within the week.

## Frozen and Canned Vegetables

Fortunately for many people who are unable to shop regularly in supermarkets, there are alternatives. Having frozen, canned, and dried foods on hand provides variety and is especially useful when shopping is not an option. Campers, hikers, boaters, and people living in remote areas rely on some forms of vegetables other than fresh.

Frozen vegetables should be solidly frozen when purchased and remain so until used. Packages of unsized vegetables are a better buy, and large bags, provided you have freezer space, are more versatile and cost less per kilogram.

When buying canned vegetables consider the use intended. Tomatoes for a sauce or soup need not be whole or of any particular size. For serving cold or in a casserole dish, you may prefer them whole and uniformly small. The other consideration is to buy a size that will be used without any waste. Large cans at a discounted price are not good value unless the whole amount is used.

Canned vegetables will have lost some of their original food value but using the juices helps to minimize this loss. Under normal conditions canned foods keep for years. Cans should not be allowed to freeze or rust. A storage temperature of 10°C or less is ideal. Higher temperatures will eventually affect the colour and flavour but will not affect wholesomeness of vegetables.

## Cooking Principles

♦ Although cooking most vegetables generally reduces their food value, there are good reasons for serving them cooked, at least some of the time. Providing variety and interest to meals is a first consideration. In spite of the appeal of salads and other fresh produce, it would be very difficult to eat only raw vegetables, and because of the bulk you would probably not be able to eat enough of them to supply your body's needs. Cooking softens the structure which reduces volume and, in many cases, makes the flavour more acceptable. When a vegetable is cooked properly, it can be digested more easily. Cooked, starchy vegetables, such as potatoes, are a good example of improved flavour and increased digestibility.

Some vegetables look more appealing when cooked, especially when colours become intensified. Cooking always destroys microorganisms that may be present. Very young children with immature immune systems are fed only cooked vegetables for this reason. Canned vegetables have been cooked at a high temperature under pressure and, therefore, are sterilized.

Properly cooked vegetables remain close to the natural colour, form, and flavour of their raw state with a minimum loss of nutrients. The principles that have been developed to achieve the desired results revolve around the minimum exposure to water and the shortest possible cooking time. Certain vitamins are destroyed when high heat is applied for an extended time. Overcooked vegetables lose their desirable colour and flavour, become mushy, and may develop unpleasant odours and unnatural flavours.

Because some vitamins are water-soluble, they will seep out of the vegetable into the cooking liquid easily. Therefore, you should reduce the amount of liquid and minimize the surface exposed to it. Use the water in which vegetables are cooked in a sauce, soup, or gravy to retain some of the vitamins.

Cooked vegetables can be a colourful, nutritious addition to a meal. Try to name the vegetables pictured here.

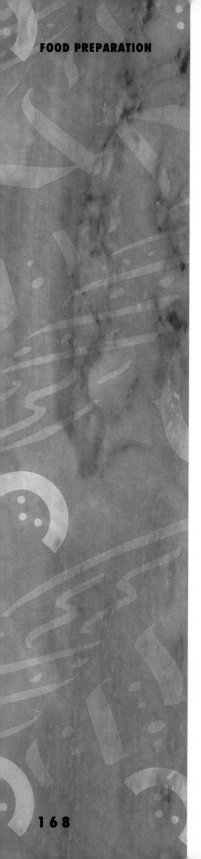

## CAREER SKETCH

THE LOCAL GROCERY STORE often provides a good opportunity for students to find part-time jobs. According to Jim Grieve, owner of Port Perry IGA, approximately 40 percent of the available jobs at his store are filled by students. Students can be found working in virtually every department. They range in age from 14–20 years old. Here are some of the students who work at the Port Perry IGA and a description of their jobs.

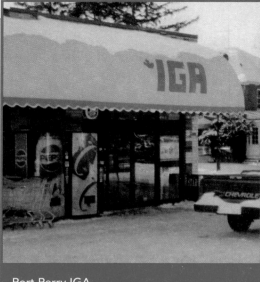

Port Perry IGA

### JASEN DAWSON, 19 — BAKERY

Dawson bakes much of the wide variety of products available at the bakery—breads, rolls, muffins, and pies. A lot of baking is done on the midnight shift, in order to have fresh products ready in the morning. Dawson is also responsible for keeping the bakery clean and for serving customers. He has been working in the bakery for over four years. "I like working with the dough and being able to work on my own. It's a fun job."

### CHRISTOPHER BRYANT, 18 — PRODUCE

Bryant is responsible for putting the vegetables and fruit on the shelves. He keeps the produce area neat and clean. He also helps customers, answering their questions about prices and locations of products. On the occasion when someone returns a spoiled product, he either replaces it or gives the customer a refund. One day a week he completely tears down the counters to thoroughly clean the produce section. "It's a good part-time job and you make good money. You have to learn good customer relations."

### RANDY GARDNER, 20 — DAIRY/FROZEN FOODS

Gardner is in his third year of working at the IGA. He works with milks, cheese, butter, eggs, and frozen foods. He stocks the shelves, does price checks, helps customers, makes signs for special prices, and organizes the cooler for the frozen foods. He has to be able to identify the boxes containing the various sizes and kinds of products. "I like the variety in this job; there's always something to do. The organizational and socialization skills will help me in my future career."

### ANNETTE STAINTON, 18 — DELI

Stainton cuts the various kinds of meats, prepares meat and cheese trays, and prepares hot foods and ready-to-cook foods such as pizzas. She serves the variety of deli products to customers. An important part of her job is keeping the deli area clean. The meat slicers and counters must be clean and sanitary. "I love dealing with the public, and the people I work with are great. It's a good part-time job."

### DAVE PHILIP, 18 — MEATS

Philip works 30 hours a week in the meat department. He packages meats that have already been prepared, such as frozen sausages and beef patties. He has been learning how to cut pieces of meat, such as pork chops and roasts. He trims the fat off meats and also makes hamburger. Like Stainton, he is responsible for the sanitation of his department. "Working with meat is a good skill to fall back on. It teaches you responsibility and how to make decisions. I also like that it's a physical job."

### MARK COSWAY, 18 — GROCERY

Cosway keeps the shelves stocked and looks after the stock in the back room. He has to keep a close watch on the items on special to make sure that they do not run low. He runs price checks and answers customer questions. "This job keeps you busy. They treat you well, and you can earn money to go to university. There aren't a lot of jobs out there, but they'll take you on here."

### MANDY BRIGHT, 18 — CASHIER

Although the main part of Bright's job is to run the grocery items through the electronic scanner and ring in prices, she also deals in public relations. She has learned how to deal with the public, including people with special needs, such as those with disabilities or seniors. She keeps a smile on her face and gauges whether the customers want to talk with her. Because many items such as produce are coded, she has to memorize the codes. This is not easy, as the codes sometimes change. She also deals with money and has to keep her till accurate. "This is one of the best jobs in town. You get paid well, you learn a lot, and it keeps you busy."

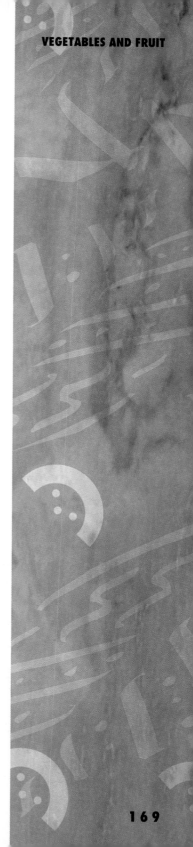

## Methods of Cooking Vegetables • The cooking method that you choose will depend to some extent on the equipment available and the other foods being served. Try to incorporate variety and interest by using different cooking methods for the foods in a meal, while at the same time utilizing energy wisely. For example, you may want to bake vegetables for dinner if the oven is already heated to cook meat or dessert. For variety you might serve a crisp, raw vegetable as well. Certain methods are more suitable to cooking some vegetables than others.

When *baked*, vegetables will retain water-soluble nutrients, but some vitamin C will be lost from high temperatures. Vegetables can be peeled or scrubbed and cooked with the skins on, baked in an ovenproof dish, open or covered, and served at the table from the baking dish. A variation is to season cut pieces, wrap in aluminum foil, and bake. Sometimes this same preparation is used to cook vegetables on the barbecue.

In *steaming*, vegetables are placed over boiling water in a container with holes in the bottom to allow the steam to penetrate. The pot is covered tightly. Since the vegetables never touch the water, water-soluble nutrients are retained. Steaming only takes a short time. Mild-flavoured vegetables, such as leafy greens and summer squash, are well suited to steaming.

More nutrients are lost by *boiling* than by any other method. To minimize loss, start with boiling water, then simmer with the lid in place for a minimum of time. More of the nutrients will be saved by using the cooking water later.

*Broiling* vegetables, such as tomato halves, sliced eggplant, and zucchini pieces, is an attractive way to garnish the dinner plate. Place vegetables far enough away from the heat source to avoid burning and broil until just tender and browned.

When *stir-frying* is done correctly, there is maximum nutrient retention. Use a minimum of oil (some pans require none), a high heat, and keep stirring constantly. Any preparation and slicing for the stir-fry should be done before cooking is started and the rest of the meal should be nearly ready to serve because this popular method takes very little cooking time. It can be used for a single vegetable or an assortment of them. When more than one vegetable is to be combined, begin with the one that requires the longest cooking time. Then, as you continue to stir, add others according to the length of time they need to be cooked. Cook only until tender and serve immediately.

*Pressure cooking* requires the use of a pressure cooker, an airtight apparatus for cooking with steam under pressure. Nutrient losses are minimal because cooking time is so short and very little water is used. However, overcooking is a danger unless timing is very accurate. Follow the manufacturer's instructions.

*Microwave cooking* is suitable for most vegetables and results in an attractive product with minimum nutrient loss. Cut vegetables in uniform pieces, place in a suitable dish, and cover the top with plastic wrap. Puncture with a few holes to allow steam to escape. Cook for time suggested by the manufacturer.

## Kinds of Salads

The possibilities for salad making are endless and only limited by the imagination of the cook. Usually a salad is cold, but there are recipes for salads served hot. Ingredients may be either raw or cooked. Meal salads usually have vegetables as their base, but fruit may also be added. When served as an appetizer or a dessert, the entire salad may be made of fruit. Here are some possibilities.

- Special small vegetable salads are sometimes served as appetizers. Raw vegetables with dip or a seafood cocktail with tangy tomato-based sauce could be used this way.

- A simple mixture of assorted greens might be served just before or immediately after the entrée. Alternatively, a similar salad may be offered at the same time as the entrée. Certainly this is the case with buffet service. Coleslaw, a salad made with shredded cabbage, and potato salad are often served with a meal.

- Main dish salads have some protein food added to them to make them heartier. Potato salad might contain hard cooked egg. When accompanied by a bread and possibly hot soup or a beverage, the salad is the main part of the meal.

A salmon and pasta salad is just one of the many kinds of salad you can make. Think of three interesting salad combinations.

## Preparing and Serving Salads

Making an attractive, appetizing salad begins with careful selection of the ingredients. In the case of a tossed green salad the most important step is choosing and caring for the green vegetables. Choose the freshest greens available and avoid any that have wilted or bruised leaves or curled edges. Do not limit yourself to iceberg lettuce unless that is all that is available. Darker green leaves have better food value. Try romaine, leaf lettuce, or spinach for a change or combine two or three varieties that give a good mixture of colour and texture. In winter, or when lettuce is very expensive, use cabbage or sliced pieces of chard, Chinese cabbage, or bok choy to add interest and extend the lettuce.

If salad greens are to be used within 24 hours, wash the vegetables thoroughly to remove dirt, spray residues, and insects. Drain and remove as much water as possible. Use a clean towel, salad spinner, or paper towel. Excess moisture increases the rate of spoilage during storage. Finally, wrap in a towel and store in a plastic bag in the refrigerator until it is time to be make the salad.

When the salad vegetables need to be stored for longer than 24 hours, simply remove damaged parts and place in a plastic bag in the refrigerator crisper. Early on the day when the salad is to be made, wash and prepare greens as described and allow several hours for them to become crisp. Here are additional tips to preparing a good salad.

- Allow enough time to chill all salad ingredients before combining them.
- Be sure the greens are crisped and dry. Salad dressings will not adhere to wet greens.
- Tear greens into pieces instead of cutting them. The salad will not wilt as quickly because the cell structure will not be as damaged. For hard vegetables, such as celery, use a very sharp knife to prevent unnecessary bruising of the cells.
- Salad ingredients should be in pieces large enough to be recognizable without settling to the bottom of the bowl. Make lettuce and other leafy greens small enough to be eaten easily. You should be able to eat the resulting salad with a fork. Finely chopped vegetables, as in coleslaw, are held together with dressing.

IT WAS THE FRUITS VS. THE VEGETABLES AND ONCE AGAIN THE TOMATO WAS FORCED TO CHOOSE A SIDE.

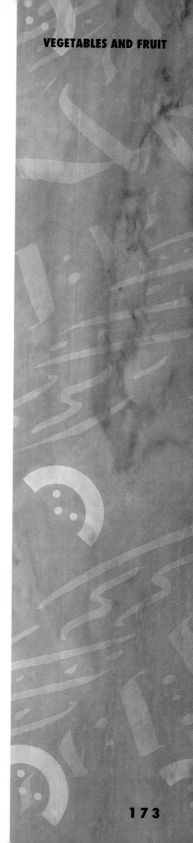

- Toss salad ingredients together gently to avoid bruising. Add dressing and any seasonings a little at a time to avoid excess, and just before serving, or offer separately at the table.
- Garnish simply with attention to natural shapes, colours, and textures of the ingredients. Serve chilled. When using individual plates, chill them. Do not let greens extend beyond the edge of the plate. The plate should "frame" the salad.

# FRUIT

**Kinds of Fruit** • Like vegetables, fruit can be classified into groups. Here is one way of thinking of the kinds of fruit and some suggestions for choosing and storing them.

*Berries* are the most perishable of all fruit. They need to be handled gently by rolling rather than dropping them into the container. When washing is required it should be done just before serving. Never allow berries to sit in water, they should be washed and drained immediately. Refrigeration is imperative to slow the action of the natural enzymes that cause spoilage. Examples are blueberries, raspberries, red currants, and strawberries.

All members of the *citrus fruit* family — lemons, limes, kumquats, oranges, and grapefruit — supply valuable amounts of vitamin C. The juiciest ones will have thin, smooth skins and a fully developed colour. All keep very well in the refrigerator.

*Tree fruit*, as the name indicates, are the product of mature trees whose blossoms have been pollinated. Some, such as apples and pears, have a central core around the edible portion, all enclosed by a protective skin. They keep for a long period of time under optimal conditions as demonstrated by the availability of certain varieties in spring. Another whole group of tree fruit contain a single seed or pit. Examples are cherries, plums, peaches, and nectarines. The fleshy, edible portion is soft, and together this group is sometimes referred to as soft fruit. They spoil much more quickly than apples and definitely require refrigeration.

The most obvious *vine fruit* are the different varieties of melons including honeydew, cantaloupe, and watermelon. When fully ripened they have a noticeable aroma, and the stem end will give way when pressed. A wide assortment of grapes also grow on vines. Choose clumps of grapes that are full and well attached to the stem. Avoid clumps with shrivelled, bruised, or decayed grapes. All vine fruits should be stored in the refrigerator.

These coconuts are from the Philippines.

Clockwise from the top left these are: watermelon; cantaloupe; pineapple; grapefruit; apples; oranges; grapes; pear; peach; cherries; blueberries; strawberries; kiwi; bananas, pomegranate

Although *tropical* and *exotic fruit* are imported from countries with warmer climates, they are well-known in Canada. Bananas, pineapple, papaya, and coconut are some of the most familiar. They are all most flavourful when fully ripened and served at room temperature. Bananas should never be refrigerated. Other tropical and exotic fruit include fig, kiwi, mango, passion fruit, and pomegranate.

### Nutritive Value of Fruit

Fruit of all kinds is valuable for the nutrients supplied. Probably most important to a healthy body is the vitamin and mineral content that fruit contributes. Because vitamin C cannot be stored in the body, a daily vitamin C-rich source is needed. A serving of citrus fruit like orange, grapefruit, or mandarins will supply enough for the day. There are other less concentrated fruit sources of vitamin C. The bright yellow or orange colour of any fruit indicates a rich source of vitamin A.

The most important mineral available from fruit is iron. Body reserves of iron can be restored by eating dried fruits such as apricots, dates, prunes, and raisins. Some fresh fruit also contain this mineral. It is well to remember that concentrations of minerals are greatest just under the skin so the skin should be eaten if at all possible. Wash fresh fruit thoroughly before eating.

The carbohydrate content of most fruit is relatively low and is primarily some form of sugar. The ripening process changes starch to a natural sugar, called fructose. Most canned fruit contain at least a small amount of added sugar. If you do not want additional kilojoules, choose water-packed fruit or discard the syrup. Enjoyed for the delicious flavour that is characteristic of all fruit, the fibre they contain furnishes bulk that acts as a natural laxative. Water is the other body regulating component of fruit.

## Principles for Preparing and Cooking Fruit

The reasons for cooking fruit are similar to those for cooking vegetables. As with vegetables, raw fruit supply more nutrients than cooked fruit. Unlike vegetables, but to the body's advantage, fruit are more frequently eaten raw than cooked. When fruit are canned, they are cooked to stop enzyme action that causes spoilage. The application of heat softens fibre and makes the fruit easier to eat and digest. Texture and flavour of some fruit are also improved by cooking. Cooking fruit provides an interesting variety of choices for our meals.

Caring for fruit once they are in your possession is a first step in presentation. Careful washing removes dust, spray residue, and other contaminants. Since cut fruit will turn brown and lose flavour and vitamins, fruit should be cut just before serving. Knives and other utensils should be sharp to prevent bruises and juice loss. Vitamin C is the vitamin most easily destroyed by exposure to oxygen, heat, and water.

As with vegetables, principles for preparing and cooking fruit have to do with preserving the greatest possible nutritive values. Here are the main issues.

- Prevent or minimize exposure to oxygen.
- Minimize the time during which cut surfaces are exposed to air.
- Wherever possible eat the skins because they have high concentrations of nutrients directly under them.
- Use as little water as possible during cooking and use the resulting nutrient-rich liquid in some way.
- Cook for the shortest possible time and only until tender.

Fruit can be cooked by several methods. They can be baked, such as baked apples with roast pork. Apples can also be baked for dessert, such as a cobbler. A variety of fruit can be baked in pies, cakes, and muffins.

Fruit are sometimes cooked in a liquid and made into a sauce. Cranberries, apples, and rhubarb are commonly made this way. The fruit are cooked in a small amount of water or another liquid. Cutting the fruit into small pieces helps to cook them quickly.

Fruit can be fried as well, but this is not as healthy a manner of eating fruit. Apple, banana, and pineapple slices are the most common fruit to fry. Microwaving fruit is more healthful as fat does not need to be added. They cook very fast in the microwave because of their high natural sugar and water content. For even heat distribution, fruit should be covered when cooked in a microwave, unless the recipe suggests otherwise.

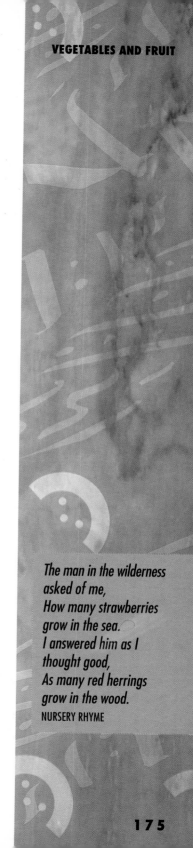

*The man in the wilderness asked of me,*
*How many strawberries grow in the sea.*
*I answered him as I thought good,*
*As many red herrings grow in the wood.*
NURSERY RHYME

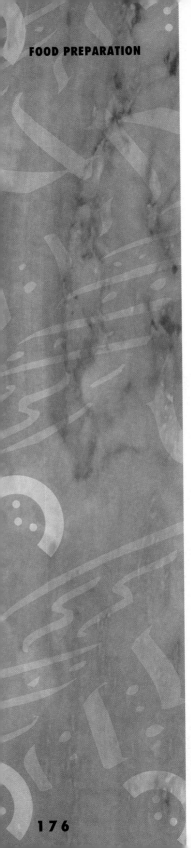

## Fruit and Their Uses

| Fruit | Description | Uses |
|---|---|---|
| Apple — Golden Delicious | Whitish-golden, tender skin, delicate flavour. | Eat out of hand; cooking; baking. |
| Apple — MacIntosh | Bright red, glossy, fragrant, juicy with very white flesh. | Eat out of hand; cooking; baking. |
| Apple — Red Delicious | Deep red, elongated shape, five knoblike points on bottom. | Eat out of hand. |
| Apple — Spy | Red with greenish streaks, mildly acidic flavour. | Cooking; baking. |
| Apricot | Yellow-orange, juicy, smooth skin. | Eat out of hand; cooking; baking; salads. |
| Avocado | Green to black. | Salads; combines well with other foods; *guacamole*. |
| Banana | Yellow (select ones not quite a full yellow). | Eat out of hand, cooking, baking. |
| Blueberries | Blue-black. | Eat out of hand; desserts; cereal topping; salads; jams, jellies; baking. |
| Cantaloupe | Netted outer surface, orange flesh. | Salads, slice and eat fresh. |
| Cherries | Dark red and purple. | Eat out of hand; desserts; jams, jellies; baking. |
| Cranberries | Red, glossy. | Sauces; jams, jellies; juices; baking. |
| Fig | Vary in colour from golden to red and purple. | Eat out of hand; preserves; dried. |
| Grapefruit | Yellow skin with white, pink, or red flesh. | Eat out of hand, peeled; juice. |
| Grapes | Green, red, and purple; seeded and seedless. | Eat out of hand; jams, jellies, preserves; salads; juices; dried for raisins. |
| Guava | Small, round, yellow and pink, white, or yellow flesh. | Eat out of hand; cooked, jellies, preserves. |
| Honeydew melon | Creamy white, greenish-white flesh. | Salads; slice and eat fresh. |
| Kiwi | Small, furry, and greenish brown. | Eat out of hand, peeled; cooked; as a garnish. |

| | | |
|---|---|---|
| Lemon | Yellow, fine-textured skin. | Garnish; flavouring; juice or beverage; desserts. |
| Lime | Green. | Flavouring desserts; garnish; juice. |
| Mango | Oval and yellow or round and greeny-red. | Eat out of hand; in a compote or salad. |
| Navel orange | Orange, thick skin. | Eat out of hand, peeled. |
| Nectarine | Yellowish with a hint of red, smooth skin. | Eat out of hand; desserts; cereal topping; garnish. |
| Papaya | Yellow and green on the outside, pink or yellow inside. | Salads; slice and eat fresh. |
| Passion fruit | Purple or golden with greenish pulp and seeds. | Salads; sauce; sorbet. |
| Peach | Yellowish with a hint of red, fuzzy skin. | Eat out of hand; cooking; baking; desserts; cereal topping; jam. |
| Pear | Yellow, may have a touch of red or green. | Eat out of hand; cooking; baking; salad. |
| Plum | Red, blue, and purple, tart sweetness. | Eat out of hand; desserts; jams, jellies; dried for prunes. |
| Pomegranate | Red with gold containing bright red seeds. | Eat out of hand; add to a fruit compote. |
| Raspberries | Red, black, and purple. | Eat out of hand; salads; desserts; jams; jellies, cereal or ice cream topping. |
| Strawberries | Deep red. | Eat out of hand; desserts; jams, jellies; salads. |
| Tangelo | Tangerine crossed with a grapefruit, thick skin. | Eat out of hand, peeled. |
| Tangerine | Orange colour, loose skin. | Eat out of hand, peeled; salads. |
| Watermelon | Green skin that may have stripes, red flesh. | Salads; slice and eat fresh. |

*Plant your seeds in a row,*
*One for the pheasant,*
*one for the crow,*
*One to rot and one to*
*grow.*
THE COUNTRY DIARY
OF GARDEN LORE

**FOOD PREPARATION**

 KEY TERMS

Use the words listed below to complete the following statements in your notebook.

bulb        water soluble
root        tropical
fructose    seed
stalk       citrus
tubers

1. The _____ of the plant functions as a corridor to other parts of the plant.

2. _____ vegetables come from the part of the plant that grows below the ground.

3. The intense flavour of _____ vegetables is their principal value.

4. _____ store the energy to nourish the growing plant and contain carbohydrates and vitamins.

5. _____ fruit contain valuable amounts of vitamin C and include lemons and grapefruit.

6. Bananas and pineapple are kinds of _____ fruit.

7. _____ vegetables are intended by nature to create and nourish a new plant.

8. The _____ vitamins will easily seep out of the vegetable or fruit into the cooking liquid.

9. A natural sugar found in fruit is _____.

FOCUS YOUR KNOWLEDGE

1. List the four major considerations in purchasing fresh vegetables.

2. What are the advantages and disadvantages of cooking vegetables?

3. Prepare a poster to illustrate the guidelines for buying vegetables and fruit.

4. Describe six tips for preparing an attractive and appetizing salad.

5. Create a chart of the five groups in which fruit are classified, giving three examples for each group.

6. List the major nutrients found in fruit and give two examples of each.

7. Explain how to care for fruit after purchase.

8. What are the five principles for preparing and cooking fruit?

## ☀ DEMONSTRATE YOUR KNOWLEDGE

1. Find recipes that feature one or more of the less common vegetables, such as artichoke, bok choy, celeriac, kohlrabi, and leeks. In groups, prepare one of the recipes.

2. In small groups, cook vegetables in different forms; for example, fresh carrots, canned carrots, frozen carrots. Compare the flavour, colour, appearance, cost, and preparation time.

3. Prepare a cooked vegetable buffet using vegetables from each part of the plant. Choose different cooking methods for each vegetable; for example, scalloped potatoes, steamed frozen peas, stir-fried zucchini/mushrooms/peppers.

4. Working in groups, brainstorm ways in which salads can be added to packed lunches.

5. Prepare baked apples in a conventional oven, a microwave, and a convection oven. Compare cooking time, flavour, and appearance.

6. Working with a partner, stir-fry a variety of vegetables. Sample the results and evaluate for flavour, appearance, and texture. Does this method not work well for any of the vegetables?

## ☀ APPLY YOUR KNOWLEDGE

1. Visit a supermarket as a class or individually. Prepare a list of all the vegetables displayed. Make a second list of any vegetable you have not tasted.

2. Compare the nutrient information on the labels of fruit packed in water, in fruit juice, or in syrup. Prepare a chart listing the kilojoules and nutrient content for each fruit.

3. Prepare a diagram to show the parts of a plant from which vegetables come. Label two examples of vegetables for each part.

4. Prepare and present to the class a brief oral report about a fruit. Outline its classification, country of origin, where it is grown commercially, its qualities when ripe, and its major uses.

5. Plan dinner menus for one week, and include a variety of vegetables and fruit. Evaluate the vegetables and fruit in the menus for flavour, colour, texture, shape, and nutrient content.

How many glasses of milk do you drink in a day?

# Milk Products

## MILK

Milk is defined as the liquid produced naturally by all female mammals to nourish their young. Therefore, it must contain all the elements needed for the life and growth of the new animal. It is not surprising then that milk is the most complete single food yet known. Some consider it to be the "perfect food." For humans, milk does not contain sufficient amounts of vitamin C, vitamin D, or iron to meet their needs. That is why infants need to be given daily supplements of these nutrients during the time when milk is their principal food. It is important that consumers understand the meaning of two terms — homogenization and pasteurization. An explanation of these processes and their function follows.

**Homogenization** ◆ Whole milk has a layer of cream, which contains the **butterfat**, on top of the skim milk. **Homogenized** milk is whole milk that has been treated to break up the fat globules (butterfat) into small particles. During homogenization the whole milk is forced under pressure through very small holes, which emulsifies the fat and distributes it evenly throughout the remaining liquid.

**Pasteurization** ◆ Raw milk has had no treatment of any kind. It may contain harmful microorganisms. **Pasteurization** destroys any harmful bacteria without reducing the nutrient value of the milk. It also kills a great many of the milk-souring bacteria to extend its storage time. Milk is pasteurized by heating it quickly to 71°C for a few seconds, then immediately chilling it before transferring to consumer-sized containers.

**Nutritional Value of Milk** ◆ Cows' milk is the kind used primarily in Canada. Milks from different animals, such as goats, are similar and contain the same nutrients although in different proportions. There is a variation in the amounts of nutrients in cows' milk, depending on factors such as the breed of cow, type of feed, and season of the year. A description of the composition of milk follows.

*Water* ◆ More than 85 percent of milk is water. That means that all of the other nutrients are contained in, at most, 15 percent of the total volume. Water is essential to human life. It is an important part of blood, the lymph system, and all the solutions that bathe the internal body cavities. Consider the fact that humans have been known to live for months without food but can exist only for a few days without water. Health professionals recommend that we drink eight glasses of water daily to replenish the body's water requirement. The water contained in milk can be a part of that amount.

*Carbohydrate* ◆ The carbohydrate found in milk is milk sugar, called **lactose**. It accounts for about 30 percent of the energy, measured as kilojoules, that is contained in whole milk and a greater proportion in skim milk.

*Protein* ◆ **Amino acids** are the building blocks of all protein foods. High-quality proteins, such as those found in milk, contain all of the essential amino acids that the body cannot make for itself. These are called complete proteins.

The main complete protein in milk is **casein**, a protein that forms the curd from which most cheese is made. Other complete proteins, **lactoalbumin** and **lactoglobulin**, are found in the whey remaining after the curd is removed. Although cheese is also an excellent source of complete protein, it does not contain these whey proteins so its amino acid composition differs from that of milk.

When combinations of foods are eaten at the same meal, the high-quality complete proteins of one food complement the incomplete proteins of other foods. For example, breakfast cereals contain incomplete plant proteins. However, when they are eaten with the complete proteins in milk, these proteins can be fully used by the body. Another good combination is yogurt or cottage cheese (complete proteins) served as a dip with vegetables (incomplete proteins).

*Fat* ◆ The fat in milk is referred to as butterfat. Milk fat is easily digested and accounts for about half of milk's kilojoule count. Skim milk is suggested

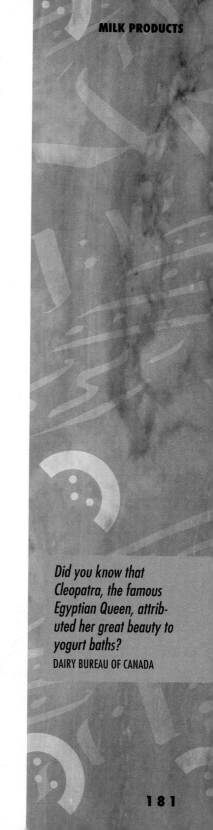

*Did you know that Cleopatra, the famous Egyptian Queen, attributed her great beauty to yogurt baths?*
DAIRY BUREAU OF CANADA

Name the nutrients a glass of milk provides.

REMINDER
• • • • • • • • • • • •

*Canada's Food Guide to Healthy Eating* Recommends

Children (4–9 years)
　2–3 servings
Youths (10–16 years)
　3–4 servings
Adults
　2–4 servings
Pregnant and Breast-
feeding Women
　3–4 servings

when foods having lower energy value are important to the individual. Unless the milk is fortified with added vitamin D, the fat-soluble vitamin D will be missing. All of the other important nutrients are present in skim milk.

*Minerals* • Calcium is considered to be the most important part of milk. When the amount of milk recommended by *Canada's Food Guide to Healthy Eating* is consumed daily, nearly all of the body's calcium needs will be met. Without milk it is very difficult for young people to get sufficient calcium for the formation of developing bones and teeth.

Milk also supplies the mineral phosphorus that is needed by all body cells to help release energy to the body. Phosphorus works with calcium and vitamin D in the formation of bones and teeth, but all three must be supplied at the same time for this to take place.

*Vitamins* • The amount of vitamin D found naturally in milk depends on the feed and sunlight available to the milk-producing animal. Because the vitamin D content of milk is small and unpredictable, government agencies have encouraged the controlled addition of vitamin D to milk. **Fortification** is the enrichment of foods with the addition of vitamins. In the case of milk, the addition of vitamin D helps the body utilize calcium and phosphorus to form and maintain strong bones and teeth. A label on the milk will indicate if, and to what extent, a milk product has been fortified.

Vitamin A is an important nutrient in whole milk. It contributes to the health of the skin and moist mucous membranes of the body, for example, in the nasal passages and digestive tract. As well, it helps maintain normal vision in dim light. Vitamin A is involved also in formation of tooth enamel. Because vitamin A is one of the fat-soluble vitamins it is present only to the degree that milk fat is present in a milk product.

Riboflavin is essential to the healthy condition and function of the skin, eyes, tongue, nerves, and digestive tract. It also assists the body cells to use oxygen, so that other foods eaten can release energy for all daily activities. The riboflavin in milk is destroyed easily by ultraviolet light. For this reason milk needs to be protected from light by its container.

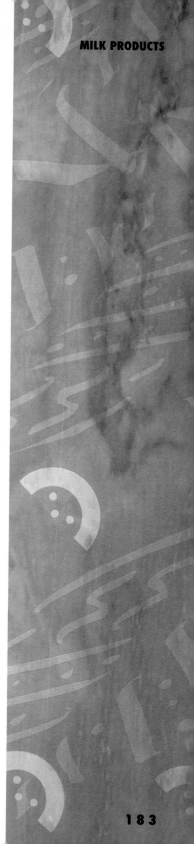

MILK PRODUCTS

## Examples of Foods in the Milk Products Group:

250 mL liquid milk or buttermilk
125 mL undiluted evaporated milk
175 g (200 mL) yogurt
50 g (2 slices) process cheese
50 g (7.5 cm x 2.5 cm x 2.5 cm) firm cheese

## Kinds of Milk and Milk Products

In Canada, *whole milk* must contain at least 3.25 percent milk fat and at least 8 percent non-milk solids. Most fluid whole milk sold is homogenized, and milk sold from recognized dairies is also pasteurized.

*Skim milk* is milk that has had most of the fat removed. Skim milk has a reduced vitamin A content, because this vitamin is held in the fat, most of which has been removed. Skim milk contains the same important nutrients as whole milk. It, of course, has a reduced kilojoule count.

*Partly skimmed milk* has fewer kilojoules than whole milk. The amount of fat that remains depends on whether it is 1% or 2%. Otherwise, partly skimmed milk contains the same nutritive value as whole milk.

*Cream* is the fatty part that rises to the top of raw whole milk. When cream is separated out, skim milk remains. Sour cream is made by adding a bacterial culture to milk solids. Government regulations control the butterfat content of different cream products such as:

• Whipping Cream — 35 percent fat; may be less in aerosol form

• Table Cream — 18–32 percent fat

• Half and Half — 8–16 percent fat and 8–16 percent non-fat solids

• Light Cream (cereal cream) — 8–16 percent fat

• Sour Cream — 10–18 percent fat

• Light Sour Cream — 1–7 percent

*Powdered milk* is milk from which all but 3 percent of the water content has been removed. Most powdered milk is made by spraying milk into a heated chamber, where it dries almost instantly and falls as a powder. Instant dissolving skim milk powder is produced by blowing this milk powder into a steam chamber where the minute particles form larger particles containing

**183**

many tiny air spaces. Powdered skim milk stores very well at room temperatures and is inexpensive and convenient to use. Powdered whole milk has a short shelf life because the milk fat that it contains will become rancid.

*Evaporated milk* is a canned milk product produced by removing about 60 percent of the water from whole, partly skimmed, or skim milk. Because of the high temperatures required to evaporate the water and sterilize the canned product, the milk protein and milk sugar become browned and give the canned milk a golden brown colour.

*Sweetened condensed milk* is a canned milk product prepared from whole milk that has been condensed to one-third of its original volume. It is a thick, cream-coloured liquid containing about 40 percent sugar that acts as a preservative. It is primarily used for baking.

Name all the dairy products pictured here.

Originally enjoyed as a by-product of butter making, *buttermilk* is now made commercially by adding a bacterial culture to partly skimmed milk. It is then held under controlled conditions of time and temperature until it reaches the desired acidity and flavour. The resulting buttermilk has a smooth, rich consistency with a tangy flavour and less than 2 percent milk fat.

*Yogurt* is made by heating pasteurized, homogenized milk and adding bacterial culture to it. The final consistency depends on the preparation techniques and holding temperatures used by the manufacturer. Whole, partly skimmed, or skim milk can be used in making yogurt. Skim milk powder is sometimes added to make a total of about 16 percent milk solids. Properly refrigerated, yogurt has a storage life of two to four weeks. It is available plain or with flavourings or fruit mixtures added and is also sold frozen.

*Butter* is a dairy product made by **churning** cream. Churning is a vigorous mixing that makes the fat particles cluster together and break away from the surrounding liquid, called buttermilk. Canadian law requires that butter contain a minimum of 80 percent milk fat. The rest is buttermilk and remaining milk solids that contribute flavour. Sometimes colouring and salt are added. Because fat-soluble vitamin A remains in the milk fat, butter is an important source of this vitamin. Butter contains only small amounts of other vitamins and minerals. It is sold in different forms.

- Salted — Added salt contributes flavour and helps preserve the butter.

- Unsalted — When heated, unsalted butter will not burn as easily as salt-ed butter. Unsalted butter is important to people on a salt-free diet, and some cooks prefer it for baking. It is sometimes called sweet butter.

- Whipped Butter — Whipping adds air and makes the butter softer and more spreadable.

A variety of *frozen dairy products* are prepared from cream, whole and/or condensed milk, and/or milk solids, sugar, and flavouring. With the use of food additives, a smooth creamy product is possible even with a low milk fat content. Air can be incorporated to increase volume by whipping the mixture during freezing. Examples are:

- Ice cream contains at least 36 percent total milk solids of which 10 percent is milk fat.

- Light ice cream contains 5–7.5 percent milk fat.

- Soft ice cream has at least 10 percent milk fat, slightly more non-fat solids, and less sugar than hard ice cream.

- Ice milk contains 3–5 percent milk fat, 33 percent milk solids, plus sugar and flavouring.

- Sherbet is a tart-flavoured product made from a sweetened fruit juice base containing a maximum of 5 percent total milk solids.

- Frozen yogurt is a tasty alternative to ice cream and contains less than 3 percent milk fat.

For an attractive presentation, try using a butter curler when serving butter. Dip the curler into warm water, then pull it over firm, but not too cold, butter. Place the curls in cold water immediately and refrigerate until ready to drain and serve.

## Cooking With Milk ◆ Many recipes ask for the milk to be heated or **scalded** as a first step. Scalding means heating the milk to just below the boiling point, about 82°C. That temperature is reached when bubbles form around the edge of the pan.

A scum of coagulated protein forms a layer on top of milk whenever it is heated. The layer may be removed by skimming or stirring, or it can be prevented from forming in the first place. However, if it is not removed the hot milk will eventually break through this tough film that holds in the steam pressure caused by heating. The result is that the milk boils over the sides of the pan.

As milk is heated, particles of milk solids settle on the bottom and sides of the pan. When allowed to overheat, the milk sugar, called lactose, browns and the solids are easily scorched. In correct terms, the lactose caramelizes.

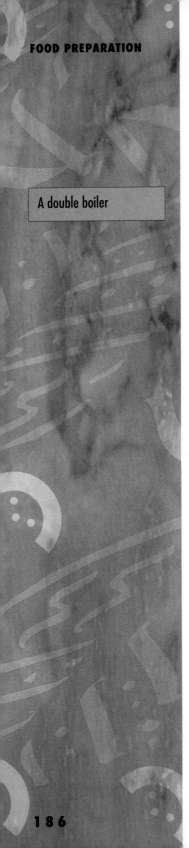

A double boiler

## Tips for Heating and Cooking Milk

- A double boiler maintains a low heat for scalding milk and prevents scorching of proteins that settle to the bottom and would otherwise stick and scorch.

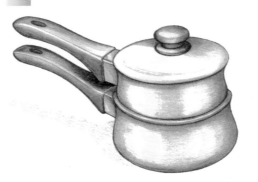

- Use a very low heat if using a saucepan. Stir with a whip occasionally to produce a foamy layer that will slow evaporation and formation of the protein film.
- When carefully monitored, a microwave is a fast alternative that minimizes required dishwashing and simplifies the scalding process. It takes about two minutes to heat 250 mL of milk.
- Cooked milk sauces, such as white sauce, or creamed soups should have a lid placed on them until serving time to prevent the formation of a thick film.
- Cooked puddings made with milk should be covered tightly as soon as removed from heat. Wax paper or plastic film works well to prevent a scum from forming on individual servings.

Milk **curdles** easily when overheated, especially under acid conditions. Casein, from the milk solids, separates from the liquid leaving an unattractive mass in a thin liquid. Three conditions contribute to this — the addition of acid foods, use of a high temperature, and using old milk. Here are some suggestions to prevent curdling.

- Use very fresh milk in heated mixtures. Lactose, or milk sugar, is slowly changed to lactic acid with age, and milk with a higher acid content will curdle more readily.
- Use a low temperature for a longer period of time when cooking milk mixtures, for example, scalloped potatoes or baked custard.
- When combining an acid vegetable, such as tomatoes, with milk, thicken either the milk or the tomato first before combining them. In the example of making tomato soup, the flour used to thicken the white sauce keeps the milk protein mixed throughout the sauce. Curdling is thus prevented when tomato is added later.

**Milk Sauces** • White sauce in the strictest sense is a sauce made from milk. In a commercial kitchen the comparable "cream sauce" is not necessarily made from cream but always from a **roux**, equal parts of fat and flour cooked together. The liquid to be added to the roux can be a meat or chicken stock thinned with rich milk or cream.

Because white sauce is a part of many recipes, such as soups, casseroles, scalloped dishes, and other sauces, knowledge of its preparation is considered important to a well-qualified cook. Many of the principles involved in making it are the same as those involved in making other sauces and in cooking other milk mixtures.

A good white sauce will be glossy in appearance, smooth and creamy in texture, of the desired consistency, and with a well-seasoned flavour. There should be no taste of raw starch remaining.

Flour tends to lump when it is combined with a hot liquid. For this reason the flour is first mixed well with the melted fat and cooked slightly without burning. This flour–fat mixture is essentially the same as a roux used by a commercial cook. The cold liquid, in this case milk, is then added a little at a time with constant stirring to keep the mixture smooth. Although a heated liquid saves time, using a cold liquid helps to further prevent lumps from forming.

After all the liquid has been added, the mixture is cooked over low heat or over boiling water, with constant stirring, until completely thickened. The sauce will stick and scorch easily if left standing over direct heat without stirring. A microwave can also be used, allowing pauses for stirring.

White sauce is an important part of scalloped potatoes. Name three other dishes that include a white sauce.

## White Sauce Ingredients and Proportions

| Thickness | Uses | Fat | Flour | Liquid | Salt |
|---|---|---|---|---|---|
| Thin | Cream soup, cheese sauce | 15 mL | 15 mL | 250 mL | 1 mL |
| Medium | Creamed vegetables, egg, puddings, sauces | 30 mL | 30 mL | 250 mL | 1 mL |
| Thick | Salad dressing | 45 mL | 45 mL | 250 mL | 1 mL |
| Very thick | Soufflé, croquettes | 60 mL | 60 mL | 250 mL | 1 mL |

## Methods for Making White Sauce

### Stove Top Method

1. Melt measured fat in heavy saucepan or in top of double boiler.
2. Stir in flour. Stir over heat until smooth but not burned.
3. Slowly stir in cold liquid and continue stirring.
4. Continue cooking over boiling water or on low direct heat. Stir constantly until sauce is thickened and smooth and all the taste of raw starch has disappeared. (This will take about 10 minutes in a double boiler and between 5–7 minutes on direct heat.)

### Microwave Method

1. Place measured fat in heatproof bowl. Microwave to melt.
2. Add measured flour and stir with wire whip. Microwave until bubbly.
3. Stir in measured liquid until mixed completely. Adding small amounts gradually prevents lumps from forming. When all liquid has been added, microwave until bubbling, stirring with wire whip part way through the time. (250 mL milk requires approximately 2 minutes to reach boil.)
4. Combine thoroughly with whip, then microwave for additional time in 1 minute periods, each followed by stirring, until the mixture is smooth and completely thickened.

*La mejor salsa del mundo es el hambre. Hunger is the best sauce in the world.*
MIGUEL DE CERVANTES

## White Sauce Has a Variety of Uses

### Cheese Sauce

To each 250 mL of white sauce, add 125 mL grated cheese and seasonings to taste. (Example: 1 mL paprika and 2 mL Worcestershire sauce.) Stir until smooth. Serve as soon as cheese is melted. Sharp (aged) cheddar is used most commonly, but others and mixtures give their own distinctive flavours. See cheeses on page 190.

## Mornay Sauce

To a thin white sauce made with 250 mL milk, cream, or half and half, add 50 mL of grated Swiss, Gruyère, or Samsoe cheese, and 30 mL grated Parmesan cheese. Heat and stir until cheese melts.

## Cream Soup

1. To 500 mL thin white sauce, add one of the following: 375 mL cream style corn, 375 mL puréed fresh or canned asparagus, 500 mL puréed celery, or an equivalent amount of other vegetables.
2. Place over low heat and bring to serving temperature or heat thoroughly in microwave.
3. Season to taste.
4. Serve hot.

# CHEESE

### Nutritional Value of Cheese

• The nutritive value of cheese is much the same as that of the milk from which it is made. A main difference is that because curd and whey are separated to make the cheese, the protein casein is the principal complete protein in cheese. The proteins lactoalbumin and lactoglobulin that remain with the whey are not present. However, the milk solids containing butterfat and lactose, and minerals and vitamins are all present.

Try to identify these cheeses—Swiss; mozerella; cottage cheese; cheddar; parmesan; processed; brie.

### Production of Cheese

• Commercial production of cheese begins by forming the curd. A culture of lactic acid is added to warm milk. This produces bacteria, which are allowed to grow until the milk reaches the acidity desired. An enzyme called **rennin** is used in the production of most cheeses. It coagulates the milk, separating the curds from the whey. Unripened cheese, such as cottage cheese or cream cheese, results when this soft curd is not treated any further. Ripened cheeses are produced by treating the curd with heat and pressure and adding cultures of bacteria or mould. The cheese ripens or cures under controlled conditions, to produce the desired type of cheese.

*Little Miss Muffet sat on
a tuffet,
Eating her curds and
whey;
There came a big spider,
Who sat down beside her
And frightened Miss
Muffet away.*
NURSERY RHYME

Did you know that there
are over 350 different
kinds of cheese?

Kinds of Cheese • Many varieties of cheese exist, from soft to hard and from unripened to ripened. Each cheese has its own distinctive flavour that results from the kind of milk and the method used.

Process cheese is made by blending one or more of the natural cheeses with other ingredients. Grated or ground cheese is first melted, pasteurized, and then blended with milk, water, or milk solids and sometimes with food colouring, seasonings, or flavourings. Pasteurization, or heating, stops bacterial and enzyme action and gives process cheese excellent keeping qualities with a relatively mild flavour. Process cheese is pliable and melts easily without becoming stringy or tough as do the natural cheeses used to make it.

## Cheese Reference Guide

| Category | Canadian Cheese Characteristics | Varieties |
|---|---|---|
| Fresh Unripened | Soft, creamy texture; slight acidic taste. | Cottage; Tuma; Quark; Ricotta; Baker's Neufchâtel; Cream; Mytzithra. |
| Soft Surface-ripened | Bloomy rind; soft, creamy texture; light aroma of mushrooms. | Brie; Camembert; Double-cream; Triple-cream. |
| Semi-soft Unripened (Pasta filata) | Cheese stretched until it becomes threadlike; supple, elastic texture; milk taste. | Fior di latte; Suris; Trecce; Bocconcini; Caciotta; Scamorza; Mozzarella. |
| Semi-soft Interior-ripened | Mild taste; supple texture; light, pleasant aroma. | Tomme; Muenster; Havarti; Monterey Jack; Casata; Saint-Paulin; Burrini. |
| Semi-soft Surface-ripened | Stronger flavour; creamy, smooth texture. | Oka; Limburger; Feta; Alpina; Serra. |
| Firm Interior-ripened | Flavour milk to sharp, depending on length and method of ripening. | Brick; Colby; Edam; Cheddar; Elbo; Caciocavallo; Camosum; Friulano; Fontina; Emmenthal; Montasio; Marble; Farmer's; Gouda; Raclette; Provolone; Swiss; New Bra; Tilsit; Saint André; Skim Milk. |
| Hard Interior-ripened | Long ripening period; sharp pronounced flavour; dry, grainy texture; excellent grating cheese. | Kefalotyri; Bra; Romano; Parmesan. |
| Blue-veined | Soft to firm texture; salty taste; nippy to strong flavour. | Blue. |

SOURCE: Dairy Bureau of Canada

## Storage of Cheese ◆

Warm temperatures cause some of the fat in firm cheese to melt and ooze out. Therefore, firm cheese should always be stored in a cool place. Soft cheeses are more perishable than firmer varieties. Cream cheese or cottage cheese should be stored covered, in the refrigerator, and eaten while fresh. Ripened cheese has a more full flavour when served at room temperature and therefore should not be served chilled.

## Cooking With Cheese ◆

Some of the same principles of cooking milk mixtures apply to cooking with cheese. Cheese is a protein food and like all other proteins is much better when cooked at a low temperature. High temperatures toughen proteins making them more difficult to digest. In the case of cheese, it also becomes stringy and difficult to cut.

Overcooking will produce the same toughening effect as cooking with too high a heat. Cheese dishes made with foods that have already been cooked should be baked in a moderate oven only long enough to thoroughly heat the mixture. If the cheese is first grated, or in the case of cottage cheese or cream cheese, sieved or mixed in the blender, it will mix more evenly and quickly with other ingredients.

### Suggestions for Cooking With Cheese

- Use a low heat. Melt cheese in a double boiler or chafing dish rather than over direct heat. Use a low setting when using a microwave to heat or cook cheese.
- The method recommended for any uncooked mixture of eggs, cheese, and milk is **oven poaching**. This means to place the cheese dish in a pan of hot water and bake it in a moderate oven until a knife, inserted in the centre, comes out clean.
- To prevent toughening, do not overcook. Cheese is cooked when it has melted.

*Did you know that ancient Greek Olympic athletes trained on a diet consisting mostly of cheese?*
DAIRY BUREAU OF CANADA

**191**

KEY TERMS

Use the words listed below to complete the following statements in your notebook.

| | |
|---|---|
| curdling | lactose |
| rennin | roux |
| homogenizing | scalding |
| pasteurizing | whey |
| casein | churning |

1. When making sauces flour and fat are mixed together to make a _____.

2. The process of _____ destroys any harmful bacteria in milk without reducing the nutrient value.

3. Most whole milk has the butter evenly distributed throughout the fluid. This process is called _____.

4. Milk sugar is also called _____.

5. A vigorous mixing of cream that causes the fat particles to cluster together and break away from the surrounding liquid is called _____.

6. _____ is the process of heating milk until bubbles form around the edge of the pan.

7. _____ will occur when an acid is added to a milk product.

8. The liquid remaining after curds are formed in cheese making is called _____.

9. The complete protein in cheese products is called _____.

10. To assist the curds to separate from the whey when making cheese the enzyme _____ is added.

FOCUS YOUR KNOWLEDGE

1. Prepare a chart showing the nutrients in milk. Include the importance of each nutrient.

2. Explain the difference between pasteurization and homogenization.

3. How is milk scalded?

4. List six examples of frozen dairy products.

5. Describe what happens to cheese when it is overheated.

6. What is the principal nutritive difference between milk and cheese?

7. Compare two different methods of preparing a sauce. Include ease of preparation and clean-up, preparation time, and the number of pieces of equipment used. Determine which method you think you would prefer.

## ☀ DEMONSTRATE YOUR KNOWLEDGE

1. Prepare a pudding or soup made with milk. Have a partner evaluate the product results based on criteria that you establish together.

2. Assemble a taste panel. Using a variety of cheeses, note the texture, flavour, and classification of each.

3. Heat milk until scalded, using a double boiler. Have your partner scald milk in a saucepan or in a microwave oven. Each record your observations for your method. Compare your results of scalding and clean-up.

4. Prepare dips from a chosen recipe first using sour cream (regular or lower fat), then yogurt, and then blended cottage cheese. Serve with raw vegetables. Compare the fat content, flavour, and texture of each dip.

5. Compare a commercially made soup or sauce with a homemade product. Compare the cost, ease of preparation, and the final product results. Which product do you rate better overall?

6. In small groups locate a method for making cottage cheese, yogurt, or butter. Prepare the product. Compare the result with a similar commercial product for flavour, texture, and cost.

## ☀ APPLY YOUR KNOWLEDGE

1. Conduct library research on the production of milk, yogurt, or frozen milk products. Outline the process in a report to the class.

2. Determine the major source of the fluid milk products in your community.

3. Make a list of milk products your family enjoys. Visit the grocery store and calculate the cost of providing a variety of milk products for your family for one week.

4. Select one cheese and investigate how it is made, where it is made, how to store it, how to serve it, and suggested ways of using it in recipes. Prepare a brief report on your results.

5. Observe the containers (glass, cardboard, plastic) in which fluid milk is available. List the advantages and disadvantages of each. Think about recycling and the loss of vitamin A through exposure to ultraviolet light.

6. In groups, devise a crossword puzzle or word game that incorporates the various types of cheese. Share the puzzle or game with another group.

# Meat and Alternatives

## MEAT

**Meat Structure** • To learn how to choose and cook meat properly, you need to first understand its structure. Strands of fibrous tissue, called **connective tissue**, hold together long hollow cells that, bound together, make up the **muscle fibres**. Within these cells the meat **extractives**, the liquid that gives meat its characteristic flavour, are found. Fat also contributes to the flavour of meat.

Connective tissue is of two kinds — **collagen** and **elastin**. Collagen is tough, elastic strands that are converted into gelatin during cooking. This is done best at a low cooking temperature for a long period of time in the presence of moisture. The meat is fully tenderized when collagen is softened sufficiently to release its hold on the bundles of muscle, allowing them to fall apart.

Elastin resists being tenderized by heat, moisture, or any other conditions. Normally, this kind of connective tissue is trimmed away before the meat is cooked. Small amounts of elastin sometimes remain in tougher cuts like stew and brisket.

Distribution of fat cells throughout the lean is known as **marbling**. As well as giving it flavour, this fat makes the meat more tender and juicy than meat that is not well marbled. For the most part, marbling is microscopic, but some cuts of meat have visible fat between the muscle fibres. Another kind of fat lies in larger, more visible deposits that can be trimmed from the meat easily. The layer of fat under the animal's skin is known as the **finish**.

The proportion of fat to lean depends on the kind of animal and its age. Veal, which is the flesh of a calf, has less finish than beef; beef, from cattle, has less finish than pork, from pigs. Lamb, the meat from a young sheep, has less fat than mutton, the flesh of the older sheep. The type of feed given to the animal and the amount of exercise it gets also influences the percentage of fat contained in meat. Range-fed cattle are usually leaner than more restricted animals fed in feed lots.

The fat of meat contributes to its kilojoule count, providing twice the amount of energy as the same mass of protein. *Canada's Food Guide to*

*Healthy Eating* recommends the trimming of visible fat from meat to reduce the intake of "empty" kilojoules. As explained in earlier chapters, fatty foods take longer to digest than low-fat foods.

## Nutritive Value of Meat

• Meat of all kinds is valued for the high-quality protein it supplies. Because it contains all of the essential amino acids in one food, this protein can be utilized by the body immediately for building and repairing. The amount of fat present depends on the cut of meat, the age and kind of animal, and the part of the animal from which it was taken. Important amounts of B vitamins are available in meat. Pork products are a rich source of thiamin; organ meats supply most of the B vitamins. The most important minerals found in meats of all kinds are copper, iron, phosphorus, and zinc. Liver is a particularly good source of iron.

## Meat Inspection and Grading

• In Canada federal veterinarians examine the animals slaughtered for food to certify that they are fit for human consumption. Some provinces also have meat inspection regulations for meat sold within their borders. Once the carcass has passed inspection it receives a brown-coloured stamp of vegetable dye with the words "Canada Approved" around a crown and the registration number of the meat plant. The same identification stamp is used on a tag or label on meat products from packing plants. Composition standards for meat products, such as sausages, meat pies, canned spreads, and luncheon meats are controlled in a similar way.

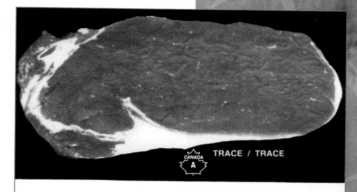

CANADA A — TRACE / TRACE

CANADA AA — SLIGHT / TRÈS PEU ABONDANT

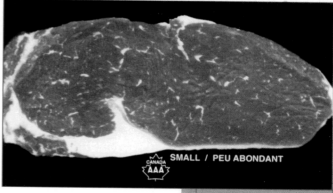

CANADA AAA — SMALL / PEU ABONDANT

Which of these pieces of beef has the least amount of marbling? Which has the largest amount?

Meat grading is carried out by personnel from Agriculture Canada. Grades are assigned on the basis of age, quality, and the proportion of fat to lean. A young animal will be more likely to produce tender meat. The colour, texture, and firmness of both the lean and fat indicate to the grader how closely the meat responds to the ideal.

Once a grade has been determined, a ribbonlike mark is placed on the large, wholesale cut. In the case of beef, the grades are as described.

*Canada Grade A (Red)* ◆ The lean from these youthful animals is firm, fine-grained, and a bright red colour with at least a trace of marbling. The exterior fat covering is white or slightly tinged with red or amber.

*Canada Grade B (Blue)* ◆ Also from youthful animals, the lean is moderately firm, ranging from bright red to medium dark red. The colour of the exterior fat may be white or have a yellowish tinge; no minimum marbling is required.

There is no longer a Canada Grade C.

*Canada Grade D (Brown)* ◆ This beef is from mature cows or steers and further grade divisions are provided on the basis of the characteristics of fat and the amount of muscling.

*Canada Grade E (Brown)* ◆ These carcasses from mature and young bulls are used mainly for processed meat products.

**Buying Meat** ◆ When comparing the price of meat, the most important factor to consider is the number of people that can be served from the package of meat. Rather than comparing the price per kilogram, you need to compare the total cost of buying enough meat to serve the family. Make your choice based on comparisons of edible cooked portions. When buying ground meat, for example, you should make your choice based on the amount of edible meat remaining after the fat has been cooked out, not on the fact that ground meat with a maximum of 10 percent fat is more expensive per kilogram than meat having up to 30 percent fat.

The following chart shows the average amount of meat required per serving. It will help you estimate the amount of meat to buy.

## Deciding How Much Meat to Buy

| | |
|---|---|
| Ground meat | 100–150 g |
| Braising meat (stew) | 150 g |
| Braising meat, bone in | 250 g |
| Chops and Steaks | 150–250 g |
| Roasts, bone in | 150–250 g |
| Roasts, boneless | 100–150 g |

SOURCE: Adapted from *Management and Foods*

> While competing, I have beef four or five times a week because I need the nutrients red meat provides, such as protein and iron. As a teenager, I stopped eating red meat, but I became weak and tired and my performance in the pool really suffered.
>
> MARK TEWKSBURY (SWIMMER)

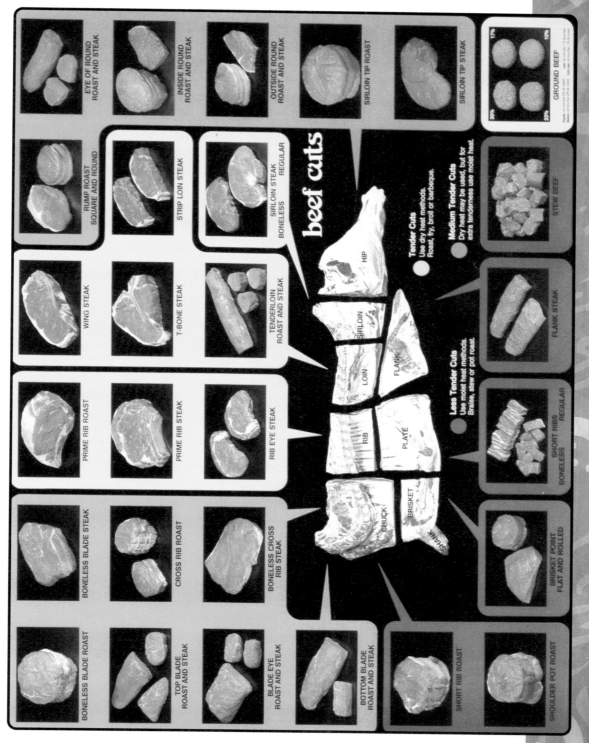

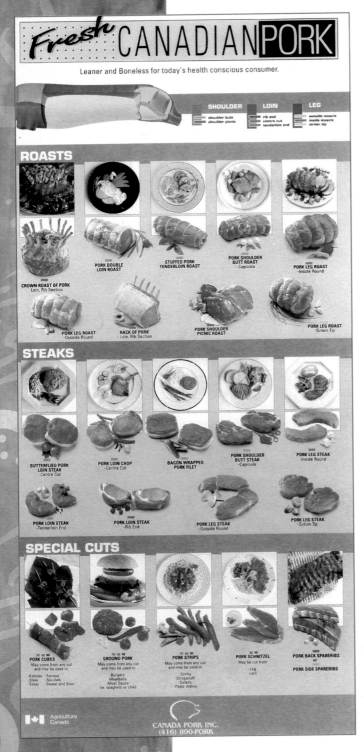

**Fresh CANADIAN PORK**

Leaner and Boneless for today's health conscious consumer.

| SHOULDER | LOIN | LEG |
|---|---|---|
| shoulder butt | rib end | outside muscle |
| shoulder picnic | centre cut | inside muscle |
| | tenderloin and | sirloin tip |

**ROASTS**

CROWN ROAST OF PORK
Loin, Rib Section

PORK DOUBLE LOIN ROAST

STUFFED PORK TENDERLOIN ROAST

PORK SHOULDER BUTT ROAST - Capicola

PORK LEG ROAST -Inside Round

PORK LEG ROAST -Outside Round

RACK OF PORK - Loin, Rib Section

PORK SHOULDER PICNIC ROAST

PORK LEG ROAST -Sirloin Tip

**STEAKS**

BUTTERFLIED PORK LOIN STEAK -Centre Cut

PORK LOIN CHOP -Centre Cut

BACON WRAPPED PORK FILET

PORK SHOULDER BUTT STEAK -Capicola

PORK LEG STEAK -Inside Round

PORK LOIN STEAK -Tenderloin End

PORK LOIN STEAK -Rib End

PORK LEG STEAK -Outside Round

PORK LEG STEAK -Sirloin Tip

**SPECIAL CUTS**

PORK CUBES
May come from any cut and may be used in:
-Kabobs  -Fondue
-Stew    -Souvlaki
-Satay   -Sweet and Sour

GROUND PORK
May come from any cut and may be used in:
-Burgers
-Meatballs
-Meat Sauce
(ie. spaghetti or chili)

PORK STRIPS
May come from any cut and may be used in:
-Stirfry
-Stroganoff
-Salads
-Pasta dishes

PORK SCHNITZEL
May be cut from
-Leg
-Loin

PORK BACK SPARERIBS
or
PORK SIDE SPARERIBS

Agriculture Canada

CANADA PORK INC.
(416) 890-PORK

## Cooking Principles

Probably the most important reason for cooking meat is to destroy harmful microorganisms. However, there are many other good reasons. Cooking usually makes the meat tastier. The extractives from the muscle tissue are released, which contributes to the flavour of the meat and the juices that may be used in gravy. Cooking also tenderizes the meat by breaking down the connective tissue. This makes the meat easier to digest. The changes in colour and the addition of sauces and garnishment make meat more appealing, as well.

## Tenderizing Meat

The ageing of the carcass before dividing it into consumer cuts is a preliminary step in meat handling. During this time when the meat is held under controlled conditions, the muscle fibres begin to soften from the action of enzymes naturally found in the meat.

One of the most important objectives of preparing and cooking meat is to make it more tender. There are a number of techniques, depending on the cut of meat. Here are some of the tenderizing methods used.

- Cutting the meat breaks the connective tissue into smaller pieces. Cutting methods include grinding, chopping, dicing, and scoring the surface. Grinding also makes elastin edible although not digestible.
- Pounding breaks down the connective tissue in the meat, making it more susceptible to the tenderizing effects of the cooking process.
- Moisture softens the collagen in tough meat, converting it to gelatin if the meat is allowed to cook for a long time.
- Pressure cooking is another moist-heat method that tenderizes the collagen, but in a much shorter period of time.

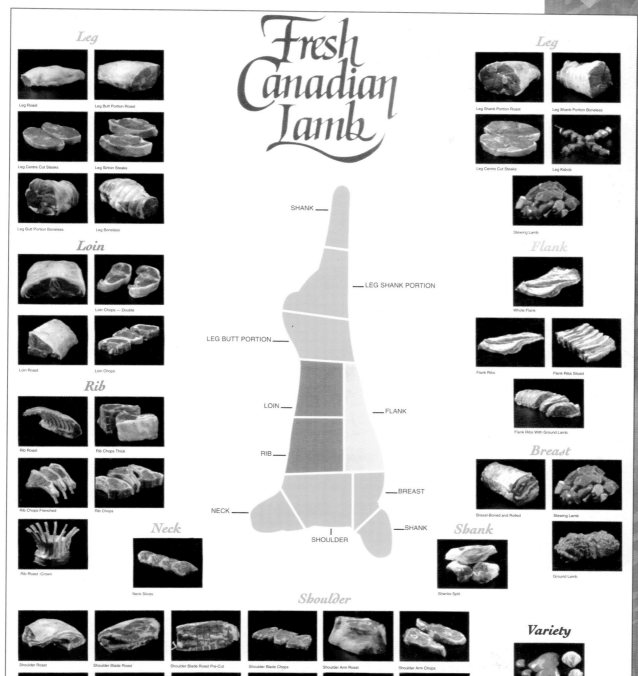

# Fresh Canadian Lamb

## Leg

Leg Roast

Leg Butt Portion Roast

Leg Centre Cut Steaks

Leg Sirloin Steaks

Leg Butt Portion Boneless

Leg Boneless

## Loin

Loin Chops — Double

Loin Roast

Loin Chops

## Rib

Rib Roast

Rib Chops Thick

Rib Chops Frenched

Rib Chops

Rib Roast -Crown

## Neck

Neck Slices

## Leg

Leg Shank Portion Roast

Leg Shank Portion Boneless

Leg Centre Cut Steaks

Leg Kabob

Stewing Lamb

## Flank

Whole Flank

Flank Ribs

Flank Ribs Sliced

Flank Ribs With Ground Lamb

## Breast

Breast-Boned and Rolled

Stewing Lamb

Ground Lamb

## Shank

Shanks Split

## Variety

Kidneys
Liver
Heart
Tongue

SHANK

LEG SHANK PORTION

LEG BUTT PORTION

LOIN

FLANK

RIB

BREAST

NECK

SHANK

SHOULDER

## Shoulder

Shoulder Roast

Shoulder Blade Roast

Shoulder Blade Roast Pre-Cut

Shoulder Blade Chops

Shoulder Arm Roast

Shoulder Arm Chops

Shoulder Boneless Rolled

Shoulder Boneless Stuffed

Stewing Lamb

Shoulder Kabob

Ground Lamb

Patties

199

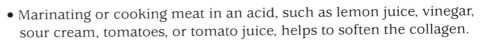

- Marinating or cooking meat in an acid, such as lemon juice, vinegar, sour cream, tomatoes, or tomato juice, helps to soften the collagen.
- Meat tenderizers contain a protein splitting enzyme, the most common of which is **papain**, an extractive from the papaya tree. When sprinkled on the surface of the meat, the enzyme breaks apart some of the collagen.

Cooking Meat ✦ Usually, cooking methods are divided into two categories — moist-heat and dry-heat processes. Tougher cuts of meat require longer cooking and one or more of the tenderizing techniques described to soften the collagen found in the muscle fibres. Tougher cuts respond best to moist methods. On the other hand, tender meat contains a protein called **myosin**, which needs only a little cooking. Indeed, when cooked too long, the muscle fibres in tender meat tend to become tougher. Tender cuts respond well to dry-heat methods.

## Moist-heat Methods

*Boiling* ✦ This method involves a large amount of water added to the pot in which unbrowned meat is placed. The meat is simmered covered, until tender.

This hearty maple stew contains beef and a variety of vegetables.

*Stewing* ✦ Meat for stew is cut in approximately 3-cm cubes, seasoned, rolled into flour, and browned in hot fat. Enough liquid to cover the meat is added, and the heat reduced; the covered pot is allowed to simmer until the meat is tender. Characteristically, vegetables are added to stew later and, if necessary, the juices are thickened before serving.

*Braising* ✦ Meat is browned on both sides in hot fat; then a small amount of liquid is added. Cooking continues at a low heat, with the lid on, until the meat is tender. Seasonings and sometimes vegetables are added. When the meat is ready to serve, juices are thickened to make a tasty sauce or gravy.

*Pot-roasting* ✦ Like braising, meat is cooked at a low temperature with moisture for a long time. The difference is that a single, large piece of meat, called a roast, is being cooked.

Vegetables are added and cooked in the same pot. Pot-roasting can take place in the oven or on a heated surface.

*Pressure Cooking* ◆ The first steps are the same as for braising except that the pot used is a pressure cooker. Once the lid is in position and properly secured, heat brings the pressure to 105 kP. With pressure, the meat cooks very quickly.

## Dry-heat Methods

*Pan Frying* ◆ As the name suggests, meat is cooked uncovered in a small amount of fat. It is a quick method of cooking thin cuts of meat.

*Sautéing* ◆ This is a quick method, similar to pan frying meat. It is done in a large, open pan, which is kept in motion, with a small amount of fat or oil. The fat or oil must be hot enough to sear the seasoned or breaded meat as soon as it is put in the pan. Heat must be kept up throughout cooking to hold in the sealed juices.

*Pan Broiling* ◆ For best results, a heavy pan that conducts heat evenly is used over surface heat, without added fat or liquid. When the meat is seared and browned on the bottom, turn it once and cook the other side. Pour off any fat that accumulates to prevent the meat from frying. Pan broiling is a convenient method for cooking steaks or chops.

*Broiling* ◆ Direct heat, usually from the top, is used. Only very tender cuts or those that have been treated by one of the tenderizing methods are suitable for broiling. There are many different specifics to this method, depending on the equipment being used. Therefore, follow manufacturer's instructions.

*Roasting* ◆ Only tender roasts can be cooked successfully using dry heat. To roast, place the large piece of meat in an open pan, on a rack if desired. A meat thermometer is helpful to determine when the meat is cooked. Insert it into the centre of the thickest part, but not against bone or into a fat pocket. The time required will depend on the size of the roast, the amount of lean, fat, and bone, the cooking temperature, the temperature of the raw meat, and how thoroughly you want it cooked. The internal temperature indicated by the thermometer is your guide; rare beef will be 60°C, well-done 75°C. See the chart on page 202.

Roast pork is the protein food in this eye-pleasing meal.

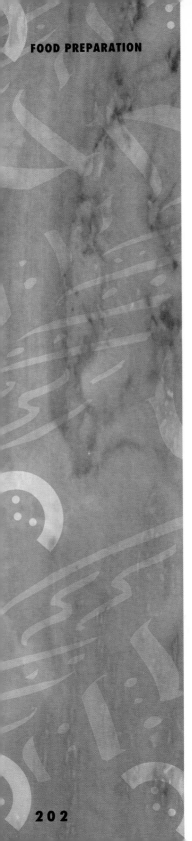

## Oven Roasting Chart
### (Oven temperature 160°C)

|  | Approximate Time per 500 g (min) | Internal Temperature (°C) |
|---|---|---|
| **Beef** | | |
| Boneless or boned and rolled | | |
|   Rare | 25–35 | 60 |
|   Medium | 30–40 | 70 |
|   Well-done | 35–45 | 75 |
| Bone-in | | |
|   Rare | 20–25 | 60 |
|   Medium | 25–30 | 70 |
|   Well-done | 30–35 | 75 |
| **Veal** | | |
| Leg | 35–45 | 80 |
| Boneless or boned and rolled | 45–55 | 80 |
| **Pork** | | |
| Leg or loin | 40–45 | 85 |
| Boneless or boned and rolled | 55–60 | 80 |
| **Ham** | | |
| Cook-before-eating | | |
|   Bone-in | 25–35 | 70 |
|   Bone-out | 35–40 | 70 |
| Fully cooked ham | 10–15 | 55 |
| Cottage roll | 30 | 70 |
| **Lamb** | | |
| Bone-in (leg, rack, shoulder) | | |
|   Rare | 25–30 | 70 |
|   Medium | 30–35 | 75 |
|   Well-done | 35–40 | 80 |
| Boneless or boned and rolled | | |
|   Rare | 25–30 | 70 |
|   Medium | 30–35 | 75 |
|   Well-done | 35–45 | 80 |

### Using the Chart

1. Times are based on the temperature of meat when taken from the refrigerator (about 5°C). To cook a frozen roast increase time by half that required for fresh or thawed meat.
2. Allow the longer times given for small roasts (2–3 kg) and the shorter times for larger, (3–4 kg).

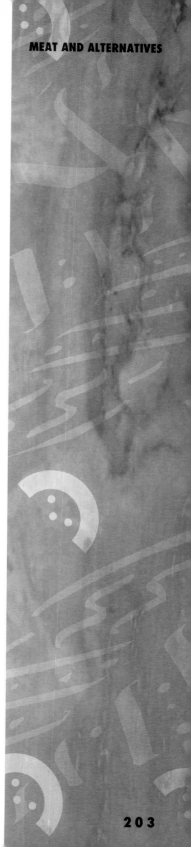

3. The approximate time required is merely a guide to know when to put the roast in the oven. An accurate meat thermometer is the only certain way to obtain meat cooked the way you want it. If the meat is being cooked from the frozen state, insert the meat thermometer part way through the cooking time.
4. Allow 10–15 minutes "resting time" after the roast is removed from the oven. It will be easier to carve since the protein tissues are set and less juice will escape.

SOURCE: Adapted from *Management and Foods*

*Barbecuing* ◆ This method is much like broiling, but the heat source, whether electric, gas, or from hot coals or briquettes, rises from under the meat. Some barbecues give a characteristic flavour, and you may or may not want to accentuate it by basting the meat with a favourite sauce.

*Rotisserie* ◆ A large, compact piece of meat is rotated on a spit. Because the rotating motion holds the juices within the meat, it is moist and full of flavour when cooked. Each kind of rotisserie equipment has its own method of operation, so follow the manufacturer's instructions.

Microwaving Meat ◆ There are certain differences between cooking meat in a microwave and in a conventional oven. Microwaved meats shrink less, do not become crisp, and have a different flavour. All visible fat should be removed before cooking meat in the microwave. You will need a special microwave thermometer, because standard meat thermometers cannot be used in the microwave.

The following tips will help you use a microwave to cook meat.

• Thaw frozen meat before cooking. Most microwaves have a special defrost setting. Follow the manufacturer's instructions.

• For roasts, use a dish just large enough to hold the meat and juices. Since bones reflect microwaves, resulting in uneven cooking, it is best to choose a boneless, even-shaped roast for uniform cooking.

• After turning the power off, allow for standing time for the meat to finish cooking and absorb the juices.

• When microwaving stews, fully submerge the meat in the liquid. Check periodically during cooking to ensure the meat is still submerged.

• When browning ground meat, put the meat in a microwave-safe colander and set over a large, glass bowl. This allows the fat to drain away during cooking.

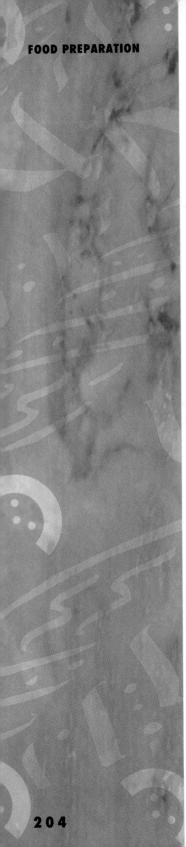

- Cook meat loaf in a round ball or a ring mould so the edges do not over-cook. Using a sauce prevents overbrowning.
- Interrupt cooking occasionally to remove accumulated fat. This allows the microwave to direct its power onto the meat instead of cooking the fat.
- Follow suggestions in the owner's manual for cooking meats, especially less tender cuts.

# POULTRY

Poultry includes chicken, duck, turkey, goose, Cornish hen, guinea fowl, and squab. Other game birds, such as pheasant, partridge, grouse, prairie chicken, and wild duck, are considered wildfowl. The principles of cooking poultry and wildfowl are somewhat different. If you are interested in cooking game birds, refer to a specialty cookbook that deals with them.

At one time, the cook had to kill, pluck, singe, draw, and dress the bird before it could be stuffed and cooked. Today all that is done for us before poultry is offered for sale in a store. Frequently, it is already cut into portion pieces and sometimes also boned.

Poultry Inspection and Grading ◆ Poultry is subject to similar health regulations as other meat. When it has passed health inspection in Agriculture Canada approved plants, the "Canada" inspection legend on the tag, bag, or insert is attached.

Poultry is also graded. Grade names are the same for chickens, stewing hens, turkeys, ducks, and geese. The grade name is either printed on a metal breast tag, as in the case of whole chickens, or printed on the transparent wrapper. Turkeys, ducks, and geese must also be marked as "young" or "mature." The grade is assigned on the basis of an evaluation of the bird compared to a standard. Factors include **conformation**, **fleshing**, fat covering, and **dressing**.

- Conformation means the appearance as affected by bone shape and normal flesh distribution.
- Fleshing refers to the distribution and amount of flesh in specific areas.
- Fat covering and its distribution in specific areas is noted.
- Dressing refers to the presence of discolouration, bruises, pinfeathers, skin tears, or any other blemishes.

Grades and the identifying colours used for poultry are outlined here.

*Canada A (Red)* ◆ This grade is most commonly available to retail consumers. Birds are a normal shape, well-fattened, and fleshed with only minor defects or blemishes. Chickens, turkeys, capons, stewing hens, ducks, and geese have individual standards to meet.

*Canada B (Blue)* ◆ These birds may have a slightly crooked keel bone (breast bone) but are otherwise normal. Not as well-fleshed or fatted as Canada A, they can have a few skin tears and other imperfections that do not seriously affect appearance or taste.

*Canada Utility (Blue)* ◆ These birds are of the same quality as Canada A but may have one or more parts, such as a wing, of the bird missing.

*Canada C (Brown)* ◆ Birds are fairly well-fleshed but may have prominent imperfections not allowed with the other grades.

Buying Poultry ◆ As with the advice given for buying other meat, the amount of poultry to buy depends on the required number of servings, the price per kilogram, and the amount of meat to bone in the package you are considering.

A whole chicken or turkey usually sells for less per kilogram than pieces. Most whole birds are about half meat and half bone. By purchasing the whole bird, it is possible to use any remaining meat in other recipes as planned leftovers. Boneless meat always costs more per kilogram, but accurately estimating amounts of meat with bone can be difficult. Base the amount to buy on 100 g of cooked meat per serving without bone or skin included.

The following tips for buying poultry will supplement the Buying Guide for Poultry, page 206.

Turkey meat can easily replace chicken or beef in a stir-fry like this. What other protein-rich food might you try?

- Choose the grade of bird, according to the way you plan to serve it.
- Fresh poultry has a clear, bright skin. A yellowish skin indicates the presence of a layer of fat. A bluish skin indicates little fat, and the bird may be tough.
- Choose frozen poultry with no freezer burn (dry, pale, frosty areas) that may indicate that it has been improperly stored or stored for too long.
- Choose frozen poultry with unbroken and unstained wrappers.

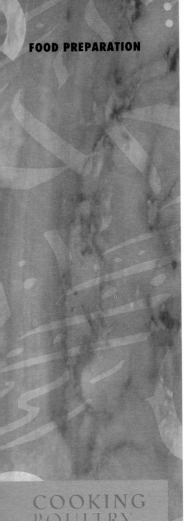

The same methods described for cooking meat are used for cooking poultry. Roasting is the one method that may be more difficult for the inexperienced cook. A Poultry Roasting Chart is included to help you roast a bird successfully.

## Buying Guide for Poultry

| Type of Poultry | Eviscerated Mass | Amount to Buy per Serving | Method of Cooking |
|---|---|---|---|
| Chicken — broiler/fryer | Up to 2 kg | 400–500 g | Fry or barbecue |
| Roaster | Over 2 kg | 400–500 g | Roast |
| Capon | 2.5–4 kg | 400 g | Roast |
| Fowl | Over 1.5 kg | 400 g | Braise, stew, or pressure cook |
| Turkey— broiler | Over 5 kg | 400–500 g | Broil, bake, or barbecue |
| Young turkey | 5–6 kg | 400–500 g | Roast |
| | over 6 kg | 250–400 g | Roast |
| Mature turkey | 5–6 kg | 400–500 g | Roast or braise |
| | Over 6 kg | 250–400 g | Roast or braise |
| Young duck | 2–3 kg | 500–650 g | Roast |
| Young goose | 4.4–6 kg | 400–500 g | Roast |
| Cornish hen | Up to 500 g | 1/2–1 bird | Broil, roast, or barbecue |
| Squab | Up to 575 g | 1/2–1 bird | Broil or barbecue |

SOURCE: Adapted from *Management and Foods*

## Poultry Roasting Chart
**(Oven temperature 160°C)**

| Type of Poultry | Eviscerated Mass (kg) | Roasting Time (h) |
|---|---|---|
| Chicken | 2–2.5 | 2 3/4–3 1/2 |
| | 2.5–3 | 3 1/2–4 1/2 |
| | 3–3.5 | 4 1/2–5 |
| Turkey — Whole | 4 | 3 3/4–4 1/2 |
| | 6 | 4 3/4 –5 1/2 |
| | 8 | 5 1/4–6 |
| | 10 | 5 3/4–6 1/2 |
| | 12 | 6 1/4–7 |
| — Halves | 2 | 2 1/2–3 |
| | 4 | 4–4 1/2 |
| | 6 | 4 1/2–5 |
| — Quarters | 2 | 3–3 1/2 |
| | 3 | 3 1/2–4 |

| | | |
|---|---|---|
| Turkey Rolls | 1.5–2.5 | 3 1/2–5 |
| | 2.5–3.5 | 5–6 |
| | 3.5–5 | 6–6 1/2 |
| Goose | 4–5 | 1 1/2–2 |
| | 5–6 | 2–2 1/2 |
| Duck | 2–2.5 | 1 1/2–2 |

Notes About Roasting Poultry:

1. Unstuffed poultry may require slightly less time to cook.
2. Begin testing to determine if the bird is cooked when it has been in the oven the shorter of two times. To do this press the thick muscle of the drumstick, protecting your fingers with a pot holder or towel, to see if it feels soft. Then check how easily the leg moves. The bird is cooked when the drumstick muscle feels soft and the leg moves readily in the joint when you lift or twist it. When pricked with a fork between the body and the heaviest part of the thigh, the juices will run clear.
3. If using a meat thermometer, insert it before cooking into the thickest part of the thigh muscle or into the centre of the stuffing. Be sure that it is not touching bone. Cooked turkey or chicken will register 85°C on the thermometer placed in the thigh; in the stuffing it will register 75°C.
4. Because geese vary in shape, their cooking times may differ. Therefore, allow an extra half hour before serving time in case more cooking time is needed.
5. Because duck has more fat, it should be roasted at a higher temperature than chicken or turkey.
6. Overbrowning may become evident as cooking proceeds. To prevent this from happening, cover the bird loosely with aluminum foil, shiny side out.
7. To prevent drying of the meat, baste the surfaces occasionally with fat and/or juices as they cook out of the bird.

SOURCE: Adapted from *Management and Foods*

# FISH AND SHELLFISH

Canadians have three oceans and hundreds of freshwater lakes and rivers to fish. We have fish of all kinds — freshwater fish, such as bass, perch, and trout; saltwater fish, such as cod, halibut, and salmon; and shellfish, such as mussels and lobster. Some fish are lean, and some are not so lean. All are a good source of protein.

Buying Fish • The most important factor in buying fish is its condition when you choose it. Packaged frozen fish should still be solid and the packaging tight to prevent entry of air. When the package is opened, there should be no evidence of frost or ice crystals and no white areas on the

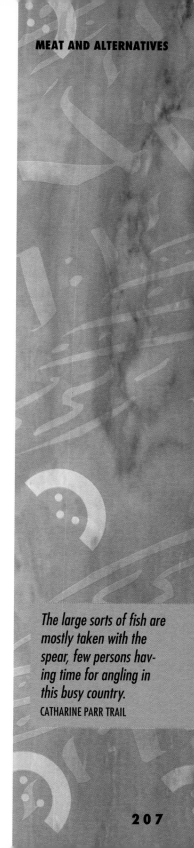

*The large sorts of fish are mostly taken with the spear, few persons having time for angling in this busy country.*
CATHARINE PARR TRAIL

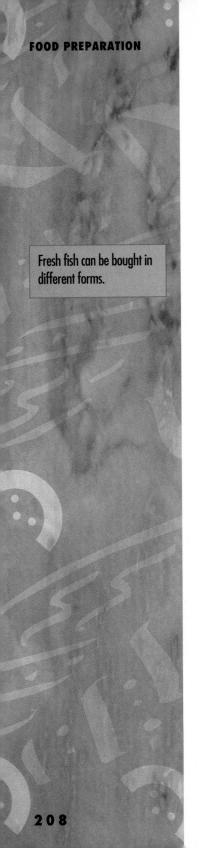

flesh that would indicate freezer burn or drying. Whole frozen fish will have a glaze of ice over the whole fish with no fading or discolouration.

Never refreeze frozen fish that has been thawed. Much of the fish and shellfish available in most stores, especially those at greater distances from the source, has been frozen soon after removal from the water. It may be displayed as fresh, and you may have difficulty knowing the difference. The best advice is to inquire before you buy, especially if you plan to freeze.

Most people prefer to buy fresh fish, and there are some good indicators to help you determine that it is fresh.

Fresh fish may have a mild fish smell, but it will not be strong or in any way offensive. If whole, the eyes should be clear and bright and slightly bulging. The entire fish will be a characteristic colour with reddish gills. Any scales will still be tight to the skin and all surfaces will be free of slime. The flesh of fresh fish should be firm. If an imprint remains when the fish is pressed, it is not fresh. Whether whole, filleted, or in steaks, the two terms used to describe the flesh of fish you will want to choose are firm and elastic. As well, fresh fish will not separate easily from the bones. These same indicators can help you choose fish that has been thawed.

Although eating habits and appetites vary, the person responsible for purchasing seafood should know from practice how much is adequate for the family meal. A general guideline is 150–225 g of edible flesh per serving. The chart on the following page will help you determine how much fish to buy.

Using Frozen Fish • Depending on the recipe or method being used, fish can be cooked either frozen or thawed.

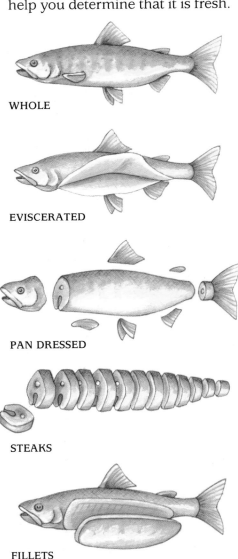

WHOLE

EVISCERATED

PAN DRESSED

STEAKS

FILLETS

Fresh fish can be bought in different forms.

Fish cooked from the frozen state will always be juicier than thawed fish. The cooking time will need to be slightly increased, but it is better to thaw only enough to make the fish easy to handle during preparation.

Because fish is so perishable, the preferable method for thawing is to leave it in the refrigerator overnight. An alternative method is to submerge the whole fish in cold running water. This method is, of course, not suitable for steaks or fillets. Whatever way you thaw fish, be careful to keep the flesh chilled throughout and cook it as soon as thawed.

| Deciding How Much Fish to Buy | 2 servings |
| --- | --- |
| Fillets, sticks, solid flesh with bones removed | 300 g |
| Steaks or slices with some bones | 500 g |
| Pan dressed, with head, tail, and fins removed | 500 g |
| Eviscerated only, head, tail, and fins remaining | 600 g |
| Whole, in the round, as taken from the water | 1 kg |

SOURCE: Adapted from *Management and Foods*

## Nutritive Value of Fish

The key nutrient that all foods of the Meat and Alternatives group have in common is protein. Fish and shellfish provide all of the essential amino acids to supply our needs for growth and repair of body tissues. Fish protein is digested easily. The kilojoule count of different species varies, and most of that variation is attributed to the proportion of fat the species contains. Most of the fat is distributed evenly throughout the flesh, although there is usually a visible fat layer just below the skin that can be removed if desired. The fat of fish contains the fat-soluble vitamins A and D. Other vitamins, including niacin and riboflavin, are found in the rest of the tissues. Minerals are an important component of all seafood. Calcium is contained in the bones, and beneficial amounts are obtained when small bones, softened by the pressure canning process, are mixed with the flaked fish flesh to make sandwiches, patties, and loaves. Other minerals found in fish include copper, iodine, and phosphorus.

## Cooking Principles

Fish is one of the easiest of the protein foods to cook. Since it contains very little connective tissue, it can be cooked at high temperatures. In fact, the cooked product is better when a high temperature is used for a short time. Low temperatures and overcooking dry and toughen the fish.

Fish should be cooked only until done. The time needed can be estimated by measuring the thickness of the piece of fish and allowing 5 minutes (10 minutes for frozen) for each centimetre of thickness. This guide works well to estimate time for baked, steamed, poached, broiled, and even fried fish.

Do you know that sqeezing a bit of lemon juice on your hands will get rid of any fishy smell?

To be assured that the fish is cooked thoroughly, pierce with a fork at the thickest part or near the bone. When the fish is cooked through, you will note these characteristics.

- Flesh pierces easily with a fork.
- Flesh separates easily into flakes.
- Flesh has lost its translucent appearance and has become opaque.
- Juices, clear in the raw fish, are now milky.

Shellfish • Shellfish are a popular protein-rich food that can be divided scientifically into two groups — mollusks and crustaceans. Clams, mussels, oysters, and scallops have very hard, protective outer shells, typical of mollusks. Crabs, lobster, and shrimp display segmented outer shells or carapaces that distinguish them as crustaceans. All shellfish are best when eaten very fresh, but most are also available frozen or canned. Availability will depend on where you live. The method of treatment and cooking differs for shellfish, depending on whether they are frozen, canned, or fresh.

## Mollusks

*Clams* • Clams are harvested commercially on both the Atlantic and Pacific coasts. They are sold alive in the shell and as fresh, frozen, and canned shucked meat. Live clams have tightly closed shells. If allowed to stand in cold, salty water for several hours, they will open and cleanse themselves of sand and grit. You can help this process by sprinkling uncooked cereal on the water.

Clams can be shucked open with a knife or steamed open. To steam, place the scrubbed shells in a steamer or a large kettle containing about 2 cm of water. Cover tightly and steam for about 10 minutes or until the shells partly open. Serve hot with sauce or melted butter. Save the clam liquid for chowder broth.

*Mussels* • Sometimes called "the oysters of the poor," mussels are, nonetheless, delicious mollusks that are cultivated and caught off the Atlantic provinces. They are sold fresh in the shell or as cooked meat. Mussels have a dark purple to black, elongated shell. They are distinguished by a beard, along the edge of the shell.

Discard any mussels with broken shells or shells that do not close after being refrigerated. To prepare, scrub mussels with a stiff brush under running water to remove sand and grit. Remove the beard with a sharp knife or scissors. Steam mussels, as you would clams, for about 10 minutes or until the shells partly open. Serve with a sauce or use in a recipe calling for cooked seafood.

How many different kinds of seafood can you find in this salad? Try to name them all.

*Oysters* • Oysters are commercially harvested on both coasts. From the Atlantic, the eastern oyster is marketed in the shell and graded according to its shape. On the Pacific coast, the Japanese or Pacific Oyster is farmed. They are available fresh, frozen, canned, and as smoked oyster meat. During the months of May through August oysters spawn. At that time their meat is thin and less flavourful. The rule of thumb is never buy oysters in a month that does not have an "r" in its name.

If you buy oysters in the shell, be sure that the shells are tightly closed. A gaping shell indicates that the oyster is dead and no longer edible. Shucked oysters should be plump, firm, and in clear liquid free of shell particles.

Oysters are toughened by high or prolonged heat. They should be cooked using a low or moderate temperature, just until they are plump and the thin edges show signs of ruffling. Oysters can also be chilled and eaten raw.

*Why, then the world's mine oyster, Which I with sword will open.*
WILLIAM SHAKESPEARE

**211**

## CAREER SKETCH

Joe Klassen, President of Joey's Only Franchising Ltd.

SOMETIMES A SUMMER JOB can lead to a full-time career. It did for Joseph Klassen. It was while working on a floating restaurant in Kelowna, British Columbia, that Klassen decided he wanted to be in the restaurant business.

Klassen began planning his restaurant in February of 1985. A seafood restaurant seemed a natural choice because many of his relatives live on the water. One of those relatives, an uncle in the commercial fishing industry, helped him to develop recipes. In September of that same year, Joey's Only Seafood Restaurant was opened. Fish and chips were a main menu item, along with other fresh seafood, such as crab, shrimp, oysters, sole, and trout.

It was not easy in the beginning. Klassen had to overcome a lack of experience, and he found that he was not taken seriously. He prided himself on the high quality of his food and excellent service, but no one seemed to know about his restaurant. By February of 1986 most of his money was gone, and he was almost ready to give up his business. Instead he persevered, and the business turned around. In a short span of time he had opened more Joey's Only restaurants. In 1989 he took on David Mossey and Jill Argue as partners to run three Joey's Onlys in Edmonton. By 1990 there were nine of the restaurants in Alberta.

Klassen had been approached regarding franchising Joey's Only almost as soon as it became successful. It was not until 1991 that he began to give it serious consideration. Mossey and Argue became full partners and the undertaking of franchising Joey's Only began. Alberta's stringent rules controlling franchising had to be met. This involved seeing lawyers, passing security checks, preparing an operational manual, and rigorous paperwork. The first franchises were in operation in 1992.

For Klassen, one of the most exciting aspects of the franchising business is getting into new territories. Opening each new restaurant brings him satisfaction. At present, there are 35 Joey's Only franchises with 75 more in the process in Ontario, British Columbia, Manitoba, and Saskatchewan. Joey's Only Franchising Ltd. is a team effort. Mossey is the vice president, heading the franchise development. Argue is the head of marketing and all advertising campaigns. Theresa Klassen is the head of accounting.

Klassen, as president, is now involved in dealing with landlords and contractors, buying equipment, and the many other aspects of setting up a franchise. This involves training staff, ordering inventory, and checking on schedules and the last-minute details of the restaurant openings. The operations manager then stays with the new Joey's Only for one to two weeks to make sure that everything runs smoothly.

Klassen has this advice for students considering the restaurant or franchising business: "Give your maximum effort. Be unique; offer something that no one else is offering. Treat everyone you meet with the utmost respect and give the best possible service and product." It is a formula that has certainly worked for Joseph Klassen and Joey's Only.

*Scallops* • Sea scallops are caught commercially in deep water off the coast of the Atlantic provinces. Some scallops are also caught off the British Columbia coast. Bay scallops, which are small, tender, and creamy pink or tan, are imported. Scallops are shelled or shucked as soon as they are caught, and the only parts eaten are the tender cubes of meat that functioned as a muscle to open and close the shell. The meat is sold fresh or frozen. Thaw frozen scallops sufficiently to permit separation before cooking.

Scallops are creamy white and have a mild flavour and a firm texture. They may be substituted in recipes calling for oysters, shrimp, prawns, or even firm white fish.

## Crustaceans

*Crabs* • Although caught in both Atlantic and Pacific oceans, most of the crabs harvested are Dungeness crabs from British Columbia. Most often, fresh crab is sold as cooked crab or cooked in the shell. When purchased alive, crabs should be cooked promptly, cleaned, and refrigerated.

To cook a live crab, plunge it head first into actively boiling sea water or fresh water with 50 mL of salt added for each litre used. Cover and simmer for about 15 minutes. Cool quickly in cold water. Crack and remove the meat.

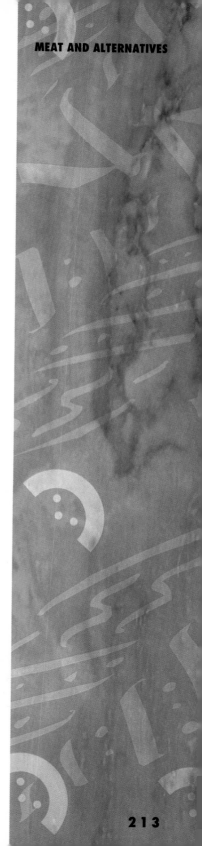

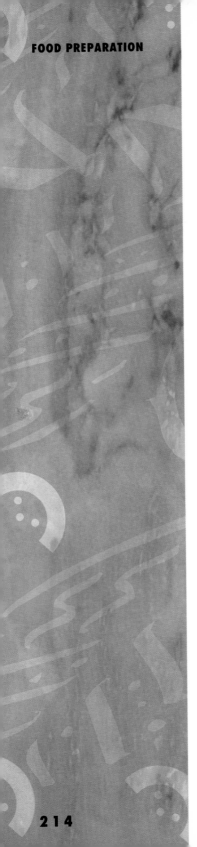

*Lobster* ♦ Lobsters are best when purchased and cooked alive. Live lobsters are bluish green to brown; when cooked they turn bright red. Cook live lobster the same way as live crabs. If you are buying a cooked lobster in the shell, check it by straightening out the tail and releasing it. If the tail springs back into a curled position, the lobster was alive and healthy when cooked.

Cooked, fresh and frozen lobster meat is sold in various sizes. Frozen lobster can be thawed overnight in the refrigerator or for several hours at room temperature. Lobster is also sold canned for use in salads and casseroles.

*Shrimp and Prawns* ♦ The coastal waters of British Columbia are the main source of Canadian shrimp. Canadians import even more than they harvest. Shellfish of the shrimp family vary in size from tiny members to large prawns. Their colours range from grey and green to pink; all turn distinctively pink when cooked.

Shrimp are sold by mass, both fresh and frozen, usually with the head removed. They also come shelled, cooked, and canned. From 1 kg of the whole shrimp in the shell — these are called "green shrimp" — you can expect to obtain about 500 g of headless shrimp or 250 g of shucked meat.

Shrimp or prawns may be cooked in the shell or unshelled, but the shells add flavour. To cook them in the shell, twist off the heads, then immerse them in well-salted, boiling water in 500-g batches. Return the water to a boil, and cook for one minute or until the shrimp turn pink. Remove immediately to cold running water. Peel by holding the end of the tail firmly between thumb and forefinger. Push toward the larger end of the shrimp to release shell.

# EGGS

*Egg Structure* ♦ Eggs are a valuable food because they contain high-quality nutrients. Although the main component of eggs is water, they also contain protein, fat, minerals, and vitamins. An egg has four distinct parts: **shell**, **shell membrane**, **albumen**, and **yolk**.

The shell is porous and composed mainly of calcium. A fresh egg has only a small **air cell,** as shown on the diagram. With age, the egg shell loses its thin, natural coating, called the **bloom,** that prevents air from passing through the pores. Then the space between the two membranes, one firmly attached to the shell and another that lies next to it, slowly fills with air to form an air cell. As water in the egg evaporates, the air cell size increases. When eggs are stored where air is dry and temperatures warm, this change occurs rapidly. It is therefore important to keep eggs refrigerated.

The egg white, called albumen, is thinnest next to the shell and becomes more liquid with age. In eggs graded A, the albumen is thick, and when an egg is broken into a flat dish is raised high and not spread out.

The yolk of a fresh egg is round and when the egg is broken into a plate, the yolk will be well raised. As the egg deteriorates, its yolk absorbs water from the white, making the yolk swell and flatten. Its colour varies with the feed of the hen. Egg yolks from other kinds of birds, such as ducks or geese, will also vary in colour from chicken egg yolks. A small, light-coloured spot on the surface of the yolk is called the **germ**. The germ is the initial source from which, in a fertilized egg, the chick eventually develops.

So that the yolk will remain in the centre of the shell, two **chalaza**, which are part of the thick albumen, anchor it. The chalaza look like whitish, twisted cords. They form an axis enabling the germ spot to remain in the centre of the egg.

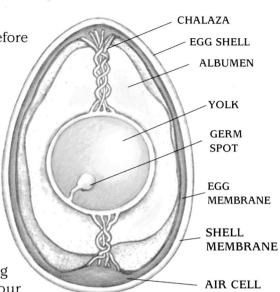

CHALAZA
EGG SHELL
ALBUMEN
YOLK
GERM SPOT
EGG MEMBRANE
SHELL MEMBRANE
AIR CELL

The components of an egg

## Egg Grading

Egg Grading ◆ Agriculture Canada inspects all egg-processing plants to ensure that the products are wholesome and processed according to sanitary standards. They also monitor the pasteurization and packaging of egg products, most of which are used in the food service industry, and the packaging and labelling of eggs in retail establishments. Imported eggs must meet the same standards, although they cannot carry the name "Canada" in the grade mark.

Registered grading stations must meet certain operation and sanitation requirements. Federal inspectors spot check both producer premises and grading stations.

Eggs are graded on:

- Cleanliness, soundness, and shape of shell. An older hen lays larger eggs with thinner shells. A shell having fine pores is preferable because deterioration of the egg will be slower.

*It has, I believe, been often remarked, that a hen is only an egg's way of making another egg.*
SAMUEL BUTLER

- Shape and relative position of yolk within the egg, as viewed during **candling**. Candling is the commercial method of rotating an egg before a bright light to reveal how the inside compares with the required internal standard.

- Size of air cell and abnormalities, if any, such as blood spots or double yolks. A small air cell indicates freshness.

## Grades of Eggs

*Canada A* ◆ These are of premium quality and in limited supply on the retail market. Eggs are clean, normal in shape with round, uncracked shells, and finest interior quality. Yolks are round and compact and surrounded by a reasonably firm albumen. Cartons are marked with an expiry date nine days from the date of grading and, if unsold by then, must be returned to the supplier.

*Canada B* ◆ Eggs are reasonably clean, slightly abnormal in shape, with uncracked shells. Yolks are moderately oblong and surrounded by albumen less firm than in Canada A. Canada B eggs are good for general cooking and baking where appearance is not too important.

*Canada C* ◆ Eggs are suitable for processing into commercially frozen, liquid, and dried egg products. Sizes are not specified, and cracked eggs may be included, as long as the contents do not leak.

*Canada Nest Run* ◆ These eggs are ungraded and sold for processing. Sizes are not specified, and the shell is cracked, but contents are not leaking.

**Buying and Storing Eggs** ◆ The size of eggs you buy should depend upon the price and the way you plan to use them. Since eggs are actually sold by mass it is possible to work out which size is most economical at any one time. Egg sizes range from jumbo to peewee.

Sometimes it is worthwhile to have more than one size of egg on hand. Most recipes are developed using medium eggs. The size of egg

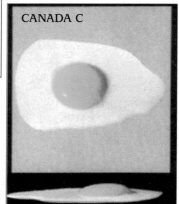

CANADA A

CANADA B

CANADA C

How is each yolk different in these three grades of eggs? How is each albumen different?

used can make quite a difference in certain recipes. For example, a cake that relies on beaten egg white to make it light will not have the desired characteristics if small eggs are used. Using more of the smaller size may work well.

If the eggs are to be scrambled or used in a sandwich, a salad, or an omelette, the size is unimportant. For serving eggs poached, fried, or boiled in the shell, a large size may be preferred. Infants and young children seem to like the smaller eggs.

When available, grade B eggs will be less expensive. They are suitable for scrambling, omelettes, general cooking, and baking. Grade A eggs look more attractive when poached or fried. They are a better choice for sponge-type cakes and meringues because the fresher, thicker albumen will hold the air beaten into them much better.

Egg freshness is maintained by refrigeration. Storing them in the carton prevents loss of moisture and absorption of odours. Strong smelling foods are easily taken up by eggs. Leftover yolks can be covered with cold water to prevent drying and drained before using. Leftover whites can be stored in an airtight container. Both leftover yolks and whites should be used within four days and *always* in recipes that require cooking.

Nutritional Value of Eggs  ◆  One to two eggs are considered one serving of the Meat Alternatives food group in a nutritionally dense form. They contain a wide variety of essential nutrients as shown in the accompanying chart.

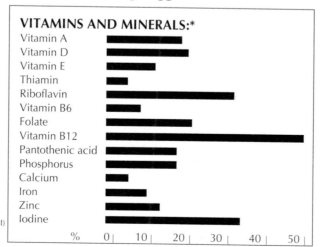

### Nutritional Profile of 2 Large Eggs

| Energy | 149 Calories |
|---|---|
| Protien | 12 g |
| Fat | 10 g |
| Carbohydrate | 1 g |

**VITAMINS AND MINERALS:***

Vitamin A
Vitamin D
Vitamin E
Thiamin
Riboflavin
Vitamin B6
Folate
Vitamin B12
Pantothenic acid
Phosphorus
Calcium
Iron
Zinc
Iodine

%   0   10   20   30   40   50

*Percentage of Recommended Daily Intake (RDI) as established by Health & Welfare Canada

SOURCE: Canadian Egg Marketing Agency

**217**

## Uses of the Versatile Egg

*Thickener* ◆ Eggs **coagulate** when heated. This means they stiffen and become firm, thickening the mixture that contains them. Sauces, custards, and some puddings are thickened with eggs.

*Leavener* ◆ Eggs hold air when they are beaten into a foam. When heated, the protein coagulates so that the foam structure is made firm and holds its shape. Sponge-type cakes, meringues, and soufflés have a high proportion of eggs that hold air and make them light.

*Binder* ◆ Eggs help bind the other ingredients in mixtures, such as meat loaf, meat patties, or flour mixtures. Once the eggs coagulate from the heat, the other ingredients stick together.

*Clarifier* ◆ Sometimes an egg is used to help clear a cloudy liquid like soup broth. Egg takes up the unwanted particles as it coagulates, and they can then be removed with the cooked egg.

*Coating Agent* ◆ Some recipes call for food to be dipped into slightly beaten egg, then rolled in a crumb mixture of bread, cereal, or crackers before being fried or baked in the oven. The egg helps the crumbs to stick to the food, and the protein–crumb coating protects the food from the intense heat of fat or oven. Meat cutlets and zucchini sticks are two examples.

*Emulsifying Agent* ◆ An **emulsifying agent** helps fat to mix thoroughly with a liquid. Eggs are used this way in mixtures to surround droplets of oil and prevent them from forming larger drops that will settle to the bottom. Mayonnaise and Hollandaise sauce are two examples.

*Crystallization Preventative* ◆ Ice crystals form when a liquid freezes. To prevent this **crystallization**, beaten eggs are included in frozen mixtures. Trapped air bubbles in the beaten egg remain in the small ice crystals preventing the formation of a large mass of frozen mixture. Ice cream, sherbet, and frozen desserts are examples.

## Cooking Principles

◆ The main principle of cooking eggs, whether alone or in combination with other ingredients, is to use a low temperature. They coagulate at a temperature of 65°C, well below boiling, which

*Why do people who enjoy chicken eggs for breakfast call crows, jays or raccoons nest robbers?*
BARRY KENT MacKAY

is 100°C. When eggs are cooked at boiling temperatures, they become tough and difficult to digest. In addition, the pan, in which eggs or a mixture containing eggs is cooked, is much more difficult to clean when a high temperature is used.

All protein foods are more tender when cooked at moderate temperatures. Eggs *cooked in the shell* require only a simmering temperature for coagulation to take place. For hard-cooked eggs, turn the heat to minimum after the water has just reached the simmer and allow to stand in the hot water to cook fully. If eggs are to be used cold, place in cold water after cooking to prevent a ring of discolouration around the yolk.

*Poach* eggs just below boiling temperature. When an egg poacher is not used, eggs will retain their shape in the water best, if the water is not boiling.

*Fry* eggs at a setting of 150°C in a pan with a fine coating of fat. If a treated pan is used, eliminate the fat or replace it with a few drops of water. To help firm the yolk, cover the pan for a few minutes.

*Scrambled* eggs can be cooked at 160°C. The higher temperature is possible because the yolks and whites are combined and the yolks coagulate at a slightly higher temperature than the whites. Sometimes a small amount of milk is added, which dilutes the egg.

An *omelette* is similar to scrambled eggs when the mixture is placed in a frying pan and rolled as it cooks. For a puffy omelette, the yolk and white are beaten separately, then folded together. Cooking is usually done in the oven. A puffy omelette has greater volume because of the air beaten into the eggs.

*Tips to Obtain Volume of Beaten Egg Whites* • A number of recipes rely on the ability of egg whites to hold air when beaten to provide leavening. Examples of their use this way are in soufflés, puffy omelettes, sponge cakes, such as angel food, sponge, and chiffon, and in meringues. Some desserts also contain beaten egg whites to make them light and, in the case of frozen desserts, prevent large crystals from forming. Here are some suggestions for obtaining and maintaining maximum volume.

• Fresh eggs give the most stable volume. They may take longer to beat to full volume, but will not lose air easily.

• To get the best volume, eggs should be at room temperature. Remove them from the refrigerator well ahead of time.

What part of the egg is most important in a soufflé?

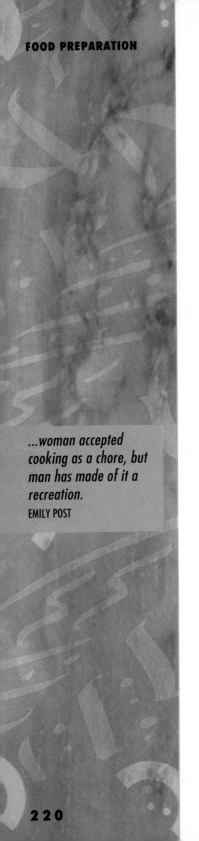

- Equipment must be very clean with no trace of fat. Plastic bowls with a scratched surface are not suitable because fat may be embedded. Be sure there is no yolk in the white when you separate the eggs. Even a small amount of yolk will prevent a foam from forming.

- Some recipes suggest the addition of an acid ingredient, such as lemon juice or cream of tartar. Acid will begin coagulation of the egg white and help to stabilize the foam.

- When sugar is called for, a finer textured product will be obtained if you use a fine-ground sugar, such as powdered (icing) sugar or berry sugar.

- Both the correct rate of beating and time of adding other ingredients contribute to success. Egg whites should be beaten to the frothy stage before anything is added. This is called an *egg white foam*. At this stage an acid ingredient can be beaten in. Sugar should be added very gradually as beating continues. This dissolves the sugar completely, and produces a fine-grained **meringue**. Meringue is the term used to describe a beaten egg white and sugar mixture. Added slowly, sugar makes the foam stronger and less air is lost. A sponge-type cake made with a strong foam will have a finer texture.

- Understand terms frequently used in recipes with beaten egg whites. In the *soft peak* stage, the meringue peaks bend over slightly. At this stage they are suitable for folding into a batter. The *stiff peak* stage has been reached when the peaks stand up straight as the beater is withdrawn. At this stage the whites will be more difficult to fold into other ingredients. If beaten further, the foam will break down and loose air.

## LEGUMES

**Legumes** are the dried seeds of a particular family of plants that produce their seeds in pods. Also known as **pulses**, they include beans, lentils, and peas. All are rich in protein, complex carbohydrates, iron, calcium, and B vitamins. Another attribute is that they contain virtually no fat, sodium, or cholesterol, but are high in fibre. *Canada's Food Guide to Healthy Eating* encourages us to eat more foods with these characteristics. For thousands of years legumes have been a staple food throughout the world. Common varieties of beans, lentils, and peas are produced in the Prairie provinces of Canada.

*...woman accepted cooking as a chore, but man has made of it a recreation.*
EMILY POST

When buying legumes in the dried form look for bright colour and uniform size. They are packaged in a variety of sizes or sold in bulk form in specialty stores and in some supermarkets. A 500-g package of beans will measure approximately 500–625 mL and yield about 1.25–1.5 L of cooked beans. Canned beans and lentils are also available for variety. They make meals easy to prepare and provide variety.

Beans, peas, and lentils are all part of the legume family.

One of the greatest advantages of these inexpensive and nutrition-packed foods is their easy storage and long storage life. They keep almost indefinitely when stored in tightly covered containers in a cool dry location. When exposed to sunlight they loose some of their colour, but provided they are in an airtight container the flavour and texture will not be affected. Over time they may become drier and harder. Once cooked, lentils and peas may be stored in the refrigerator for 3–4 days. They may be frozen for up to six months. Canned beans, peas, and lentils have the same good keeping qualities as any other canned vegetables.

Cooking Legumes • Wash legumes to remove dust and any lumps of dirt or stones that may be mistaken for a bean. While inspecting for foreign materials remove any damaged legumes. The next step in preparing a variety of dried beans is to soak them. Remove any legumes that float. Split peas and lentils, mung beans, and black-eyed peas do not require soaking. Here are three methods for soaking. For each, use 750 mL of water for every 500 g of beans.

- The traditional method is an overnight soak. Cover the beans with cold water and allow them to soak overnight in the refrigerator. Drain before cooking. Beans soaked this way cook in less time and keep their shape better.

- To quick-soak beans, cover them with water and bring to a boil. Boil for two minutes. Remove from heat and allow to stand for one hour. Drain before cooking.

- You can even use your microwave to soak beans. Combine beans and water in a 4-L microwaveable dish. Cover and microwave on high power until boiling (15 minutes). Let stand for one hour, then drain.

To cook beans follow the general rule of 750 mL of water for every 250 mL beans. Cooking times will vary with the kind of bean. If they are to be used in a soup or casserole that involves further cooking, simmer until just barely tender. Pierce with a toothpick to test.

Some recipes recommend that red kidney beans be boiled hard for 10 minutes at first to reduce stomach upsets that may result when they are eaten. Adding 15 mL of oil will prevent foaming that occurs during boiling. Do not add salt or other seasonings until after the beans have become tender, as seasonings may toughen the outside and lengthen the cooking time.

| Type of Legume | Cooking Time | Soak Required |
| --- | --- | --- |
| Lentils | 30–45 minutes | No |
| Lentil purée | 45–50 minutes | No |
| Split peas | 35–45 minutes | No |
| Split pea purée | 45–60 minutes | No |
| Black-eyed peas | 30–45 minutes | No |
| Whole peas | 1–1 1/2 hours | Yes |
| Kidney, pinto, navy beans | 1 1/2–2 hours | Yes |
| Soybeans | 1 1/2–3 hours | Yes |
| Canned beans and legumes | Heat thoroughly | No |

**Kinds of Legumes** ◆ A great variety of legumes are available. Each has its own identifying characteristics, but in most recipes substitutions can be made.

*Black-eyed peas* or *cowpeas* are native to Africa and popular in South America, India, and the southern United States. These little beans with the "black eye" are attractive to children. They cook in a relatively short time and are used in stews, soups, salads, and casseroles.

*Chick peas* have a savory flavour and, depending on the type, of which there are many, cook in 30 minutes to 3 hours. They are available canned, split, or ground into flour. Chick peas are included in many traditional recipes including *falafel* and *humus* from the Middle East.

*Fava beans* or *broad beans* have been cultivated since the Stone Age and are thought to be the original bean variety. They are popular in the Middle East and Italy. In Canada we can buy them fresh or frozen. They have a

*Looks can be deceiving — it's eating that's believing.*
JAMES THURBER

tough skin but can be chopped in a food processor with seasonings added to make a good dip.

*Whole dried peas* can be used in soups and stews where they take a little longer to cook than *split peas*. The split and skinned versions of dried peas can be made into a good purée for serving with vegetables. They are called soup peas in North America, and in the United Kingdom they are familiar as mushy peas.

*Lentils* are used in the Mediterranean and Middle East to make soups, stews, salads, and sauces for pasta. In India they are made into spicy *dials*. There are several types of lentil: small and brown, split orange-red, dark greenish-grey (puy lentils), and larger, whole green lentils. Although they can be cooked without soaking, soaking will shorten cooking time a little.

*Lima beans* are probably better known in the fresh form as *butter beans*. They are native to South America, and although they grow in different sizes, they are all flat and kidney-shaped. They are a tasty bean with a mealy texture that absorbs other flavours well. In the southern United States they are popular in *succotash*.

*Mung beans* are small, round, and usually green, although there are also black and yellow varieties. They are cultivated widely in China and India and known there as *mung dal*. Mung beans are the kind that are frequently sprouted and used in salads and stir-fries as bean sprouts.

*Pinto beans*, native to India, are popular there and in the Caribbean. They are also called *gunga peas*. Pinto beans can be used like red kidney beans in casseroles and in mixed-bean salads, where they add colour and variety.

*Red kidney beans* are one of the most useful of the legumes. They are available both dried and canned. They are the bean of choice to make chili and are used to make the popular Mexican dish called *refried beans*, in which the cooked beans are fried like a large potato cake.

*Soybeans* are thought to have originated in eastern Asia. They have been grown for thousands of years in China, where they are known as "meat without bones" because of their high protein content. Soybeans have a strong flavour and need flavourful condiments if they are to be eaten as legumes. Soy beans are preferred when made into many other products including bean sprouts, soy sauce, soy flour, soy milk, and tofu.

*White beans* are an all-purpose bean that absorbs other flavours well. Native to Guatemala and southern Mexico, they are used for baked beans in Britain. In France they are called *haricots* in the popular and filling *cassoulet*. Also known as *navy beans* they are used to make *Boston baked beans*, a traditional dish in North America.

## IDEA
••••••

Grow your own bean sprouts. Soak 50 mL of mung beans overnight. Drain, place the beans in a 1-L, wide-mouthed, glass jar, and cover the opening with cheesecloth. Store the jar on its side in a dark, warm cupboard. Rinse and drain the beans three times daily. Sprouts should develop in six to eight days.

# TOFU

Soy beans are used to make a non-dairy liquid called soy milk. This milk is a useful substitute for people who are allergic to other milk or who are following a vegetarian diet.

**Tofu** is the curd made from soy milk. Often referred to as bean curd, it is made by curdling the mild, white milk of the soybean. The valuable protein it contains makes it an excellent meat alternative. Approximately 75 mL or 100 g is considered one serving of tofu. Minerals and some vitamins are obtained from it in varying amounts. The other advantage of tofu is that it has no cholesterol and is very low in carbohydrates and kilojoules.

In its basic form tofu is a soft, white substance that resembles cheese, but has a bland flavour. Its advantage lies in the many ways that various cutting, mixing, and pressing techniques can alter its form. It easily takes up other flavours to provide variety to the vegetarian diet. Whether you are a practising vegetarian or simply wish to reduce the amount of meat, dairy products, and eggs you eat, tofu may be your best alternative. Compared with many other protein foods it is relatively inexpensive.

The adaptable tofu is becoming more readily available in Canadian supermarkets as its merits are becoming better known. Look for it in the produce section or in the dairy section with the cheese. It will be packaged in a solid block or several cakes together, packed in water, and sealed in plastic containers. Tofu can also be found in natural food stores or Asian specialty food stores.

Solid tofu will keep for a week when refrigerated and the water covering is changed daily. Soft tofu comes vacuum-packed and can be kept unrefrigerated until the package is opened. When beaten to a smooth consistency, soft tofu is popular for dips, dressings, and desserts. It can be blended in a food processor or blender with fresh strawberries and a small amount of honey. Tofu is suitable for use in a variety of main dishes, breads, desserts, soups, salads, and for any meal, snack, or party. Tofu in any form is a useful and nutritious food for babies, children, and seniors since it is soft and easily digested.

## Using Tofu ◆ 
Although it has an inconsequential and bland flavour, tofu takes on the flavour of other foods. Especially good results are obtained by marinating it in a tasty liquid, and then using it as a snack or appetizer or in other dishes.

*Of soup and love, the first is best.*
SPANISH PROVERB

- Put tiny tofu cubes into your favourite vinaigrette salad dressing several hours ahead of serving time. Use the tofu dressing on any green salad to make it more filling and increase its food value.

- A marinade of tamari sauce, oil, vinegar, and seasonings will flavour chunks of tofu when left for several hours. Add the flavourful pieces to cooked rice or other cooked grains or pulses.

- Steamed or stir-fried vegetables can be made into a more satisfying meal by the addition of marinated cubes of tofu. For this, try combining lime or lemon juice, tamari sauce, garlic, pepper, and a touch of honey.

- Tasty kabobs result when cubes of marinated, firm tofu are threaded onto skewers alternating with mushrooms, small tomatoes, onions, and other vegetable pieces. The marinade could be a mixture of soy sauce, brown sugar, mustard, and vinegar. Brush with oil before cooking on the barbecue grill or under the broiler.

This may look like a regular hot dog, but it is actually a veggie wiener made with tofu.

Other Vegetable Protein • Textured vegetable protein is another alternative to tofu and can be used in many of the same ways. Purchased in assorted shapes and sizes, it needs to be reconstituted. Package instructions will describe how to soak in hot water or for more flavour, in a stock, overnight. Reconstituted textured vegetable protein can be added to ground meat to replace one-third to one-half of the meat. This kind of protein is useful because it adds moisture and a more chewy texture than some of the other ingredients available for vegetarian meals. It can add bulk, nourishment, and flavour to lentil and nut dishes as well as to burgers, loaves, and shepherd's pie. Any of these protein alternatives can be mashed, mixed with seasonings, and formed into burgers. The burgers can be coated with flour or dipped in egg, coated with bread crumbs, and fried in oil or baked in the oven on an oiled or coated baking pan.

# FOOD PREPARATION

## KEY TERMS

Use the words listed below to complete the following statements in your notebook.

| | |
|---|---|
| candling | elastin |
| finish | coagulate |
| tofu | albumen |
| collagen | myosin |
| legumes | chalaza |

1. Tough, elastic strands of the connective tissues of meat, called _____ , are converted into gelatin during cooking.

2. _____ is resistant to tenderizing with heat, moisture, or other methods. Usually it is trimmed away before the meat is cooked.

3. The layer of fat under an animal's skin is known as the _____ .

4. The principal protein in tender meat, called _____ , needs only a little cooking to make it palatable.

5. The egg white is also called the _____ .

6. The yolk of the egg is anchored in the centre of the shell by two _____ .

7. _____ is the commercial method of rotating an egg before an intense light to reveal how it compares with the required internal standard.

8. When heated, eggs _____ or stiffen and become firm, making the mixture that contains them thicker.

9. _____ are the dried seeds of plants that produce their seeds in pods.

10. _____ is the curd made from soy milk.

## FOCUS YOUR KNOWLEDGE

1. Name and briefly describe the grades of beef in Canada.

2. Prepare a chart to illustrate the major nutrients found in meat, poultry, fish, eggs, and legumes.

3. List six ways in which meat can be tenderized.

4. List the factors that are considered in assigning a grade to poultry.

5. What differences are there in the temperatures used for cooking meat, poultry, and fish?

6. List four characteristics that indicate fish is thoroughly cooked.

7. Name and describe briefly the four parts of an egg.

8. Describe the difference between the soft and hard peak stages in preparing meringues.

9. Describe briefly the preparation that must be given to legumes prior to cooking.

## DEMONSTRATE YOUR KNOWLEDGE

1. Collect pictures of different types and cuts of meat and prepare a bulletin board to illustrate the types of meat, cuts, and cooking methods.

2. Prepare identical quantities of ground beef using beef with different percentages of fat. Note the price of each and weigh the portions before and after cooking to determine the percentage of fat loss. Evaluate the beef for flavour and cost.

3. On a large map of Canada, tack names of fresh and salt water fish and shellfish on appropriate lakes, rivers, and oceans.

4. In small groups, find a recipe using different types of fish and shellfish for an hors d'oeuvre, appetizer, salad, and main dish. Prepare one of the recipes.

5. Prepare scrambled eggs three ways: using egg yolk only, the whole egg, and an egg substitute. Compare the flavour, appearance, texture, fat content, cost, and ease of preparation.

6. In small groups, find a recipe using legumes for a main dish, soup, and salad. Prepare one of the recipes.

7. Locate and prepare a recipe using tofu.

## APPLY YOUR KNOWLEDGE

1. In small groups, create a word search or crossword puzzle using the key words and other significant words in the chapter.

2. Collect bones from various types and cuts of meat. Boil the bones to clean them of any meat. Prepare a bulletin board, labeling the bones according to whether the cut containing the bone was tender or less tender.

3. Interview a vegetarian to ask why meat is omitted from his or her diet and what alternative foods he or she chooses to meet daily protein requirements.

4. Prepare a poster to illustrate safety and sanitation procedures when handling, preparing, cooking, and storing poultry.

5. Brainstorm ways to include eggs in the diet of a person who must control cholesterol and fat intake.

6. Research the history and use of legumes throughout the world. Prepare a brief report on your findings.

# Other Foods

*Canada's Food Guide to Healthy Eating* includes an additional category called Other Foods. Health and Welfare Canada States: "Other Foods are a broad range of food items that Canadians commonly eat or drink that do not belong in one of the four food groups."

The Other Foods category includes:

- Foods that are mostly fats and oils, such as butter, oil, and salad dressing.
- Foods that are mostly sugar, such as candy, cake, and jam.
- High-fat and/or high-salt snack foods, such as potato chips, pretzels, and crackers.
- Beverages, such as coffee, tea, and soft drinks.
- Herbs, spices, and condiments, such as parsley, cinnamon, and ketchup.

As explained in Units 1 and 2, the food habits and eating pattern that you develop over time affect your general health. However, including or excluding any one food generally will not improve or adversely affect the outcome of long-term food habits. A healthy pattern of eating regular, nutritious meals and snacks will not be destroyed by eating one particular food, or meal, or even all the meals in a single day that may be less nutritious or higher in fat or kilojoules. Similarly, the careful selection of nutritious foods for a short time will not undo the harmful effects of poor choices made over a lifetime.

Health and Welfare Canada states, "It is the average of what people eat over time or the pattern of eating that is important to health." With this as a framework for your understanding of the impacts of the Other Foods category, let us look at each of the five groups that are included.

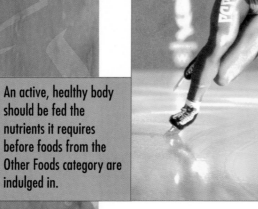

An active, healthy body should be fed the nutrients it requires before foods from the Other Foods category are indulged in.

# FOODS THAT ARE MOSTLY FATS AND OILS

This group includes animals fats, such as butter and lard, vegetable fats, such as margarine and shortening, and the oils from which they are made. It also includes mayonnaise and other oil-based salad dressings.

You have already learned about butter from reading Chapter 8. *Lard*, another animal fat, is rendered from pork. Lard produces a flakier texture in biscuits and crusts than other solid fats, but is less suitable for cake baking. Lard should be stored in the refrigerator.

*Margarine* contains refined vegetable oil, water, and salt. Almost all margarines are vitamin-enriched. Since butter and margarine are similar in moisture content, margarine may be substituted for butter in both baking and cooking.

*Vegetable shortenings* can have a polyunsaturated oil base — soybean, corn, cottonseed, peanut — that is hydrogenated to convert them to saturated fats. Vegetable shortenings have a better creaming quality than lard, so they are more suitable than lard for making fine-textured cakes.

*Vegetable oils* are 100 percent fat and come from a variety of sources. Corn, cottonseed, olive, soybean, sesame, safflower, sunflower, and peanuts are the major sources. The oils pressed from these seeds, fruits, and nuts are distinguished by their smoking points (the temperature at which they begin to smoke). Some oils, such as corn and safflower, have a higher smoking point than oils, such as peanut and sesame. Olive oil, which has the lowest smoking point, is more suitable for salad dressings than for exposure to heat.

Some fats and oils are necessary to the body, because they are important sources of fatty acids where fat-soluble vitamins are stored. Margarine is also a source of vitamin D. However, a high-fat intake is associated with a number of serious diseases and contributes to obesity. A major goal of the nutrition recommendations that accompany *Canada's Food Guide to Healthy Eating* is to reduce the amount of fat eaten. A general recommendation is that no more than 30 percent of the total intake of kilojoules should come from fat. That may seem to be a high percentage until you remember that 1 g of fat has twice the number of kilojoules as 1 g of protein or carbohydrate.

Pastry • One of the more popular foods with a very high fat content is pastry. This family of products is made from a mixture of flour, fat, and water, milk, or cream. Sometimes egg or sugar is added, depending on the recipe. The main differences are related to the kind and amount of fat used and the method of mixing and later manipulation.

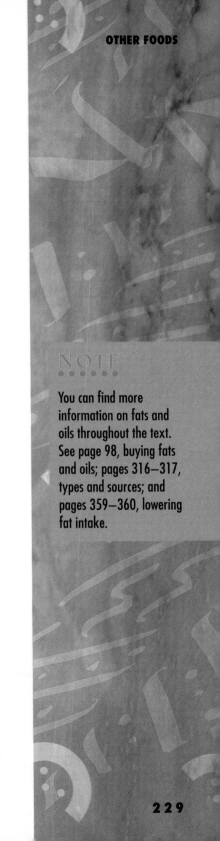

NOTE

You can find more information on fats and oils throughout the text. See page 98, buying fats and oils; pages 316–317, types and sources; and pages 359–360, lowering fat intake.

These dessert tarts are made with pastry. Name three other uses of pastry.

Pastry has many uses. As a main course, it can be used in two layers encasing meat/poultry, vegetables, and gravy in a meat pie. Wrapped around sausages and baked, it makes a tasty snack food. For dessert, pastry can be used either in two layers with fruit fillings or as single-crust pies or tarts with custard or cream fillings.

Although pastry has little nutritional value, when combined with other ingredients, nutrition may be improved. A good example is a single-crust dish known as quiche. The filling of eggs, milk, vegetables, and protein (meat, fish, and/or cheese) provides added nutritional value.

*Making Pastry* ◆ Any standard cookbook will have recipes for making pastry. A variety of ingredients and methods can be used. The choice of fat, whether shortening, margarine, butter, lard, or oil, will give different characteristics of tenderness and flavour to the product.

Pastry is one of the more difficult flour mixtures to prepare successfully. The techniques used build upon those practised in making biscuit and muffin doughs described in Chapter 3. The following recipe for pastry is versatile in commercial or quantity food operations, and most inexperienced cooks can achieve an acceptable product in their first attempt. The recipe yields enough pastry dough for three double-crust pies or six single crusts.

## Dependable Pastry

| | | | |
|---|---|---|---|
| 1500 mL | sifted all-purpose flour | 450 mL | lard |
| 15 mL | salt | 1 | egg |
| 5 mL | baking powder | 5 mL | lemon juice or vinegar |
| | cold water | | |

1. Sift and measure dry ingredients into a very large bowl.
2. Cut lard into dry ingredients using a pastry blender, until pieces resemble rolled oat flakes.

3. Break egg into a liquid measure. Beat with fork, add lemon juice or vinegar, and add cold water to make 175 mL total liquid. Beat again with fork.
4. Pour liquid ingredients a little at a time over the flour–fat mixture, tossing lightly with a fork after each addition.
5. Work the dough until evenly moist, then form into a large ball. Divide into single portions, and wrap with plastic wrap until ready to use.

## FOODS THAT ARE MOSTLY SUGAR

This group includes all forms of sugar, honey, maple syrup and other syrups, and most jams, jellies, marmalades, and conserves containing more sugar than fruit. It also includes snack items, such as all candy, candy floss, marshmallows, popsicles, and sherbet. Like fat, these contribute energy but few nutrients. The principal concerns about their use are:

• Whether adequate amounts of the other four food groups have been supplied.

• Whether these sugary foods are replacing more nutritious choices required by the body.

• Whether your energy need and activity level will balance the amount eaten.

Although *Canada's Food Guide to Healthy Eating* does not specifically recommend a reduction in the amount of sugar and sugar-laden foods eaten, the principle of moderation applies here too. Of particular concern are people with low energy needs.

Sugar in our food comes in many forms. Whether derived from sugar cane, sugar beets, or maple tree sap, the same sweetening result occurs in foods to which the derivative is added. Here are some of the forms of sugar in food.

*Granulated sugar* is sucrose in the crystalline form from beets or cane. It is the most common form used commercially or in homes. Fine granulated sugar, made by passing the crystals through sifting screens, dissolves quickly. It is popular for use with fresh fruit, in beaten egg white or whipped cream mixtures, and sprinkled on baked products, such as cookies or doughnuts.

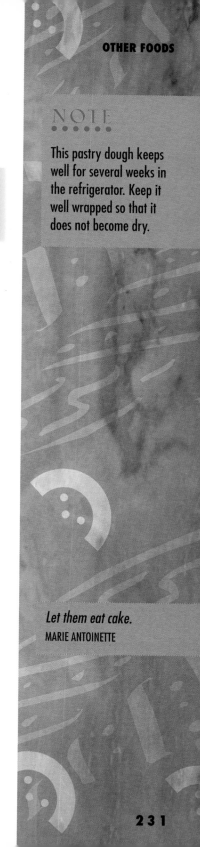

**NOTE**

This pastry dough keeps well for several weeks in the refrigerator. Keep it well wrapped so that it does not become dry.

*Let them eat cake.*
MARIE ANTOINETTE

*Icing sugar* is pulverized granulated sugar to which a small amount of starch or other anti-caking ingredient has been added. The starch absorbs moisture in the air and helps maintain the powdery texture of the icing sugar. It is used to make uncooked frostings and is dusted over cakes, cookies, and squares to make them more attractive.

*Brown sugar* is a more moist, refined sugar that comes light or dark. Molasses gives it colour and flavour. The darker sugar is more strongly flavoured. Brown sugar is enjoyed sprinkled on hot, cooked cereals and is used in baking cookies, bars, and cakes.

*Molasses*, which is rich in iron, comes in three types. Unsulphured molasses, made from the juice of sun-ripened cane, is the best tasting. Sulphured molasses is a by-product of the cane and beet refining process. The third type, blackstrap molasses, is a waste product. It is the unpalatable residue from the third boiling of the cane. It contains few sugar crystals but plenty of iron and other minerals. Molasses from sugar beets is not suitable for table use, but it is valuable in making cattle feed and manufacturing yeast and citric acid.

*Maple syrup* and *maple sugar* are made by boiling the sap of the sugar maple to evaporate the water content. Maple sap, like water, boils at 100°C. It becomes syrup at 104°C. To make maple sugar, the sap is boiled to 112°C, beaten until it thickens, then poured into moulds. Maple syrup is popular on pancakes, waffles, and French toast. It is also used in special desserts and sauces. Maple sugar is eaten as candy or used like brown sugar.

*Honey* is a natural sweetener made by honey bees from the nectar of flowers. The different plants from which the nectar has been obtained affect the colour and flavour of the honey. Honey is sold in two basic forms: comb and extracted. The latter, however, can be either liquid or crystallized. In baked products less honey is required to give the same sweetness as sugar. Honey also attracts moisture, so products containing honey stay moist longer.

*Corn syrup* is a clear, thick, sweet liquid made by hydrolyzing the starch from corn. Generally, corn syrup is used in canning and jelly making. It also appears as a sweetener in many commercial products. It is valuable in making cooked frosting and some candies.

All of these forms of sugar are used in different ways and for different reasons in food. Usually, their sweetening properties determine their use. The fact that sugar will crystallize is used to advantage in candy making. The caramelization that occurs when sugar is heated contributes to the attractive colour of baked goods. Flavour and aroma changes give foods other pleasing characteristics. In jams, jellies, marmalades, and other preserves, the high concentration of sugar acts as a preservative.

# HIGH–FAT AND/OR HIGH–SALT SNACK FOODS

Most young people will be familiar with foods in this group. They include chips of various kinds, pretzels, and puffs. How many varieties can you name?

Most of these items originate from foods that are included in one of the four food groups. However, they are so highly refined and processed that little of the original nutrient value remains. For example, potato chips are derived from potatoes, a vegetable in the Vegetables and Fruit group. After processing has been completed there is very little of value from the original potato. Pretzels, made from a flour base in the Grain Products food group, have little remaining other than kilojoules and salt.

With some concern, health professionals are finding that Canadians consume far more sodium than they require, most of it as salt used in food preparation both commercially and at home. Here are some specific suggestions for reducing the amount of salt in your food.

- Choose highly salted snack foods less often.
- Reduce the amount of regular salt used in cooking. This includes the salt found in seasoning salts, salted condiments, and sauces like soya sauce. Experiment with herbs and spices instead.
- Taste the food on your plate before you add salt. Then add only a little salt, if any.
- When shopping, read labels on all foods, then select foods that are unsalted or have less salt or sodium listed.

Other suggestions for reducing the salt in your foods can be found in other sections of this book that are related to shopping and making food

selections both at home and in commercial eating establishments. Similarily, because it is such a major health issue, suggestions for reducing fat in food are contained throughout.

## BEVERAGES

Water is essential to life and is the preferred beverage. It is an energy-free way to quench thirst and replenish fluids lost during elimination of body wastes. Drinking water is the best way to replace fluids lost through perspiration during a strenuous workout or other physical activity. Water is not the only way to replenish body fluids. Milk, fruit, and juices provide water, but with the additional benefit of their nutritive value.

Coffee, tea, cocoa, and cola all contain **caffeine**, a stimulating drug. Moderate amounts of up to 400–450 mg of caffeine daily are not considered to be a health risk or to have adverse affects during pregnancy. It is important to note that caffeine can cross the placenta and stimulate the fetus. Similarly, caffeine in the beverage of a breast-feeding mother will affect the child. Excessive consumption of these beverages should be avoided. Moderation is the key.

You may be interested to compare the average caffeine levels of some commonly used products.

> How many cups of filter drip coffee could one drink and still be within the moderate consumption of caffeine?

> Look here, Steward, if this is coffee, I want tea; but if this is tea, then I wish for coffee.
> PUNCH

| Caffeine Source | Caffeine (mg) |
|---|---|
| Coffee, 175 mL cup* | |
|   Automatic percolated | 72–144 |
|   Filter drip | 108–180 |
|   Instant regular | 60–90 |
| Tea, 175 mL cup | |
|   Weak | 18–24 |
|   Strong | 78–108 |
| Cola Soft Drinks | |
|   355-mL can | 28–64 |
| Cocoa Products | |
|   Chocolate milk, 250 mL | 2–8 |
|   Hot cocoa, 175 mL | 6–30 |

*Most coffee mugs hold more than 175 mL of beverage.

# HERBS, SPICES, AND CONDIMENTS

A dish may be packed full of nutritional value, but if it lacks a pleasant flavour, it will not be enjoyed. In the art of cooking, seasonings are the magic pigment that adds life to culinary creations. Here is a simple way to think of seasonings.

- Spices are parts of aromatic plants grown in the tropics.
- Herbs are the leaves of aromatic plants grown in the temperate zone.
- Seeds are the fruit or seeds of herb plants.

While herbs and spices do not contribute much in the way of nutrients, they are an excellent way to give foods extra flavour and to reduce the use of salt. Herbs can be used fresh or dried. The general rule when substituting fresh for dried herbs in a recipe is to use three times as much of a fresh herb as dried. Freshly picked herbs should be stored in a jar of water or loosely wrapped in a plastic bag in the refrigerator for a day or so. Dried herbs should be stored in airtight bottles, in a dark place away from heat, if possible.

Spices bring the world together. Imagine, paprika from Hungary, cinnamon from Sri Lanka, ginger from Africa, and turmeric from Jamaica all available in Canadian supermarkets. Spices are best bought in small quantities and stored in airtight jars in the dark. This ensures the spices are at their peak flavour. Some spices can be bought whole and ground as needed. Others are commonly bought already ground and ready for use.

Condiments are made with herbs and spices to accompany other foods. Pickles, relishes, chili sauce, ketchup, horseradish, and mustard are a few examples.

While it might be obvious that chili powder is the spice used to make chili con carne, did you know that you can perk up egg dishes or cottage cheese by adding a little chili powder? A Herbs and Spices Chart on pages 236–240 has been included to show you which herbs and spices can enhance particular foods.

Which of these are herbs and which are spices? Which are neither herb nor spice? Clockwise from the top left are dill; minced onion; mustard seeds; crushed red pepper; star anise; black pepper corn; nutmeg; cinnamon; chili powder; paprika; bay leaves; whole coriander; ginger; cloves; curry; sesame seeds; fennel seeds; tarragon.

| | SOUPS AND SAUCES | MEAT AND POULTRY | FISH | SALADS | VEGETABLES AND FRUIT | EGGS AND CHEESE | GRAINS |
|---|---|---|---|---|---|---|---|
| **ALLSPICE** <br> *Spice* <br> Pea-sized fruit of West Indian tree. Flavour resembles a mixture of cinnamon, nutmeg, and cloves. Purchase whole or ground. | Gravies <br> Meat sauce <br> Tomato sauce | Marinades <br> Pot roast <br> Pork and poultry <br> Stews | Boiled fish <br> Pickled herring | Fruit salad | Red cabbage <br> Squash <br> Sweet potato | Pickled eggs | Breads and baking |
| **ANISE** <br> *Seed* <br> Licorice-flavoured fruit of an annual plant of parsley family. Grown in Spain, China, and Syria. Used in baking and candy making. | Barbecue sauce | Boiled chicken <br> Poultry dressing | Pickled fish | Dressing for fruit salad | Spiced beets | Devilled eggs | Baking |
| **BASIL** <br> *Herb* <br> Aromatic leaves and tender stems of plant cultivated in western Europe. Flavour strongly suggestive of anise. | Seafood cocktail <br> Soups <br> Tomato sauce | Beef stew <br> Lamb chops <br> Sausage | Shellfish <br> Sole | Coleslaw <br> Potato salad | Peas <br> Potatoes <br> String beans <br> Squash <br> Fruit compote | Cottage cheese <br> Omelette | Macaroni <br> Rice |
| **BAY LEAVES** <br> *Herb* <br> Smooth, shiny, aromatic leaves of laurel tree from eastern Mediterranean countries. Chef's favourite the world over. | Soups <br> Spicy sauces <br> Tomato juice | Game <br> Heart <br> Kidney <br> Oxtail <br> Poultry <br> Stews | | Seafood salads | Carrots <br> Potatoes | Omelette <br> Scrambled egg | |
| **CARAWAY** <br> *Seed* <br> Dried fruit of plant grown in northern Europe, notably Holland, and Asia. Popular in German and Austrian cookery. | | Kidney <br> Liver <br> Pork <br> Hungarian goulash | Boiled crawfish | Beets <br> Coleslaw <br> Stuffed celery | Cabbage <br> Potatoes <br> Onions <br> Sauerkraut <br> Turnips | Cheese spreads <br> Cottage cheese | Bread <br> Noodles <br> Pastries |
| **CARDAMOM** <br> *Seed* <br> Aromatic, tiny seeds that range in colour from white or pale green to almost black. Grown in small pods in India, Guatemala, and Sri Lanka. | Bean and pea soups <br> Tomato juice | Hamburger <br> Liver <br> Pork <br> Seasonings | Pickled herring | | Spiced beets <br> Melons | | Rice pilaf |
| **CAYENNE** <br> *Spice* <br> Spicy, small peppers. A pungent plant grown in Mexico, Japan, and Nigeria. | Sauces for meats and vegetables <br> Tabasco | Pork sausage <br> Seasoning | Barbecued fish <br> Broiled fish | Red cabbage slaw | Avocado dip | Cheese croquettes <br> Cream cheese dip <br> Welsh rarebit | |

| | SOUPS AND SAUCES | MEAT AND POULTRY | FISH | SALADS | VEGETABLES AND FRUIT | EGGS AND CHEESE | GRAINS |
|---|---|---|---|---|---|---|---|
| **CELERY SEED** Minute, seedlike fruit of the parsley family. Used whole or in the form of celery salt. | Boullion Minestrone Sauces Tomato juice | Croquettes Casseroles Lamb Marinade Meat loaf Spareribs Stews | Baked stuffed fish Broiled fish Fish chowder | Aspic Lettuce salad Potato salad Salad dressings | Beets Lima beans Potatoes Tomatoes | Boiled, fried, and scrambled eggs | Breads |
| **CHILI POWDER** *Blend* Blend of chili peppers and other spices that can be bought whole, flaked, or ground. Pungent flavour varies from mild to very hot. | Gravies Oyster cocktail Tomato sauce | Ground meat Hamburgers Stew seasoning | Shellfish | Garnish for vegetable salads | Vegetarian chili | Cottage cheese Egg dishes | |
| **CINNAMON** *Spice* Aromatic bark of cinnamon tree can be bought in pieces or ground. Has a warm, fragrant flavouring. Grown mostly in Sri Lanka. | Sauces Soups | Ham glaze Meat loaf Porkchops Sauerbraten Stews | Fish stock Pickled herring | Fruit salads | Squash Sweet potatoes Fruit drinks Fruit compotes Melons Poached fruit | Cottage cheese Cream cheese French toast | Baking Buttered toast |
| **CLOVES** *Spice* Dried, nail-shaped flower buds of a tree of the myrtle family grown in Indonesia, Madagascar, and Zanzibar. Has natural antiseptic and preservative properties. | Bean, split pea, and potato soup | Beef stew Baked ham Corned beef Pork Poultry Sausage seasoning | Baked fish Boiled fish | Pickled beets | Beans Onions Squash | Cheese fritters Pickled eggs | Baking |
| **CORIANDER** *Seed* Fragrant, dried seeds that have a mild, slightly burnt-orange flavour. Grown in Argentina. An essential ingredient of curry powder and garam masala. | Boullion Egg sauces Tomato sauce | Pork Poultry Sausage seasoning | Stuffed fish | Marinated vegetables Mixed green salads | Green beans Mushrooms | | |
| **CUMIN** *Seed* Small, dried fruit whose taste and shape resemble caraway. One of the oldest spices. Grown in Cyprus, Iran, and Syria. | Chutney Curry sauces Soup | Barbecued meats Beef Pork Stews | Boiled shellfish | | Onions Peas Vegetable casseroles | Cheese omelettes Curried eggs Stuffed eggs | Rice |

| | SOUPS AND SAUCES | MEAT AND POULTRY | FISH | SALADS | VEGETABLES AND FRUIT | EGGS AND CHEESE | GRAINS |
|---|---|---|---|---|---|---|---|
| **CURRY POWDER** *Blend* — Blend of coriander, turmeric, fenugreek, cumin, and chili. An exotic flavour with unlimited uses. | Curry sauces Soups | Beef Lamb Poultry Veal | Fish mousse Shellfish Shrimp curry Tuna curry | French dressing | Vegetarian curry | Cream cheese Curried eggs Devilled eggs | Rice |
| **DILL** *Seed* — Dried fruit of annual plant of parsley family with a warm, aromatic taste. Grown in Europe and India. | Cucumber soup Fish sauce Meat sauce | Creamed chicken Lamb chops Sausage seasonings | All fish and seafood | Coleslaw Cucumbers Potato salad | Brussels sprouts Cabbage Carrots Cauliflower Green beans | Cheese dips Cottage cheese | Pasta |
| **FENNEL** *Seed* — Dried fruit of parsley family, grown in Europe, India, Lebanon, and Argentina. Anise flavour helps cut the oiliness of foods. | Soups Fish sauces | Roast pork | Boiled fish | Seafood salads Salad dressing | Eggplant Potatoes | | |
| **GINGER** *Spice* — Root of tuberous perennial plant, grown in Asia, Africa, and West Indies; has a citruslike smell and hot flavour. Available fresh or dried and ground. | Glazing sauce Soups Sweet and sour sauce | Chicken Ham glaze Marinades Pot roast | | Fruit salad | Carrots Sweet potatoes Compote of dried fruit | | Baking |
| **MACE** *Spice* — Lacy covering surrounding the kernel inside the apricot-like fruit of a tree of the myrtle family. Flavour slightly reminiscent of nutmeg. Grows in Grenada, Indonesia, and India. | Béchamel sauce Delicate soups Hard fish sauces | Cambridge sausage Stews | Oyster stew Scalloped fish | Salad dressings | | Creamed eggs Welsh rarebit | Baking |
| **MARJORAM** *Herb* — Perennial of mint family; imported from France and Dominican Republic. Delightfully fragrant. | Soups Cream, brown, sour cream sauces | Beef Chicken Goose Lamb Mutton Pâté | Broiled, baked, and creamed fish Oyster stew | Chicken salad French dressing Seafood salad | Carrots Eggplant Green beans Mushrooms Peas Spinach | Omelettes Scrambled egg | Stuffings |
| **MINT** *Herb* — Apple mint, spearmint, and ginger mint are only a few of many varieties grown in temperate zone. Strong, sweet flavour with pleasant aftertaste. | Chutney Fish sauce Mint jelly Mint sauce Soups | Lamb Veal stew | | Coleslaw Mixed greens | Beets Carrots Eggplant Peas Potatoes Squash Fruit compote | Cream cheese | |

| | SOUPS AND SAUCES | MEAT AND POULTRY | FISH | SALADS | VEGETABLES AND FRUIT | EGGS AND CHEESE | GRAINS |
|---|---|---|---|---|---|---|---|
| **MUSTARD** | | | | | | | |
| *Seed* White, black, and brown, seeds of annual plant of mustard family. Grown domestically and imported from Italy, Denmark, British Isles, and Netherlands. | Cream of celery soup Lentil soup Mushroom soup Sauces | Ham Hamburger Hash Pickled meat Roast beef Spareribs Tongue | Devilled crab Scalloped fish | Coleslaw Cucumber and dill Garnish Potato salad Salad dressings | Beets Cabbage Green beans Sauerkraut | Cheese dishes Cheese spreads Devilled eggs | Sandwiches |
| **NUTMEG** | | | | | | | |
| *Spice* Kernel of the nutmeg fruit. Grown in Grenada, India, and Indonesia. Freshly grated flavour is superior to ready-ground. | Cream sauces Soups | Meatballs Stews | Fish cakes Fish casserole Lobster Shrimp | Fruit salad | Cabbage Carrots Cauliflower Eggplant Green beans Mushrooms Onions Squash Spinach | Creamed eggs Custard Eggnog | Crust of meat pie Rice pudding |
| **OREGANO** | | | | | | | |
| *Herb* Dried leaf of perennial of mint family. Intense flavour similar to marjoram. Grown in Mexico, Italy, Greece, Chili, and France. | Gravies Meat sauces Tomato sauces Tomato soup | Beef stews Chicken Lamb Marinades Mexican dishes Pork Shish kabob Veal | Baked, broiled fish Butter for shellfish Fried fish Shellfish | Mixed greens Potato salad Seafood salads Salad dressings | Cauliflower Green beans Lima beans Mushrooms Potatoes Turnips | Boiled eggs Omelettes | Pasta dishes Pizza Stuffing |
| **PAPRIKA** | | | | | | | |
| *Spice* A mild, heat-free member of pepper family with an agreeable, slightly sweet taste. Grown in Spain and Hungary. | Chicken soup Cream sauce | Pork chops Roast chicken | Fried fish Shellfish | Garnish | Guacamole | Cheese dip Cottage cheese Egg dishes | |
| **PARSLEY** | | | | | | | |
| *Herb* Native of Mediterranean area. Now grown domestically. Distinctively mild, agreeable flavour. | Garnish Herb bouquet Sauces Soups | Lamb Stews Veal | All fish | Green salads Potato salad | Potatoes | Creamed, scrambled eggs Omelettes | Pasta Stuffings |
| **POPPY SEED** | | | | | | | |
| Tiny seeds of poppy plant. Widely used in Indian and Jewish cookery. Has nutty flavour and crunchy texture. Best are from Holland. | Curry sauces Garnish for cream soups | Beef casserole | Broiled and fried fish | Fruit salad Salad dressing | Asparagus Broccoli Cauliflower Potatoes Spinach | All egg dishes Cheese spreads Cream cheese | Pasta Baking |

| | SOUPS AND SAUCES | MEAT AND POULTRY | FISH | SALADS | VEGETABLES AND FRUIT | EGGS AND CHEESE | GRAINS |
|---|---|---|---|---|---|---|---|
| **ROSEMARY** *Herb* Sweet, fresh-tasting herb of mint family grown in France, Spain, and Portugal. Also known as Rosa Maria. | Chicken, pea, and spinach soup Fish and meat stocks Sauces | Beef Game Lamb Partridge Poultry Veal | Baked fish | Fruit salad Mixed greens | Cauliflower Green beans Potatoes | Custard Omelettes Scrambled eggs | Rice pilaf Stuffings |
| **SAGE** *Herb* A strongly flavoured herb of the mint family. Grown in Yugoslavia and very popular in North America. | Manhattan chowder | Goose Turkey Veal | Baked fish | Seafood salad Salad dressings | Lima beans Onions Tomatoes | Cheese dips Cottage cheese | Stuffings |
| **SAVORY** *Herb* A peppery herb of mint family; has a distinctively warm, aromatic flavour. Imported from France. | Bean and pea soup Consommé Tomato soup Vegetable soup | Chicken Hamburgers Lamb Liver Pork Veal Stew | Baked and broiled fish Fish chowder | Mixed greens Potato salad Tomato salad | Beans Cabbage Eggplant Peas Sauerkraut Squash Tomatoes Turnip | Cream cheese Devilled eggs Omelettes Scrambled eggs | Stuffings |
| **TARRAGON** *Herb* Aromatic leaves of a perennial Old World herb imported from France. | Chicken soup Tomato soup | Beef Chicken Lamb Meatloaf Mutton Sweetbreads Turkey Veal | All fish and shellfish Seafood cocktail Seafood dip | Aspic Chicken salad Mixed greens Salad dressings Seafood salads | Asparagus Beans Beets Chard Cucumber Peas Spinach | All egg and cheese dishes Omelettes Stuffed eggs | Pasta Stuffings |
| **THYME** *Herb* Leaves and tender stems of a garden herb. Imported from France and Spain. Distinctive flavour. | Fish and meat sauces | Game Meatloaf Pork Poultry Stews Veal | All fish Clam chowder Fish chowder | Aspic Chicken salad Mixed greens Pickled beets Seafood salad Tomato salad | Beets Carrots Green beans Mushrooms Onions Peas Potatoes Spinach | Cheddar cheese Cottage cheese Egg and cheese dishes | Dumplings |
| **TURMERIC** *Spice* A powder with a slightly peppery odour; prepared from the underground stem of an East Indian perennial. Imported from Haiti and Jamaica. | Fish sauce | | Barbecued salmon Clam chowder | Seafood salads | Beans Cauliflower Cucumber Onions | Devilled, scrambled, and shirred eggs | Rice |

## ☀ KEY TERMS

Use the words listed below to complete the following statements in your notebook.

| | |
|---|---|
| beverages | fats and oils |
| spices | sugar |
| herbs | caffeine |
| other foods | pastry |
| condiments | salty snack foods |

1. _____ are a broad range of food items that Canadians commonly eat and that do not belong in the four food groups.

2. The group containing _____ includes animal and vegetable fats and foods such as mayonnaise.

3. A popular food made from a mixture of flour, fat, and water is _____.

4. _____ in food can be derived from cane, beet, or maple tree sap.

5. _____ include various kinds of chips, pretzels, and puffs.

6. _____ include tea, coffee, soft drinks, and fruit-flavoured drinks.

7. _____ is a stimulating drug found in coffee, tea, cocoa, and cola drinks.

8. Pickles, relish, chili sauce, ketchup, and mustard are examples of _____.

9. _____ are the parts of aromatic plants grown in the tropics.

10. _____ are the leaves of aromatic plants grown in the temperate zone.

## ☀ FOCUS YOUR KNOWLEDGE

1. What foods comprise the Other Foods category in *Canada's Food Guide to Healthy Eating*?

2. Why have nutritionists recommended reducing our daily fat intake?

3. Briefly discuss the versatility of pastry.

4. Briefly describe the forms of sugar used in food preparation.

5. List five suggestions for reducing the amount of salt in your food.

6. Name five condiments and some foods they may accompany.

## ☀ DEMONSTRATE YOUR KNOWLEDGE

1. Prepare a display of fats, grouped according to animal, vegetable, and "hidden" fats.

2. Categorize foods that you consumed over the weekend into the four food groups plus Other Foods. Circle in orange foods high in fat, in purple those high in sugar, in pink those high in caffeine, and in brown those high in salt.

3. Read the labels from a group of canned and packaged foods in the food lab. Group the foods in three categories according to those highest in fat, sugar, and salt.

4. In small groups prepare a standard recipe for cookies, cake, muffins, or a beverage. Compare the flavour, texture, sugar content, and kilojoules with a similar product made using an artificial sweetener.

5. Prepare a steamed vegetable (corn, carrots, peas) and include salt as a seasoning. Prepare the same product, but use a herb (basil, dill weed, chervil) in place of salt. Compare the flavour and sodium content of the two products.

6. In small groups prepare pastry using a standard method from a cookbook and the Dependable Pastry method on pages 230–231. Compare the products for ease of preparation, flakiness, tenderness, and flavour.

## ☀ APPLY YOUR KNOWLEDGE

1. Using a web diagram, brainstorm hidden sources of fat found in foods.

2. Prepare a chart of foods containing natural carbohydrates and refined and processed carbohydrates. Compare the kilojoules and nutritional content.

3. Discuss ways in which the total quantity of fat, sugar, and caffeine can be reduced in one's daily diet.

4. Prepare a one-page report on a spice or herb, outlining its origin, history, and uses.

5. Prepare a graph to illustrate the nutrients found in 250 mL of skim milk, 2% milk, apple juice, orange juice, and cola.

6. As a class, survey the teachers in your school to determine whether they drink regular or decaffineated coffee or regular or herbal tea. Prepare a poster to illustrate the results of your survey.

# Unit Overview

## ☀ REVIEW YOUR KNOWLEDGE

1. Name five grains and describe their uses.
2. Explain the role of the ingredients in a flour mixture.
3. What are the classifications of vegetables?
4. List three qualities to look for when buying fresh fruit.
5. Describe the characteristics of a good white sauce.
6. Outline the problems that can occur when you cook milk, and describe how to prevent them.
7. What is the most important factor to consider when buying fish?
8. What is tofu, and how is it made?
9. Briefly explain the role of Other Foods in *Canada's Food Guide to Healthy Eating*.
10. Why is it necessary to include some fats and oils in the diet?

## ☀ EXTEND YOUR KNOWLEDGE

1. Research one of the grains discussed in chapter 6. Answer the following questions in a report: Where does it grow? How is it processed? How is it used as a food? Which cultures are likely to include this grain in the diet, and why?
2. Interview family members or friends from various cultures to learn the types of salads commonly served in different countries. Gather recipes for each type of salad. Prepare a chart of the salads for at least five countries.
3. Write and present orally a brief report on the steps involved in cheese making.
4. Prepare a report on the fish industry in Canada. Include past history, the present situation, and future predictions. Include visuals in your report.
5. Research one of the following topics:
   a. the process of hydrogenating fats
   b. the process of decaffeinating coffee
   c. the history of tea
   d. the Japanese tea ceremony
   Prepare a video presentation of your findings.
6. Interview the manager of a meat department to learn the training required, the specific challenges of the position, and the safety and sanitation practices that must be observed. Also discuss current consumer trends in the purchase of meat, poultry, and fish.

# A Global Perspective

In Unit 1 you learned that your early food choices were influenced by your cultural background. As you grow older and meet more people, you become familiar with foods from other cultures. These foods may then become a part of your own eating patterns. If you compare the foods you ate as a preschooler with what you eat now, you will likely find that many foods you enjoy now are not from your own cultural group. You even expand your vocabulary as you become familiar with foods from other cultures.

Before people from across the oceans came to what is now known as Canada, Native peoples demonstrated a rich culture based on the animals and plants available to them. As others came to this land the pattern of the lives of these original peoples changed. Today they live beside new Canadians.

The cultural groups that settled in Canada brought from their homelands a wide variety of foods. As each ethnic group became larger, importing or production of specific foods in Canada became possible. Whole industries revolve around meeting the food needs of a wide

variety of cultural groups. Which ethnic groups in your community are large enough to support restaurants and markets?

Because meeting food needs is a huge industry and has global implications, you need to be aware of your responsibilities when making food choices. How do your food choices affect land use in other countries? What can you do to reduce waste and misuse of resources in our country as well as in others? Like all parts of life, making wise decisions is a matter of choice. Are you making globally responsible food choices?

CHAPTER 11
Canadian Food Heritage

CHAPTER 12
Cultural Foods

CHAPTER 13
Global Food Issues

This line drawing depicts a traditional method of hunting walrus. Try to picture a modern hunting method.

# Canadian Food Heritage

## NATIVE PEOPLES

The Inuit are Native people who live mainly in the arctic regions of Canada. Their name means "chosen and true people" or "the people." The ancestors of today's Inuit were dependent on the mammals and fish that inhabited the land. The Arctic is a vast land with many species of animals. The species that made up the principal diet of the Inuit depended on seasonal availability and on whether the people were nomadic or more settled. Whales provided a very important part of their food.

Regardless of which large animal was killed — whale, seal, walrus, caribou, or musk ox — a successful hunt could mean food for many people for many days. Once the hunters were welcomed back from the hunt, everyone joined in the work of breaking the animal down into manageable pieces for all to share. The Inuit had a well-defined system of group

effort. Each person understood his or her role in caring for the group's needs. If the hunters were unsuccessful, it sometimes resulted in death by starvation of whole communities.

In the icy North everyone had to work quickly while the fresh carcass was still warm. No matter how skilled, one person could not cope with the skinning and quartering of a large animal in frigid weather before it froze solid. Sea animals were broken down right on the beach. Moving such a large carcass was virtually impossible given the tools and transportation methods available.

All arctic animals have a thick layer of fat between the skin and the bone and muscle, to insulate them against the cold. This fat, known as *blubber*, formed a very important part of the diet to provide energy stores for people in this cold region. Blubber also had many other uses. For example, it was the source of oil burned in lamps.

Also important to the diet and clothing needs of some Inuit people were the huge migrating herds of caribou. Caribou hunting did not take place in deep winter. The meat was too lean and the fur too thick then. The better time for hunting was summer and autumn when the caribou were well fed.

A variety of methods were used to catch fish depending on the part of the Arctic and on the season. When lakes were frozen, the fish could be caught with a jig lowered through a hole chopped in the ice. In summer, handmade spears were used to catch fish. Both fish and caribou were sun-dried to feed the people during the lean days of early winter before the ice was strong enough to permit hunting seals and other sea mammals.

Most of the traditional food-gathering methods have now been adapted or abandoned for a more modern lifestyle made possible by new technology available to people of the North. Presently, every major Inuit settlement has an airstrip with regular flight service interrupted only by bad weather. Settlements complete with homes, schools, stores, churches, and hospitals have developed since the rapid expansion of airlines and telecommunication systems. Many Inuit travel by snowmobile instead of sled and dog teams in winter, and motorboats instead of kayaks in summer. Hunting is accomplished with guns; woolen clothing and rubber boots replace traditional clothing; wooden homes have replaced snow houses and skin tents.

Over time, however, contact with non-Natives has had enormous cost. Contagious diseases have wiped out entire groups. Replacement of game meat with the available, often cheaper, starchy food from the south has contributed to poor health and susceptibility to disease. Canadian Inuit suffer the worst tooth decay of any people in the world. Loss of land, culture, and personal identity has led to broken lives for many Inuit. Mistakes of the past cannot be undone. However, efforts to improve health and living conditions and to educate young people about their cultural heritage and prepare them for a modern society are being made slowly.

The various regions in Canada have their own types of soil, forms of vegetation,

This modern Inuit settlement is Pond Inlet, Northwest Territories. Notice the icebergs in the background.

and species of fish and game. Different groups lived in these geographic areas. Some lived entirely by hunting and fishing; others cultivated the land.

## Eastern Woodlands

The wooded highlands of Ontario, Quebec, and the Atlantic provinces were occupied by groups of the Eastern Woodlands. These groups spoke languages belonging to two unrelated families, Iroquoian and Algonquian. The Algonquin are a group of communities of Algonquian-speaking people. They continually moved to new fishing and hunting groups according to the changes in the seasons. The white-tailed deer was perhaps the most important game animal, except in the north where moose were found. They used all of the animal — flesh, bone, skin, and sinew. Nothing was wasted.

In spring entire families travelled to fishing sites at the mouths of creeks and rivers or to the seashore for shellfish and eels or seals. During this season the northern Ontario Ojibwa groups of the Algonquian-speaking people camped in the maple groves to make large quantities of maple syrup and sugar. Wild rice grew abundantly around the lake shores. The Ojibwa people collected it to supplement their diet of berries, fish, and meat.

The groups of the Iroquoian-speaking people occupied the green, fertile basin of southeastern Ontario and its extension along the St. Lawrence valley. The Iroquois and Huron were two of these groups. Agriculture was so important to them that the sites for their encampments were chosen mainly for the fertility of the soil. Their main crop was corn, the only native cereal, planted in small mounds set a few feet apart. Squash, sunflowers used to make oil, and several varieties of beans were placed between the mounds. Fishing, hunting, and gathering supplemented domestic crops.

## The Plains

The Plains people of the central Prairies lived a nomadic life, with small bands travelling from place to place in search of game, such as antelope, elk, and deer. However, the most important animal to the Plains people was the buffalo. Buffalo meat was the mainstay of their diet. The hides were used to cover their homes and to make clothing and floor covers. Sinew provided the thread to sew these items. Bones were

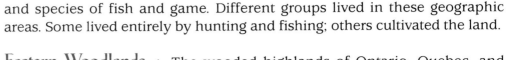

This Algonquian encampment was drawn in 1872.

fashioned into tools, such as knives and needles, and the horns were made into cups, spoons, and clubs. It is not surprising then that these people devoted nearly all of their energies to hunting this animal that was so important to their lives.

## British Columbia ◆ 
Coastal British Columbia groups have always relied heavily on salmon. It is said that there were two hundred ways to cook it. A favourite way to cook salmon fillets was to broil them in racks alongside the outdoor fire. A wooden trough caught the dripping grease, which was a favourite finger-dipping sauce. Strips of salmon were dried and smoked and nibbled on like candy during the winter months. Other seafood enjoyed by coastal groups included herring, cod, halibut, clams, oysters, octopus, and crab. Wild berries, onions, ferns, and seaweed were eaten fresh and dried for winter. Certain groups placed great importance on the small oolichan fish, which is so rich in oil it can be burned like a candle when dried. First Nations people living on the Coast made oil from the oolichan for trade.

The Plateau, an area separated from the west coast by the Cascade Range and from the plains by the Rocky Mountains, was home to various First Nations with different origins, languages, and cultures. Fish and game in fairly equal measure were the staple foods. Migrating salmon were available during the summer. Plentiful wild berries and roots were gathered and dried in the sun to preserve them for times of less abundance. Plateau people generally suspended their meat and fish on sticks and roasted them over a fire. A few First Nations peoples living nearest the sea adopted the Coast practice of boiling their food in watertight wooden boxes. Boiling in waterproof kettles of bark or woven spruce roots was a cooking method familiar to all Plateau people.

## Northern Canada ◆ 
Scattered groups of First Nations peoples lived in the basins of the Mackenzie and Yukon rivers. They all spoke dialects of a single language, Athapaskan. Life was difficult in the regions they inhabited. There was far less game than in the woods of Ontario, Quebec, or the Maritimes. The climate was harsher, and changes of seasons were more severe.

These Northern people were primarily hunters who relied less on their assorted weapons than on snares of caribou rawhide to trap caribou, beaver, and hare, and farther south, bear, moose, and buffalo. Most of the groups used the rivers and lakes in summer, where they fished with nets of twisted willow bark or rawhide, hand lines, weirs, and traps.

With few exceptions, the people of the First Nations were considered equals. Not even the chief was above other members of the group. Helping

*The caribou are everything, the centre of our whole livelihood. All of our food, our culture, our dances, our spiritual connections are with the caribou. Indigenous people around the world have a sacred animal. Well, the caribou, that's ours.*
NORMA KASSI
(THE GWICH'IN NATION)

249

These fish caught on the Mackenzie River are being dried for future use.

The first settlers came from many different countries as do new Canadians. What is your cultural heritage?

others was the norm. Like the Inuit, each member of the group shared the responsibility for food gathering. Food that was not used had to be dried and put away for winter. Firewood had to be collected and stored. During the summer months, most groups dried game meat in the sun to make *pemmican*, which is much like beef jerky. This may have been Canada's first convenience food. It was readily available during long trips and required no cooking.

There were many differences among the First Nations. These were the result of the geographic areas in which they lived and the events in their history. The groups mentioned here are only a few of many that populated Canada from coast to coast to coast. The cultures of the Inuit and the First Nations made Canada a multicultural country long before the arrival of the first settlers.

## CANADIAN REGIONAL FOODS

When the first settlers came in search of a new home, they brought with them food habits that were different from those of the First Nations peoples. Some travellers came to discover the mystery and fortune of the Western world, others to find a better opportunity for their families. With the arrival of each new group have come new ideas about food preparation and different eating patterns. Over time, people have come from every continent and country on earth. Each contributes to the mosaic of cultures that make up the nation.

Food in Canada is as diverse as the cultural backgrounds of the people. Some recipes are distinctively regional; others are adaptations of old-country favourites. Many are simply very popular ways of serving foods produced in Canada.

Early life in this huge country was undoubtedly difficult, and Canadians have proved their durability by overcoming many hardships. Everything prepared for the daily meals of early settlers had to be cultivated or foraged from the surrounding lands. At some times of the year, foods served were repetitive. Thick, hearty soups were served often in settlers' homes because they made a little food go a long way.

Potatoes had many uses in the kitchens of the early settlers. The residue squeezed from the grated pulp became starch for the family laundry. Potatoes were used to soothe headaches and make yeast for bread. Small pieces made good corks for bottles. During long winter evenings, slices of potato were often cooked over an open fire until brown, much like young people today might toast marshmallows. Grated raw potatoes, salted and cooked on the griddle, became potato pancakes.

Apples are Canada's most important fruit crop, and apple desserts are served year-round. The Annapolis Valley in Nova Scotia and the Okanagan Valley in British Columbia are major apple-growing areas. Peaches are the most important soft-tree fruit in Canada. They are grown mainly in Ontario and British Columbia. Plums are cultivated in all provinces. Rhubarb desserts appear as a springtime treat across Canada.

Berries of all kinds, especially wild ones such as blueberries in the Atlantic provinces and saskatoons on the Prairies, are used in many recipes. Blueberries are an important source of income in northern Ontario, Quebec, and the Atlantic provinces. All of these fruits are enjoyed in a variety of pies, puddings, cobblers, crumble, and buckle, each with its own additional ingredients to make it distinctive.

The only places in the world that produce maple syrup are Ontario, Quebec, New Brunswick, Nova Scotia, and northeastern United States. Quebec produces nearly 90 percent of the Canadian supply. Approximately 10 L to 15 L of sap yields 1 L of syrup.

Maple trees were the only source of sugar for many pioneer families in eastern Canada. Each spring they stockpiled enough rich, brown cakes of maple sugar to last all year. Though there is now a wide choice of sweeteners available, maple sugar is still preferred by some people, especially in areas where it is produced. Using a sharp knife, the sugar is shaved into

feathery bits to sprinkle on cereals, buttered toast, and desserts. Sugar pie, a Quebec specialty, is one of the sweet delicacies created with maple sugar.

Canada's coastline extends over 240 000 km, and considering both freshwater and saltwater, the country boasts over 150 species of fish and shellfish. From traditional lobster of the Atlantic, to assorted interior lake and river fish, to the Pacific salmon, fish is an important food in Canada.

Canadian cities from coast to coast offer a wide selection of multicultural cuisine, from Chinese and Japanese of Vancouver, to Ukrainian of the Prairies, to Italian in Toronto. Many other nationalities are also represented in the country.

The regions of Canada are an outcome of their geography, peoples, and history. The foods of each area have subtle differences because of these factors. But transportation and trade between provinces and other countries have also softened the boundaries. A logical division for reasons of describing regional foods is Atlantic Canada, Quebec, Ontario, Prairie Provinces, British Columbia, and northern Canada. Here is a brief description of the bountiful foods enjoyed in each of these areas.

## Atlantic Canada

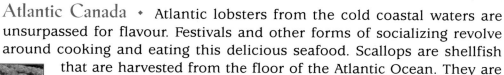

Atlantic lobsters from the cold coastal waters are unsurpassed for flavour. Festivals and other forms of socializing revolve around cooking and eating this delicious seafood. Scallops are shellfish that are harvested from the floor of the Atlantic Ocean. They are sold by weight as shucked meat, usually in frozen form.

*Fiddleheads*, a New Brunswick delicacy, are young fronds of the ostrich fern that grow abundantly in shady, moist, wooded areas. The name comes from the tightly curled top that resembles the end of a violin. Marketed fresh during May and June, they are also available frozen and canned. Their cooked flavour resembles that of asparagus.

Potato growing is highly specialized in New Brunswick and Prince Edward Island. Growers in these two provinces produce the main portion of certified seed potatoes shipped to foreign countries, making potatoes an important export crop.

The term Acadian refers to the French heritage of the Maritime provinces. One Acadian specialty using potato is *râpée pie* or *pâté à la rapture*. The meat from cooked fowl is layered with puréed potatoes in a baking pan. In some parts of New Brunswick and Nova Scotia this pie is served on Sunday, and festive occasions. *Colcannon* is of Scottish and Irish origin. It is a combination of cooked potatoes, turnips, and cabbage mashed together.

Potatoes growing in red soil are a familiar sight in Prince Edward Island.

Homemade baked beans and steamed brown bread have long been traditional for supper on Saturday night in the Atlantic provinces. Pea soup served there is a mixture of dried split peas, diced potatoes, and celery simmered in a ham bone broth.

Partridgeberries are also known as mountain cranberries, rock cranberries, and lingonberries. This fruit of a dwarf, glossy-leaved, trailing evergreen plant grows on rocky, open soil throughout the northern barren lands and in Newfoundland and Nova Scotia. Though shaped like blueberries, these scarlet berries are sour like cranberries. A great variety of berries are to be found in specific regions of these provinces.

## Quebec

Quebec is the centre of the French culture in Canada. It boasts a cuisine known worldwide for its special blend of wholesomeness, flair, and finesse. Probably the best-known of many French-Canadian specialties is *tourtière*. It is a meat pie of ground pork. Traditionally tourtière is served in French-Canadian homes on Christmas Eve after midnight mass.

*Cretons* is an old French-Canadian favourite meat spread made with seasoned ground pork, kidney, and lard. It has remained so popular that it is now made commercially and sold in supermarkets. Traditionally served on bread for breakfast or lunch, the spread is also good on crackers or toast at snack time.

Another French-Canadian dish known by nearly as many names as there are methods of preparation is *cipate (six-pâtes, chipalle, sipaille, sea-pie)*. In early days the pie was made from partridge, duck, wild rabbit, and other game. The modern version uses combinations of chicken, pork, veal, and beef.

Pea soup served in this area contains whole yellow peas, salt pork, savory, parsley, bay leaf, and a little hominy. When the maple sap is running, dumplings called *grand-pères*, are served with maple syrup for dessert in many French-Canadian homes.

## Ontario

The culinary roots of this area, originally known as Upper Canada, are a strong mix of Scottish, Irish, and English. Soups and sauces were everyday components of their meals. The best-loved part of Upper Canadian meals were the desserts. Canadians of Scottish descent are as proud of their shortbread as were their ancestors, whose recipes have been handed down from generation to generation. Many homemakers make large quantities of shortbread each year before Christmas to give to special friends and to serve during the festive season.

*I feel a recipe is only a theme, which an intelligent cook can play each time with a variation.*
MADAME BENOIT

## CAREER SKETCH

JOY HANLEY was born in Inverness, Cape Breton Island, and now lives in Charlottetown, Prince Edward Island. Hanley speaks to varied audiences on the topic of entrepreneurship. She has the knowledge and experience to speak about this topic, because Hanley is an entrepreneur.

Her career started in 1975 when Hanley, with her husband Ray, opened the Little Christo's Pizza Restaurant in

Joy Hanley, chef and entrepreneur, with her husband, Ray

Charlottetown. Future expansion included two more restaurants and the Joy Hanley's Silver Catering Company, a full-service catering company listed in the prestigious *Who's Who of Canadian Catering*. Currently, Hanley is president of Fine Foods Investments, a frozen pizza processing company. Her businesses employ, on average, 70 people.

Hanley has been involved heavily in professional organizations as a member and director. She has received numerous awards for her entrepreneurial skills. These include the P.E.I. Business Woman of the Year, the Prince Edward Island Entrepreneurship Advancement Award, and the Atlantic Nominee/National Finalist for the Canadian Woman Entrepreneur of the Year.

How has she been so successful? Her university and culinary education taught her how to think and organize her time. She also learned about research and development. Entrepreneurship requires motivation and strong organizational skills. Hanley also has the ability to recognize market demand and is willing to listen to her patrons. Fine Foods Investments insists on pizzeria-quality standards of excellence for its frozen pizza. Only the freshest vegetables, premium meats, and an award-winning mozzarella cheese are used. By focussing on the meal niche, the Hanleys have done well in a market previously dominated by multinational food companies. Their trade motto is "You'll taste the difference pizzeria quality makes."

When questioned about the stress involved in being an entrepreneur, Hanley states, "Stress energizes me. It is not a tiring force. My husband and I are good long-term planners and this helps alleviate a lot of stress." The most exciting aspect of entrepreneurship for Hanley is launching a new business and watching all the planning come together and work well. Being married to another entrepreneur has been a great asset. They provide a support system for one another and make sure they balance family with work.

When Hanley speaks to students in high schools, she wants to inspire them and enable them to make informed decisions when considering their career options. She stresses that students should get involved in debating clubs and do as much public speaking as possible. This helps in learning negotiating skills. In her words, you need to "think globally, looking beyond your immediate community" when starting a business today.

As early as 1786, Swiss Mennonites arrived in Upper Canada from Pennsylvania. Later, immigrants from Germany, the Netherlands, central Europe, Hungary, the former Czechoslovakia, Italy, India, and the West Indies have stimulated interest in new foods and flavours.

Wild rice grows in shallow water in the marsh areas of certain freshwater lakes and rivers from New Brunswick to southeastern Manitoba. Native peoples gather most of the crop in the same way as their ancestors, by beating it into their canoes using paddlelike flails. Shipped far and wide, wild rice is served most often with game or poultry.

Prairie Provinces • Huge tracts of fertile plains furnish the main ingredients of hearty Prairie food. Wheat and other grains are the basis for the breads and biscuits served daily. Grasslands support large herds of beef cattle that yield a meat that is served regularly and proudly.

More than 75 percent of the Canadian crop of honey is produced in the Prairie provinces. Prairie honey, mainly from alfalfa and clover, is noted for its fine quality, colour, and uniformity.

Whitefish is the most valuable variety of fish caught by commercial fishers in the

These bees are busy making honey in Saskatchewan.

northern lakes of Manitoba, Saskatchewan, and Alberta. Goldeye, a fish found in Manitoba and parts of Alberta and Ontario, is a delicacy prized by gourmets the world over. It is smoked and sold whole.

Saskatoons are small, sweet, purplish berries that grow wild in the Prairie provinces. They are used in pies, preserves, and jams in much the same way as blueberries are in eastern Canada.

Important contributions to the food patterns of the Prairies have been made by Mennonite settlers since they came to Manitoba from Russia in 1874. Mennonites from other countries followed. The Mennonites are a religious–cultural group, primarily interested in farming, and their foods reflect the foods of their roots — German, Swiss, Dutch, Ukrainian. Doukobors and Mormons, religious groups from Russia and the United States, respectively, as well as settlers from Iceland and Scandinavia, also brought food habits and customs that are now part of Prairie tradition.

## British Columbia

Fish and assorted seafoods are the principal specialties of this coastal province. Salmon, both wild and cultivated, cod, halibut, tuna, and herring are caught for export and are available at most markets and food stores. Popular seafoods include prawns and shrimp, oysters, clams, crabs, and mussels. Restaurant cooks and homemakers alike create an interesting assortment of dishes that reflect the cultural heritage of a mix of people from different national origins. Chinese, Japanese, Thi, Italian, and Vietnamese cultural foods are evident. Lamb, pork, and beef from locally raised animals appear on menus along with a tremendous range of fresh vegetables and fruit of all kinds.

As mentioned earlier, fruit is an important crop grown for export and local use. Tree fruits, as well as berries, are harvested and frozen, canned, and made into juices and drinks. Loganberries are grown commercially in British Columbia. A hybrid of the blackberry and raspberry, they are very large, deep red berries with small seeds and an acidic flavour excellent for pies.

This man is raking berries off the plants during the cranberry harvest in Richmond, British Columbia.

## Northern Canada

*Sourdough* is an international pioneer food well known to early explorers in the North of Canada. Sourdough is a dough containing active yeast, saved from one baking to the next. When added to a flour mixture it makes it rise and become light. If flour and sugar are added to the "starter" regularly, it can be kept active indefinitely. Fresh yeast was extremely difficult for pioneer cooks to get before sophisticated transportation systems were in place. When they were able to get it, frequently the yeast would be dead after exposure to extreme conditions of time and cold. Poor yeast caused baking failures that disappointed the cook and wasted scarce supplies. Sourdough was the solution, as it was readily available and reliable if looked after carefully. Sourdough was so essential to people in the North that they carried their pots of starter close to their bodies as they travelled and slept in order to keep it warm. Eventually the people who depended on it came to be called "sourdoughs." Sourdough is still used in the North, but Canadians living in more southern regions can easily find sourdough bread in grocery stores, bakeries, and frequently enjoy it with restaurant meals.

*Bannock* is a flat, round, unleavened cake introduced to Canada in the very early years by settlers from Scotland and northern England. Originally, this bannock was made from oatmeal, or rye or barley meal and contained no leavening. As a quickbread it is almost universal. In Scotland it is called *griddle scones*; in Russia, *lepeshki*; in Germany, *hefekuchlein*; in Hungary, *langos*; in Spain, *malasadas*. Jewish people have three names for three varieties: *levivot, lehem metugan,* and *matzo*. First Nations people call it *pakwejigan*. They add a leavening agent such as soda, yeast, or baking powder and bake it over an open fire or fry it in oil on a pan or griddle.

Have you ever seen bannock being made?

Arctic char, or *ilkaula* as the Inuit call it, is distinctively Canadian, for it is found nowhere else in the world except in our northern glacial streams. Neither trout nor salmon, the fish has a rare quality and flavour that captures the best of both fish.

 KEY TERMS

Use the words listed below to complete the following statements in your notebook.

- tourtière
- bannock
- fiddleheads
- Inuit
- sourdough
- cipate
- pemmican
- ilkaula
- blubber
- colcannan

1. _____, the name used by certain Native peoples, means "chosen and true people."

2. A fat known as _____ formed a very important part of the diet for those living in the arctic region.

3. During summer months most First Nations peoples dried game meat to make _____.

4. _____ are young fronds of the ostrich fern.

5. _____, of Scottish and Irish origin, is a combination of cooked potatoes, turnips, and cabbage mashed together.

6. A French-Canadian meat pie of ground pork is a _____.

7. _____ is a dish originally made from wild rabbit, partridge, and duck.

8. _____ is a flour–yeast mixture that makes flour mixtures containing a small portion of it rise and become light.

9. _____ is a flat, round bread originally made from oat, rye, or barley meal and containing no leavening.

10. _____, or arctic char, is a distinctively Canadian fish, found nowhere else in the world.

FOCUS YOUR KNOWLEDGE

1. What methods were used to catch fish in different parts of the Arctic?

2. What problems for the Inuit have resulted from their contact with non-Natives?

3. List the types of fish enjoyed by coastal British Columbia First Nations peoples.

4. Explain why potatoes were important to early Canadian settlers.

5. Briefly describe three traditional meat dishes from Quebec.

6. What is Goldeye?

7. Why was sourdough an important pioneer food?

8. Describe the difference between bannock and pakwejigan.

## DEMONSTRATE YOUR KNOWLEDGE

1. Prepare a chart of early Inuit peoples including the part of Canada in which they lived, principal diet, and significant features. For example, the chart for the Iroquois nation would look like this:

| IROQUOIS | SOUTH EASTERN ONTARIO | CORN, SQUASH, SUNFLOWERS, FISH, GAME | AGRICULTURE WAS OF GREAT IMPORTANCE |
|---|---|---|---|
|  |  |  |  |

2. In small groups, plan five dishes in which apples are the principal ingredient. Prepare one of the dishes.

3. Plan a day's menu for a family of four in one Canadian region using that region's local foods.

4. Role play an early settler from one of the Atlantic provinces and from British Columbia, discussing the similarities and differences in the foods they eat.

5. Locate a recipe for sourdough or bannock. Prepare it with a partner.

6. Role play a First Nations parent or early Canadian settler explaining his or her cultural food heritage to a school-age child.

## APPLY YOUR KNOWLEDGE

1. In small groups, discuss the foods that one of the Native groups described in this chapter might have included in a main meal.

2. As a group, determine the foods from your area that early settlers used as the basis of their meals. Plan a menu for a breakfast including these foods. Compare the breakfast of pioneer Canadians with a breakfast meal that you eat.

3. Prepare an organizer of foods, by region, that were available to early settlers. Group foods according to *Canada's Food Guide to Healthy Eating*.

4. Research one early Canadian group. Report on the recipes they used or foods they prepared, the availability of foods, and the foods for special occasions.

5. Write an essay describing your own food culture. Include a description of the region in which you live, the specific foods your family eats from this region, and other aspects that have influenced your food choices.

# Cultural Foods

Canadians are fortunate to experience foods from countries around the world. Whether from travelling or the enjoyment of local restaurants, markets, or neighbours, Canadians are becoming increasingly familiar with the foods, food customs, and even recipes from other lands. Many are proudly reviving their own cultural heritage as well.

Often traditional recipes are adapted because of the cost or availability of certain ingredients. Other recipes are changed to suit individual tastes. Sometimes these changes are toward more healthful eating, sometimes not.

The countries included in this section provide a sampling of the diversity of foods that contribute to the Canadian dining experience both at home and in restaurants. They represent only a small segment of the more than one hundred cultural origins that make up the rich multicultural Canadian population. Many of the food terms may be new to you. Some of them are explained here; others you will have to look up in a dictionary. The language of food is important to your understanding.

## BRITISH ISLES

Daily English foods are simple, well cooked, and unadorned. Roast beef with Yorkshire pudding, a traditional dish from northern England, is enjoyed throughout the country. Boiled vegetables, particularly potatoes, onions, and cabbage, are served with it. Another favourite is fish and chips, with malt vinegar and salt, served in a newspaper cone. Also traditional in most of England are *shepherd's pie*, made from ground meat with a whipped potato topping, and steak and kidney pie, a stewlike mixture in a pastry crust. Roast or boiled lamb is a favourite meat, which is often garnished and served with a mint or Cumberland sauce. Condiments, such as pickles and chutneys and spicy bottled sauces, are used to flavour cooked foods rather than adding herbs and spices during cooking. Boiled or steamed puddings often complete an English meal. Fruits are most often eaten as preserves, jams, and marmalade. Plum pudding served with a hot sugar sauce or a cold hard sauce is traditional, especially at Christmas. Because of Great Britain's former global colonial empire, many foods, such as Indian Curry, are popular among the British people.

High tea is still served in the late afternoon and sometimes takes the place of the evening meal. Otherwise, dinner is served rather late in the evening. Offered at afternoon tea are small sandwiches or thin slices of buttered bread, cold meats, *scones* (a type of baking powder biscuit), fruit or pound cake, and of course, tea. Various regions add their own specialties. For example, the southwest is famous for Devonshire tea, named after the area of Devon. It is also called cream tea. Devonshire cream is a rich, clotted cream, much like whipped cream, which is taken from the surface of quickly scalded and cooled whole milk. It is served with berry jam and fresh scones.

High tea in the British Isles includes many types of sweets along with sandwiches or scones and, of course, hot tea.

There are many other regional specialties such as *Cornish pasties*, named for Cornwall. Pasties are a mixture of diced or ground beef or mutton, diced potatoes, onions, carrots, and turnips wrapped in a short pastry. Traditionally, the crescent-shaped pasties are eaten from the hand, much as Canadians eat hot dogs or hamburgers. A variety of meat pies are consumed throughout the country. *Eccles cakes*, originally from the northwest, are another national sweet. These cakelike pastries, filled with currants and dried fruit, are often served at tea time or at the end of a meal.

Scottish food and cookery is practical and nourishing. The Scots eat a substantial breakfast — oatmeal porridge served hot with milk, Aberdeen sausage, fried *kippers*, and lots of *bap* (a soft breakfast roll) with plenty of hot tea. Of course, no breakfast is complete without Dundee marmalade. The heaviest meal, served at noon, usually includes a meat and vegetable soup and a dessert of steamed pudding or egg custard. *Cockaleekie* soup, made from boiling fowl, leeks, and barley or rice is strong flavoured and very nourishing. It originated in the early seventeenth century. The evening meal may be *stovies* (a dish made with potatoes, beef or mutton or leftover meats, and vegetables cooked for a long time over low heat). A bowl of hot oat barley porridge and milk may be served for the evening meal.

How many of these Scottish foods have you heard of or tried? — *cockaleekie soup; bannock; hattit kit; cullen skink*

Shortbread, made from flour, sugar, and butter, was perfected in Scotland; numerous varieties are now found in many parts of the world. This cookie is served widely for teas and desserts and is made in special shapes for Christmas.

The celebrations of *Hogmanay* (New Year's Eve) and Burns Night, commemorating the birth of the Scots poet Robbie Burns, bring forth the traditional *haggis*. Minced heart, lungs, and liver of a sheep are mixed with suet, oatmeal, and seasonings, stuffed into the animal's stomach, and boiled. The steaming haggis is skirled (accompanied by bagpipes) to the table and ceremoniously slit open.

Irish cooking is simple and plain and makes use of the products of the country, particularly potatoes. Whether boiled, baked, roasted, or fried, the Irish eat a lot of potatoes. Potatoes are also used in a varity of recipes including potato bread, potato pie, potato soup, and potato–apple cake. The versatile potato is the main ingredient in *boxty* (Irish pancakes).

## Scones

Makes 8–12

| | |
|---|---|
| 225 g | all-purpose flour |
| 5 mL | baking powder |
| | pinch salt |
| 50 g | butter or margarine |
| 30 g | sugar |
| 150 mL | sour milk (or fresh milk with 15 mL lemon juice or vinegar added to make 150 mL) |

Grease and flour a baking sheet. Combine the flour, baking powder, and salt in a bowl. Cut in the fat until the mixture resembles fine bread crumbs. Stir in the sugar. Add sufficient milk to mix to a fairly soft dough and knead very lightly.

Turn onto a floured surface and roll or pat out to 2.5-cm thickness. Cut with 5-cm rounds and place on the baking sheet. Brush tops with milk.

Bake at 230°C for about 10 minutes until well risen and golden brown. Cool on a wire rack. Serve split and buttered.

The Irish also eat a lot of fish and different parts of the island have fish specialities. Herring and mackerel may be grilled or broiled. Lobster is sometimes wrapped in clay or in a crust made from flour and water and baked on an open fire, but it is never served with fancy sauces. The delectable, pink

Dublin prawns are in such demand all over Europe that the Irish rarely get to enjoy them.

The national dish of Ireland is Irish stew. This is made from less tender cuts of lamb or mutton and root vegetables, such as potatoes, carrots, turnips, parsnips, and onions, with simple seasonings of salt and pepper. Long, slow cooking in a heavy pot and a light flour thickening of the gravy produces a deliciously flavoured food. Often it is served with Irish soda bread. Sweets and baked goods highlight all special occasions. Buttermilk or tea with milk accompany meals and snacks.

Simplicity and plain cooking also typify Welsh meals. A plate of freshly boiled ham with *tatws slaw* (mashed potatoes with buttermilk), leeks, tomatoes, *crempog* (buttermilk cakes), and a few slices of *bara brith* (bread filled with currants) spread with Welsh butter, and lots of hot tea is a typical evening meal in Wales. Special occasions and Sunday dinners include roasted pork, lamb, or mutton, several well-cooked vegetables, and a slow-baked rice pudding or spongecake.

*Welsh rarebit* (a cheese and bread dish) is a traditional Welsh recipe. A mixture of strong-flavoured Cheddar cheese, mustard, and salt and pepper is placed on bread and broiled. *Caerphilly* (a soft, gentle, unripened cheese) originated in Wales as a miner's food. Today it is popular all over Britain.

## CHINESE

Chinese cuisine is well known throughout the world. A well-prepared Chinese dish is a balance of contrasts that appeal to the five senses. Great care is taken in the selection of the foods so that all will harmonize or provide interesting contrasts in texture, colour, aroma, and flavour. Time is devoted to carefully cutting and preparing the food before it is cooked to accomplish this. Preparation and cooking are quite separate procedures. Cooking begins only when all ingredients are assembled and ready, so that foods will not be overcooked.

Most main course foods served in China are combinations of ingredients chosen on the basis of what is available and what they will contribute to the finished dish. In earlier times the lack of refrigeration led to the use of fresh poultry and freshly picked vegetables. Preservatives, such as brine, soy sauce, and spices, are important, and many dried foods are used. Frequently, ingredients

> How many of these Irish foods have you heard of or tried?
> — *dulse champ; boxty bread; Dublin coddle; singing hinnies*

> How can you tell from this photograph that presentation is very important in Chinese cuisine?

How many of these Chinese foods have you heard of or tried?
— *congee; dim sum; moon cakes; thousand year eggs*

include mushrooms, bamboo shoots, eggs, pork, and water chestnuts. Vegetables, whether fresh, dried, or salted, are used generously with meagre amounts of meat and fish. *Tofu* (soybean protein) may supplement the small amount of animal protein used. Fish of all kinds play an important role in the special dishes across China. Chinese people do not consume many sweet foods. If dessert is served, it will be fresh fruits or special puddings.

Preparation involves careful cutting, slicing, and chopping so that foods will cook quickly. Cooking techniques are stir-frying, deep-frying, simmering, and braising. Of these, stir-frying is used most often. For this, a heavy shallow pan called a wok is used. Vegetable oil is heated to sizzling before the ingredients are added. The high heat seals the natural juices of the food and constant stirring prevents sticking. Stir-frying preserves the crispness, flavour, and colour of the vegetables. The short cooking time required also helps retain the important vitamin content. Very little liquid is used in most recipes. Before the dish is served, any juices from the food are thickened slightly, usually with a corn starch solution that results in a clear gravy.

There are four main schools of Chinese cooking: Guangdong (Cantonese), Sichuan (sometimes spelled Szechuan), Shandong, and Huaiyang. Each utilizes the local foods available in the specific geographical area of China. The first Chinese who immigrated to Canada in significant numbers came from Guangdong province, in the south around Canton. That explains why cooking from this area is well known in metropolitan areas. Some familiar Guangdong foods in Canada are *egg foo yung* and *egg roll*. *Dim sum* is an assortment of steamed, dough-wrapped meat, fish, or vegetables. It is served in small, single portions from wheeled carts in restaurants.

Sichuan province, the inland region, has produced more highly seasoned food than the other three provinces. Sichuan peppercorn is grown widely in this cold, mountainous area. This popular, fiery hot variety, which seems to have no flavour at all when first tasted, has a delayed and lasting taste. The fungus called *cloud ear* is a frequent ingredient in Sichuan cooking. Among the popular Sichuan dishes are fish-flavoured chicken, mapo beancurd, and sautéed carp.

In the southern coastal Huaiyang province, rice is the staple food. Here the finest soy sauce is produced and used liberally. Foods developed in the coastal region are often salty or sweetened with sugar, and many dishes have a gravy. As could be expected, a wide range of seafood is used. A well-known specialty is *bird's nest soup* made by simmering a swallow's nest in broth, usually chicken flavoured.

In the large northern area lies Beijing (formerly Peking) where Peking duck originated. From south of Beijing comes a well-known dish of sweet-and-sour fish. Lamb or mutton is the basis of *Mongolian hot pot*. Meat is frequently cooked at the table in hot liquid, or barbecued. The staple food of the Shandong school is wheat flour, which is used to make a variety of noodle, pancake, and dumpling dishes. Unlike the other regions, cooking of northern Shandong school is lighter and more subtly seasoned, often with garlic and green scallions, a kind of onion.

For breakfast most Chinese would have *congee* or *jook*. This is a hot rice gruel garnished with flavourful tidbits and pickles. It would be accompanied by tea. In northern China, however, people would be more likely to have steaming hot noodles, wheatcakes, or dumplings with tea. Little time is spent on the noon meal, and it is often taken on the go. Foods might be hot or cold noodles with condiments, dim sum, or a lighter version of the evening meal. The evening meal is usually rice or noodles combined with other ingredients to provide a harmonious blend of flavours, textures, and colours. For special occasions, tureens of soup of different varieties may punctuate the serving of other dishes.

## Stir-Fried Mixed Vegetables

Makes 4 servings

| | |
|---|---|
| 125 g | fresh bean sprouts |
| 125 g | snow peas or broccoli flowerets |
| 2 | medium carrots |
| 45 mL | vegetable oil |
| 125 g | bamboo shoots |
| 5 mL | sugar |
| 5 mL | salt |

Wash bean sprouts in cold water and drain. Wash and snap off both ends of snow peas. If pea pods are large, cut in half. Wash broccoli flowerets if using. Cut carrots into thin slices. Rinse bamboo shoots and slice.

Heat oil in a wok or large skillet. When oil is hot, add snow peas or broccoli, carrots, and bamboo shoots. Stir-fry for 1 minute. Add bean sprouts, sugar, and salt. Stir-fry for 1 to 2 minutes.

Vegetables should be cooked but still crunchy. Serve immediately.

# FRENCH

French cooking is world famous. The classical or haute cuisine refers to the cooking practised by the best chefs. It originated with the chefs of Catherine de Medici of Florence who married Henry II of France in 1533.

All French cuisine places a great importance on sauces, and the basic principles of sauce making are well understood by all French cooks. The broth or bouillon base for the sauce must be obtained from the same substance as the main ingredient in the dish. For foods that have no suitable broth, egg and butter sauces, such as *Béarnaise* or *Hollandaise*, are made. Other sauces are made from broth or cream, thickened with eggs or flour, and enriched with butter.

The breads of France are a study in themselves. The shape of the loaf is peculiar to each region. It might be flat to fit snugly into a hunter's bag or long and thin to be packed in a shepherd's cape pocket. *Croissants* are flaky, yeast pastry. *Brioche* (a yeast dough, rich with eggs) is usually served fresh at breakfast with very strong coffee. Breads are always on the table for each meal from the first course until the meal is completed.

This is one familiar French bread. What kinds of French bread have you tried?

Meal patterns of the French focus on dinner, traditionally served in the middle of the day. An appetizer, such as anchovies or sardines, a pâté, or fresh cheese tart precedes the main course based on meat, fish, or poultry. A vegetable may be served with this course, but more often the vegetable dish follows the main course. It might be a vegetable soufflé, baked tomatoes, or fresh seasonal vegetables. To refresh the palate, salad follows the main part of the meal. Usually it is fresh greens tossed with a simple oil and vinegar dressing. Dessert is seldom part of the noon meal. Instead, cheese is served with fresh fruit, in season. Special occasion desserts may be *crème caramel* or *crème brulée* (a baked caramel custard), apple tart, or fresh wild berries with cream.

Provincial French cooking is a simpler method of cooking based on regional produce and traditions. But some dishes, like *crêpes* (very thin pancakes usually folded or rolled up with a filling) and one-dish meals like soups and stews, are enjoyed throughout France. Shared boundaries with several other countries and the sea, influence cooking practices throughout the regions of France. A study of these reveals some of the specialties of France.

## Cheese Omelette

Serves 1–2

| | |
|---|---|
| 3 | eggs |
| | salt to taste |
| | freshly ground black pepper to taste |
| 15 mL | butter |
| 30 mL | cheese |
| 2 mL | soft butter |

Break the eggs into a small mixing bowl. Add salt and pepper. Stir briskly with a table fork 20 to 30 seconds or until the whites and yolks are blended. Heat a 20-cm omelette pan until hot. Drop in the 15 mL butter and swirl it in the pan to melt it quickly and coat the pan. Do not let the butter brown.

Pour in the eggs and shake the pan over high heat. The eggs will set quickly from the bottom of the pan. Stir the still-liquid eggs on top with the flat of a fork without disturbing the bottom eggs . Once the egg mixture is set, sprinkle the cheese over the egg.

Remove from heat. Using fork, lift the edge of the egg and fold it over the centre to the far edge of the pan. Tilt the pan and roll the omelette over onto a plate. Brush the top with the soft butter and serve immediately.

*Quiche Lorraine* originated in the northern region. This tart, made from eggs, cream, cheese, and bacon, has many regional adaptations. From the mountainous regions bordering Switzerland comes the cheese called *Comte*, which is a French version of the famous Swiss *Gruyère*. Dishes prepared in this region often include wild game such as hare, venison, and boar. The Germanic influence is evident in the north by the popularity of heavy sausages and sauerkraut.

The province of Alsace is world famous for its *pâté de foie gras*, which is made from the liver of specially fed geese. In the south of France a similar pâté is prepared with the extravagant addition of *truffles*. These fungi grow underground, which makes them difficult to locate, thus adding to their expense. A little farther south is the province of Bourgogne. World-known dishes, such as *beef Bourguignon* and *coq au vin*, made with beef

How many of these French foods have you heard of or tried?
— *pâté de fois gras; cuisses de grenouilles; quenelles; bouillabaise; escargots*

*If I can't have too many truffles, I'll do without truffles.*
COLETTE

267

and chicken respectively, feature a sauce made with red wine originally from this region. The wine is gently simmered with the meat juices until all the alcohol evaporates, leaving a flavourful broth ready for thickening.

Spanish influence, such as Basque, is noticeable in the southernmost provinces, where omelettes are prepared with green peppers, tomatoes, and ham. In the province of Bordeaux, *Roquefort* cheese is made from sheep's milk.

In Provence, on the Mediterranean Sea, much of the cooking includes garlic, olive oil, and tomatoes. Foods here are more highly seasoned with fresh and dried herbs than in the north of France. Fish from the neighbouring seas are used in making the famous stewlike soup called *bouill-abaisse*. Farther east, Italian influence is shown by the preparation of the vegetable dish *ratatouille* and of *salad niçoise*. *Cassoulet* (a slowly baked casserole of meat and small dried beans) shows ancient Roman influence on the southern French regions.

Normandy and Brittany along the northern coast supply milk for *Camembert* (a soft-centred cheese) and fish and lamb for the French markets. It is believed that the delicate crêpe originated in Brittany.

## GERMAN

The main German meal often includes a meat attractively arranged.

German cooks excel in the preparation of hearty, healthful foods. Veal, pork, and chicken are used widely and almost always in serving size pieces arranged in a sauce. Veal and pork cutlets are called *wiener schnitzel* and *schwiener schnitzel*, respectively. Wiener schnitzel, which originated in the Austrian capital of Vienna, is known worldwide. These are very thin cutlets of veal, breaded and sautéed in butter. They are extremely tender and flavourful. Served with a slice of lemon, mashed potatoes, and applesauce, this meal is listed on almost every menu in Germany and Austria. Chicken can be prepared in a similar manner and served hot or cold.

*Sauerbraten* is typical of the German specialty of sweet and sour flavours. Tough cuts are tenderized in a spiced marinade sweetened with sugar and made "sour" with vinegar. It is traditionally served with cooked red cabbage and fluffy potato dumplings called *kartoffelklösse*. *Westphalian ham* is a specially smoked ham, cut paper thin and served raw on slices of rye bread. *Spargle* (white asparagus) is always a popular food in the southern regions of Germany. There are a great variety of sausages ranging from *bratwurst*, a very large, pale-coloured, mild variety, to tiny, highly spiced sausages served with sauerkraut. German cooking excels in imaginative ways in cooking vegetables, particularly potatoes. Five or six vegetables are often served at a meal. *Spätzle* are tiny, dumplings that resemble rice or grated potato. They are served instead of potatoes in some meals.

## Apple Pancakes

Makes 16–20

| | |
|---|---|
| 4 | medium tart dessert apples |
| 15 mL | lemon juice |
| 500 mL | water |
| 275 g | all-purpose flour |
| | pinch of salt |
| 3 | eggs, separated |
| 450 mL | milk |
| 30 mL | sugar |
| 5 mL | cinnamon |

Peel, core, and thinly slice the apples. Place them in a bowl with the water and the lemon juice. If necessary, add more water to cover the apples.

Mix the flour, salt, egg yolks, and milk in a large bowl to make a smooth batter. Beat the egg whites until stiff, and fold in with a metal spoon.

Heat a non-stick frying pan to approximately 190°C. Drop in about 15 mL of batter for each pancake. Fry lightly until the underside is brown. Turn each pancake carefully and cook on the other side. Remove from the pan and arrange drained apple slices on the top of each pancake. Combine sugar and cinnamon and sprinkle some on top of the apple pancakes. Continue making pancakes until all the batter has been used up.

A great deal of fruit are used in German cookery, particularly in baked goods and desserts. *Kuchen* (cakes) may be filled with fruit. Fruit may also be used as a layer on top of cake with a clear gelatin glaze. Large portions of whipped cream are used as a garnish. The variety of cakes are endless and they are often elaborately decorated.

How many of these German foods have you heard of or tried? — *topfen kuchen; sauerbraten; schnitzel; rollmops; kartoffelpuffer*

The German people enjoy bread. Large, crusty buns made in pinwheel sections, called *bratchen*, are eaten in the morning as a light breakfast. Canadians know them better as kaiser rolls. Rye and pumpernickel breads are eaten at mealtime. Hot, salted pretzels, sometimes shaped as huge loops, are eaten during the day and in the evening. Strong coffee is a popular beverage.

## GREEK

Greek cooks were experimenting with seasonings and developing sauces as early as 500 B.C. Much later the Romans and even later the Turks developed a taste for Greek foods and refinements of cookery. Because Greek cuisine has been successfully adapted and renamed by Italians and Turks, its Greek origins are often forgotten.

Greek cooking reflects the kinds of foods grown in Greece. *Moussaka* is a traditionally native food. This casserole consists of layers of sliced eggplant, ground lamb, and a cream sauce with cheese. Similarly, *souvlaki*, a very popular snack that consists of pieces of broiled lamb or goat on a bamboo skewer, was a derivative of the well-known Turkish *shishkabob*. The modern version of souvlaki is small cubes of beef, pork, lamb, or chicken placed on a swordlike skewer alternately with tomatoes, onions, peppers, and other vegetables. *Gyrros* is a large pork roast cooked as it rotates on an electrically powered spit that is positioned perpendicular to the floor. Thin pieces of meat are shaved from the roast and eaten as a snack or a small meal with bread or on a bun, much like our hamburger.

This Greek salad is accompanied by pork souvlaki and rice.

Traditionally, many Greek foods are served *avgolemono*, which means with an egg and lemon sauce. The sauce is made of well-beaten eggs, into which lemon is blended gradually. It is often poured over braised meat, fish, or vegetables or added to soup broth just before serving. Sometimes the sauce is thickened with cornstarch and accompanies foods such as *dolmas*. Dolmas are vine leaves stuffed with a mixture of onions, rice, finely ground lamb, parsley, pine nuts, and currants, and then simmered in stock.

Varieties of fish and other seafoods are found in the waters around the Greek peninsula and the islands. Eel and octopus are popular. They are boiled, baked, or grilled and served plain or with many different sauces. Fish soup with rice is often made and served avgolemono.

## Salad

Serves 4–6

| Dressing | | | Salad | |
|---|---|---|---|---|
| 500 mL | olive oil | | 4 | tomatoes, cut in wedges |
| 250 mL | lemon juice | | 1 | cucumber, thinly sliced |
| 5 mL | dried oregano | | 3 | medium onions, peeled and thinly sliced |
| 1/2 | clove of garlic, peeled and minced | | 125 g | feta cheese, cut in small pieces |
| 5 mL | salt | | 125 mL | black olives |
| 3 mL | pepper | | | |
| 5 or 6 | celery leaves, chopped | | | |

Combine all the ingredients for the dressing in a bowl or jar. For more flavour, make the dressing in advance to allow the flavours to blend.

In a large bowl, combine the tomatoes, cucumber, and onion. Stir or shake the dressing well and pour on just enough to moisten the vegetables. Toss the vegetables well to make sure they are all coated with dressing.

Arrange the olives and cheese on top of the salad and serve.

*Phyllo*, popular throughout the Mediterranean, is a pastry used in the preparation of both savoury and sweet dishes. The dough is made of flour and water and pulled carefully by hand until it is paper thin. Then it is draped over sheets and left to dry. Today, most cooks use commercially made phyllo. *Baklava* is one dessert made with phyllo. It is a sweet, sticky, compact, and delicious pastry made by alternating layers of phyllo with a mixture of finely chopped nuts, cinnamon, and sugar. The pastry is baked and, like many Greek sweets, while hot from the oven is steeped in a honey syrup, making it very rich.

*Feta* is a white, crumbly goat's milk cheese, salty but mild in flavour. It is used in salads, sandwiches, and cheese pies. It is also eaten plain with olives or fresh fruit. There are many other Greek cheeses.

Another milk product consumed in large amounts is yogurt, called *yaorte*. In Greece it is served at breakfast, for desserts, often with honey, or as a dressing or seasoned dip for vegetables and bread.

How many of these Greek foods have you heard of or tried?
— *feta; taramosalata; baklava; loukomathes*

## CAREER SKETCH

Shrikala Baljekar-Grewal, food editor

SHRIKALA BALJEKAR-GREWAL is a food editor because she loves food, eating, and cooking. She finds food to be a creative, colourful subject. Food is also a topic common to everyone. As Baljekar-Grewal states, "Everyone eats." Food is such a vital part of life it crosses gender, age, and culture.

At the University of Bombay, India, Baljekar-Grewal began writing for the college magazine and newsletters. She first decided to work as a journalist because "Journalism got into me." In India she worked for such magazines as *Flair, Technocrat,* and *Savvy.* Her on-the-job training taught her how to work under pressure and meet deadlines. In Canada, she joined the staff of *Star India Journal,* a weekly newspaper, in 1991. Its circulation is 10 000 across Canada.

Her duties are wide in range. Because there are only six employees, "Everyone does everything." In addition to writing a weekly food column and an "Eating Out" column she is responsible for restaurant advertising, the magazine section, Kids' Corner, music reviews, and the classifieds. "Producing a weekly newspaper requires a lot of work. This is where my integrated experience as a layout designer, reviewer, writer, and editor have served me well."

She covers an endless variety of topics in her food column, mostly dealing with Indian food. She has discussed regional and seasonal foods, diet foods, snacks, curries, food for working women, cooking methods, sweets, holidays, and one-dish meals. Each food column contains two or three recipes for her readers to try. Baljekar-Grewal is at the level of experience where she can just look at the ingredients of a recipe and know what it will taste like.

Baljekar-Grewal aspires to one day writing a book on Indian foods. "Each of the many states of India offers its own unique cuisine. No two states eat the same kind of food." It is a topic worth exploring.

Any students interested in becoming a food editor must love food. Baljekar-Grewal states, "You need to know what you are writing about. You should have highly developed taste buds. Use your senses; learn to appreciate food. Yet as a food critic, never let your biases interfere with your writing. Don't let your tastes rule your typewriter." It also helps to know about food photography and what is happening in the food industry. But above all else, you must appreciate food.

An important primary industry of Greece is the growing of nuts, particularly almonds. This explains their use in the preparation of so many foods. A mixture of dried nuts and raisins served in bowls makes the perfect nutritional confection. Hot roasted chestnuts are sold by vendors along city streets.

Thick, black coffee, a pleasant relic from the Turkish occupation of Greece, is served throughout the day. Morning coffee is important; coffee with a sweet pastry may be enjoyed in late afternoon. Greek guests may also be offered a cool glass of water and *spoon sweets*. This is a small dish of thick sweet preserve much like jam.

## INDIAN

*This description of Indian food was written by Shrikala Baljekar-Grewal, the person who is profiled in the Career Sketch on page 272.*

To define a traditional Indian meal is as difficult as defining a traditional European meal. Each of the many states of India offers its own unique cuisine, with varying ingredients and cooking methods used. No two states eat the same kind of food.

There are several reasons for the range in food tastes. People eat what they grow and the produce that is easily available. For instance, the staple in northern and central India is wheat, the region's main crop. Whole-wheat flour has been consumed daily for centuries as unleavened, stove-top, dry-roasted, flat bread called *rotis*, *phulkas*, or *chapattis*.

In southern, eastern, and coastal India, rice is available in many varieties: short grain, long grain, round grain, parboiled, red rice, puffed rice, and flattened rice are several. Thus, rice is the staple food of people living there. In the coastal states, fish and coconut are also an integral part of every meal. Western India grows and consumes a mix of wheat and rice, as well as flours milled from whole-grain barley and millets.

Another reason for the rich diversity of Indian cuisine is historical. Waves of foreign invaders seeking riches eventually became settlers. Each group of people, from the earliest Aryans to the last of the British, contributed to the developing cuisine. For example, the more than 300-year reign of the Mughals gave birth to one of India's most popular and well-known subcuisines — *Mughlai*. Served in restaurants in northern India and abroad, this cuisine is best known for its rich lamb, mutton, chicken, and egg preparations that most likely originated and evolved in the royal kitchens of the sixteenth to nineteenth century monarchs.

Religion has also played an important role. Most Hindus from early times were vegetarians, and this continues today. Many devout Jains do not even eat onions, garlic, or other strong herbs or condiments, in addition to not eating meat. Beef is taboo for all Hindus, just as pork is for the Muslims. Only the Christians eat both pork and beef, as well as other non-vegetarian produce. However, even the most strict Indian vegetarian is ensured of a protein-rich diet due to the daily inclusion of *daals* (lentils), pulses, cereals, and legumes in their meals.

There are some common threads in the cuisine of India. Milk and its by-products, such as yogurt, butter, and *ghee* (clarified butter used as a cooking medium) are commonly consumed throughout India. Spices and condiments are another common link.

Spices not only provide flavour, colour, and taste to food, they are considered therapeutic as well. The cooking step called *tarka/vaghaar* is fairly common throughout India. This procedure involves tempering lentils or vegetables with various ingredients in a little hot ghee or oil. In the west and south, these ingredients might be a combination of mustard seeds, asafoetida, curry leaves, turmeric, dry red chilies, and garlic. In the north, turmeric, onions, and cumin seeds, with or without green chilies, tomatoes, ginger, or garlic are the preferred tarka.

Spices are used whole or powdered, singly or in combination, and are usually called *masala*. *Garem masala* is a combination of ground spices, similar to allspice. From red chilies, cumin seeds, coriander seeds, and turmeric to peppercorns, cloves, allspice, cinnamon, cardamom, and many more, spices are a national favourite.

A wide range of hot or sweet pickles (mango, lime, chili, or vegetables), preserves (vinegared baby onions

A *thali* is a large, flat metal steel or silver plate, adorned with tiny metal bowls for each vegetable and lentil dish.

and carrots in the north), freshly ground chutneys (coconut, coriander, mint leaves), and fried or roasted crisp *papads* (sun-dried, rolled out rounds of lentils and spices) accompany the meal.

Salads are made with plain raw vegetables, such as sliced onions, tomatoes, cucumbers, radishes, and carrots. Sometimes they may be combined with yogurt and condiments to make a cool, refreshing *raita*. Beverages include plain water or a cold glass of *lassi* or *chaas* (whipped yogurt or freshly churned buttermilk).

All Indian meals include one, sometimes even two, desserts either with or after the meal. The wide range of Indian sweets, called *mithai*, include *burfie* (soft fudge), *kheer/payasam* (semi-liquid, milky pudding), and *halwa* (mashed or cubed pudding). These are made and enjoyed in all Indian homes, especially during a festive occasion, such as a wedding, a birth, or one of the many Indian festivals.

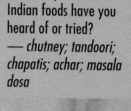

How many of these Indian foods have you heard of or tried?
— *chutney; tandoori; chapatis; achar; masala dosa*

## Lentils With Onion and Garlic

Serves 4–6

| | |
|---|---|
| 60 mL | vegetable oil |
| 3 mL | whole cumin seeds |
| 4 | cloves garlic, peeled and finely chopped (or less, if desired) |
| 1 | medium onion, peeled and chopped |
| 200 g | lentils, washed and drained |
| 720 mL | water |
| 3 mL | salt |
| 1 mL | cayenne pepper |

Heat the oil in a heavy pot over medium heat. Stir in the cumin seeds, then add the garlic. Stir-fry until the garlic turns a medium brown. Add the onion. Stir-fry until the onion pieces begin to turn brown at the edges.

Add the lentils and the water. Cover and bring to a boil. Turn heat to low and simmer for about an hour, or until lentils are tender.

Add the salt and the cayenne. Stir to mix and simmer gently for another 5 minutes.

After dessert, *paan* (betel leaves filled with betel nuts, aniseeds, perhaps dry, dessicated coconut, sugar candy, and other ingredients) may be served. Paan is a good digestive enjoyed throughout India.

Indian food, no matter from which part of that huge country it originates, can be inspiring, invigorating, and inventive. It all depends on the cook's creativity in mixing and combining the various ingredients, herbs, and spices to achieve the culinary masterpiece that we call Indian cuisine.

# ITALIAN

Pasta is a staple food of Italian meals. However, the type of pasta and the way in which it is prepared and served vary greatly from one region to another. In the northern regions the pastas are of the flat noodle type that are often cooked fresh at home and are usually made with eggs. A traditional northern pasta dish might be *fettuccine al burro* (egg noodles with butter and cheese), *tortellini* (pasta rings stuffed with chicken and cheese), or the famed *lasagna* (broad noodles baked with meat, cheese, and sauce). Bolognese sauce is a popular spicy tomato sauce containing meat and served with many pasta dishes. Butter is commonly used for cooking in the north.

In the southern regions the land is less fertile and the country less populated. Cooks almost always use olive oil in place of butter, since olive trees thrive in the warm climate of southern Italy. Here the pastas are made with less expensive ingredients and are of the dried string or tubular type, including spaghetti and macaroni. These are often manufactured commercially and made without eggs. In the south, spaghetti is served with rich, highly seasoned tomato sauces. One of the southern pastas, *ravioli*, is stuffed with a tasty meat or cheese mixture and served with a pungent tomato sauce. Spinach is often mixed with the meats of pasta dishes and is also used to make green-coloured pastas.

Almost as basic as pasta are Italian cheeses. Each region has specialties, used all over Italy. *Gorgonzola* is a blue-veined cheese with a lightly spiced, sharp flavour. *Mozzarella* is a mild, slightly sour cheese, often used on pizza and in

Do you think this pasta dish is typical of northern or southern Italy? Why?

pasta dishes. When ripened for less than three months *provolone* is a delicate, creamy cheese; when older it is excellent for cooking. *Parmesan* is a sharp, salty cheese excellent for seasoning pastas and salads. A fresh, unsalted variety, similar to cottage cheese, is called ricotta cheese. It is used in sandwiches and lasagna.

Fish from the surrounding seas is a very important food in most parts of Italy. Frequently, it is served simply and without a sauce. Quantities of shellfish, eels, octopus, prawns, swordfish, dogfish, and scampi (large shrimp) found mainly in Italian waters are other offerings from the sea. Some seafoods appear in casseroles, stews, and other dishes rich with olive oil, tomato sauce, garlic, capers, and black olives.

## Potato Gnocchi

Makes approximately 2 dozen

| | |
|---|---|
| 500 g | potatoes (before peeling) |
| 5 mL | salt |
| 125 mL | all-purpose flour |
| 10 mL | butter |
| 1 | egg, beaten |
| | salt and pepper to taste |
| 30 mL | Parmesan cheese |

Wash, peel, and quarter the potatoes. Cook them in boiling, salted water until tender, approximately 15 to 20 minutes. Drain thoroughly. Mash potatoes finely with a fork or masher.

Place the potatoes in a bowl. Add the flour, 5 mL of the butter, the beaten egg, and salt and pepper to taste. Knead until the mixture is smooth. With damp hands, shape pieces of the mixture into small balls.

Drop the balls into a saucepan of boiling water. Cook until the gnocchi float to the top. Lift out of the pan with a slotted spoon and transfer to a warm dish. Top with pieces of the remaining 5 mL butter. Sprinkle with the Parmesan cheese. Serve immediately.

How many of these Italian foods have you heard of or tried?
— *panettone; spumone; rissotto; polenta; panzarotti*

Veal is generally preferred to beef. Chicken and lamb are eaten also. Pork is especially popular in processed form. *Prosciutto* ham is a favourite. Salami is produced in various forms in most of the provinces. The area around Bologna is an important sausage-producing region. This is where the large sausage made of beef, veal, and pork got its name.

Olives grown in several parts of the country are used in many recipes. They have an important place in the Italian appetizer, *antipasto*, and are frequently eaten alone, either plain or stuffed with pimento, almonds, or anchovies. Mushrooms and truffles are frequently incorporated in the flavourful sauces used for meat and pasta.

Traditionally, whenever the noon meal is eaten at home, it is the main meal of the day. To begin, a pasta dish or soup is served. The soups of Italy are rich and hearty and often contain some form of pasta. *Minestrone* is a thick, vegetable and pasta soup that could also be a full meal. It has many regional variations.

After the soup or pasta course comes the main dish. It may be fish or meat accompanied by vegetables or larger servings of pastas in a sauce containing chopped meat or seafood. Salad is more filling than the classic French salad of tossed greens. As well as lettuce, it contains tomatoes and other vegetables. As in France, it is usually served after the main course.

Pizza, a familiar national dish, has its roots in the southern regions of Italy. Originally it was eaten as a snack food. Cheese, tomatoes, peppers, olives, anchovies, shrimp, and sausage are common toppings. The ingredients used vary greatly from region to region.

A meal may be ended with cheese or fresh fruit, or both. Elaborate desserts are saved for meals with guests or special occasions. A rich frozen dessert made with cream and eggs is called *spumone*. Many forms of *gelati*

Did you know that there is a Historical Museum of Spaghetti? It is called the *Museo Storico degli Spaghetti* and is located in Pontedassio, Italy.

(ice cream) and *granite* (sherbet) are made into artful desserts. Visitors to Italy are delighted with the wide range of ice cream offered for sale in all Italian markets.

## JAMAICAN

Surrounded by the sea and covered with lush vegetation, resulting from its warm, humid, climate, Jamaica is a year-round food basket. Good food is plentiful. The excellent growing climate produces a wide variety of vegetables and fruit, which are available at outdoor markets frequented by most cooks. Because of the transportation distances involved, imported foods are very expensive.

Business people traditionally eat a large main meal, or dinner, at noon. A supper is then served late in the evening. Most main dishes are spicy hot, and curried dishes are a specialty. Meats used include chicken, pork, and goat. Available beef tends to be tough because of difficulties involved in feeding the animals and ageing the meat. Most beef is ground into minced beef to be used in different ways. One important traditional dish is curried goat served with rice. Others include oxtail served as a stew on a bed of rice with lima beans and pigstail with red kidney beans also served on a bed of rice.

The ocean provides shrimp, lobster, sea turtle, conch, and a variety of fish. Tiny coral reef fish are fried whole until crispy. Six to eight of them make a single serving. Local lobster are actually crayfish since they have no claws. The smaller-sized ones are called chicken lobster. Most shellfish are enjoyed curried, and fish chowders are popular.

Vegetables are plentiful. What Canadians know as avocados grow very large and in the market are called pears. Sweet peppers of many kinds are available. *Cho cho* is a mild-flavoured local vegetable commonly steamed and served with butter and pepper. *Ackee* is another mild-flavoured vegetable. When cooked it has the colour and consistency of scrambled eggs. It is best known as the national dish of *salt fish and ackee*. The saltiness of the fish is complemented by the addition of the ackee.

Clockwise from the top, these Jamaican foods are curried chicken, rice and beans, and grilled snapper.

Yams differ from the Canadian sweet variety and are available as negro yams, yellow yams, or sweet yams. They are often served with salt fish.

Many tropical fruits contribute to the meals of Jamaicans. Bananas are served fresh, fried, or in banana fritters. Green bananas are boiled and served with dumplings. *Plantain* is shaped like a banana, but larger (20–30 cm), and is less flavourful than bananas. When cooked, usually fried, its sweetness is accentuated. Papaya, called *pa pa*, pineapples, and mangoes are all familiar.

Wonderfully flavoured coffee grown in the mountain areas is enjoyed very strong. Local almonds, cashews, and coconut are incorporated into many dishes. Sugar cane fields yield refined sugar, but also brown sugar, molasses, and several beverages.

*Tasty patties* are a very popular fast food. These are made of pastry filled with highly spiced minced meat and eaten out of hand as Canadians would eat a hot dog. At Easter, *bun and cheese* is served. The "bun" part looks like dark fruit cake and is made the same way. However, the flavour of the spices used, especially of cinnamon, are more distinctive. As the name suggests, a slice of cheese is served on each slice of "bun."

How many of these Jamaican foods have you heard of or tried?
— *jerked chicken; escovitch; goat meat curry; ackee and rice*

## Sweet and Tangy Grapefruit

Serves 6

3 grapefruit
1 can sweetened condensed milk
   nutmeg
6 cherries
6 fresh mint leaves or lime leaves

Cut each grapefruit in half crosswise. With a sharp paring knife or a serrated grapefruit knife, take out the sections carefully, leaving the rind intact. Put the sections in a medium-size bowl.

Pour the milk into the bowl and mix gently with the grapefruit. Spoon the grapefruit back into the grapefruit halves.

Sprinkle each half with nutmeg. Chill. Serve decorated with cherry and a fresh mint or lime leaf.

Serve as a dessert.

# JAPANESE

The changing seasons, the ocean, and the atmosphere play an important role in the choices, the method of cookery, and the arrangement and service of foods in Japanese cuisine. With such sensitivity, cooking and eating that appeals to all the senses becomes an artistic experience.

Japanese food staples include rice, fish and seafood, vegetables, and tea. In the mountainous regions and when rice crops fail, yams and taro provide an alternative staple. Vegetables include sprouts, roots, many types of mushrooms, and varieties of seaweed. Japanese recipes frequently use water chestnuts and cucumbers. Salting, pickling, and drying for fish and vegetables provide increased choices. Noodles are also enjoyed and may be used as a main dish or snack. Seasonal fruits are snacks or desserts.

In Japanese cookery, the arrangement, number, colour, and shape of the foods are as carefully considered and planned as their flavour combinations. Great pride is taken in the presentation of the food. An example of this care is *sushi* which is frequently arranged in a floral design. Sushi (vinegared rice dishes) are eaten as appetizers or as snacks and are prepared in varied forms: cakes, balls, wrapped, or rolled and sliced. A favourite sushi combination is very thin strips of raw fish carefully combined with vegetables and rice and wrapped with seaweed into bite-size morsels.

Vegetables are served in many ways, both raw and cooked. One of the most interesting ways is *tempura*. Vegetables are dipped in a light-coloured batter and quickly deep-fried in hot oil and served with dipping sauces. Thin slices of meat or fish or seafood are also cooked this way. Tempura is of Portuguese origin.

*Nabemono* is another interesting cooking method. This one-pot cookery is done in a heating unit, such as an electric skillet, at the dinner table. Each guest selects food, such as thinly sliced meat or poultry or seafood and a variety of vegetables, from an attractively arranged platter and cooks it in broth. *Sukiyaki, shabu shabu,* and *yosenabe* are three recipes cooked the "*nabe*" way. A Japanese sweet version of soy sauce, *shoyu,* is used for dipping. Grilling or broiling as methods of cooking are also commonly used for fish, meats, and vegetables.

**Have you ever tried sushi?**

International Society for Educational Information, Inc.

**281**

## Peanut Chicken

Serves 6

| | | Sauce | |
|---|---|---|---|
| 1 | egg | | |
| 30 mL | cornflour | 60 mL | rice vinegar |
| 2 mL | salt | 120 mL | water |
| 6 | chicken breasts, | 60 mL | sugar |
| | skinned and boned | 120 mL | tomato ketchup |
| 45 mL | vegetable oil | 30 mL | cornflour |
| 50 g | peanuts, chopped | 2 mL | salt |
| 1 | green onion, chopped | | |

Lightly beat the egg with the cornflour and salt to make a batter. Coat the chicken breasts with the batter. Heat the oil in a deep frying pan. Fry the chicken breasts until golden and cooked through, approximately 20 minutes.

Meanwhile, make the sauce. Place all the ingredients in a saucepan and bring to the boil, stirring. Simmer on low heat until thickened.

Drain the chicken well on paper towels. Slice into pieces. Arrange on a serving dish and pour the sauce on top. Sprinkle with the peanuts and green onion.

How many of these Japanese foods have you heard of or tried? — *tofu; red bean cake; sashimi; yakitori*

Breakfast in Japan is usually rice with egg or a hot, nourishing soup made with *miso* (fermented soybean paste). Tea is the favoured beverage. Lunch is frequently taken in a restaurant or as snacks from vendors. It might be sushi or noodles with sauces and fish or vegetable garnish. A family dinner may be boiled or steamed fish, garnished with condiments and vegetables artfully presented. Clear soup with garnishes begin the meal; rice and pickles may complete it. Fruit desserts are common. Dinnertime is frequently used as a time to socialize. However, traditionally, entertaining guests is done in restaurants.

## MEXICAN

Despite Spanish and Portuguese influence since the fifteenth century, Mexican cooking remains strongly native due to its very large Native population. Corn is one of the most basic foods in Mexican cookery. However, even many thousand of years ago, the Mexicans realized the inadequacy of corn alone in maintaining healthy bodies. They learned to add dried beans to corn mixtures to supplement the corn's inadequate protein content. The beans also provide certain of the missing minerals and vitamins. The corn and dried bean combination along with other vegetables grown in Mexico formed a reliable food foundation for the population. Other foods grown in abundance were many species of squash and pumpkins, sweet potatoes, tomatoes, many varieties of chili peppers, both hot and mild, and also many fruits and nuts. More than 90 varieties of chilies, ranging in hotness and pungency, are used in Mexican cookery.

*Tortillas* could be considered the bread of Mexico. These are flat, pancakelike, unleavened breads or cakes. The dough from which they are made is called *masa*. It is made by crushing kernels of dried corn that have been soaked in lime water. The masa is patted into shape and cooked on a hot griddle for one or two minutes. In the north of Mexico, however, tortillas are made from wheat flour rather than corn. Tortilla making is now mechanized, and in Mexico tortillas can be purchased at a tortilleria. Tortillas are as versatile as any pasta. They can be fried, shredded like noodles, layered in casseroles, stacked, or used to wrap or scoop up foods. *Refried beans* are a traditional accompaniment to tortilla dishes.

Try to name all the Mexican foods in this photograph.

*Enchiladas* are an adaptation of the tortilla. The basic tortilla is dipped into a green or red tomato sauce and heated quickly on a griddle. It is then filled with a mixture of meat, onion, cheese, and tomato, rolled to a thick cylinder, and served with a sauce, usually of tomatoes.

*Tacos* are the Mexican fast-food equivalent of a hamburger or hot dog. Most tacos are made with a crisp, fried tortilla folded so it can be filled with a spiced meat mixture topped with shredded lettuce, grated cheese, chopped tomato, and olives. A soft taco is a tortilla wrapped around some favourite filling of meat, cheese, bean, vegetable, or a mixture of these foods. A favourite filling for either is *guacamole*, a mixture of mashed avocado, tomato, onion, and chili.

Red snapper and shrimp are popular seafoods in Mexico. They may be grilled and served simply with a wedge of lime or combined with spicy

How many of these Mexican foods have you heard of or tried? — *frijoles refritos; chorizo; tostadas; huevos rancheros*

tomato and olive sauce, and served with potatoes. Tomatoes and hot chilies are often used with spices, such as cinnamon, cloves, and coriander, in dishes with pork, veal, or poultry. One such dish has another interesting ingredient — chocolate. *Mole poblano de guajolote* means turkey in chocolate and chili sauce, but chicken and pork are often prepared and served in the same sauce.

It was Mexico that introduced chocolate to the modern world when the Aztecs shared their secret with the Spanish explorer Cortés. Mexican chocolate is a combination of chocolate, sugar, cinnamon, and almonds. It is consumed mainly as a beverage, such as in Mexican hot chocolate. It is also used as an ingredient in desserts or as a rich sauce over ice cream.

## Green Chili Salsa

Makes 250 mL

|  |  |
|---|---|
| 1 | medium tomato, peeled and cut |
| 1 | 125 g can of green chili peppers, drained |
| 1 | small onion, chopped |
| 1 | clove garlic, chopped |
| 30 mL | fresh cilantro, cut up |
| 15 mL | olive oil |
| 2 mL | salt |
|  | pepper to taste |

Combine all ingredients in a blender. Cover and blend until mixture is fairly smooth. Pour into a small saucepan.

Bring mixture to a boil. Cook and stir over medium heat about 5 minutes or until slightly thickened.

Serve with tortilla chips or tacos.

# SCANDINAVIAN

Denmark, Norway, and Sweden share similar food and food customs. Each country, however, has its own specialties. A varied selection of food is served at every meal, but methods of preparation and cooking are simple, enhancing natural ingredients and fresh flavours. Smoking, pickling, and brining are used widely for meats and fish.

The most popular form of meal service is the *smorgasbord*, which features specialties from all the Scandinavian countries. Food is arranged on the buffet table with artistic skill as the cook combines the colours, shapes, and textures. In addition to the cold foods offered — meat, fish, shrimp, smoked salmon, herring, boiled potatoes, eggs, and salads — one or two hot dishes are included. The smorgasbord may be offered at any meal, including breakfast. Individuals take small servings of several similar foods and repeatedly return to the table for additional kinds of foods.

### Lacy Potato Pancakes With Chives

Serves 4

| | |
|---|---|
| 4 | medium-sized baking potatoes |
| 30 mL | fresh chives, chopped |
| 3 mL | salt |
| | freshly ground pepper to taste |
| 30 mL | vegetable oil (or non-stick cooking spray) |

Peel and finely grate the potatoes into a large mixing bowl. Do not drain off the potato water that will accumulate in the bowl. Working quickly to prevent the potatoes from turning brown, mix them with the chopped chives, salt, and pepper.

Heat the oil in a 25–30-cm skillet over high heat. The pan must be very hot, but not smoking. Lower heat to medium-high.

Using 30 mL of potato mixture for each pancake, fry two or three at a time. Flatten them with a metal spatula to about 7 cm in diameter. Fry each batch of pancakes for 2 or 3 minutes on each side, or until they are crisp and golden. Serve immediately.

Another specialty of the Scandinavian countries is the *smorrebord*, known to most Canadians as open-faced sandwiches. Thinly sliced, buttered breads are topped with decoratively arranged combinations of foods. Many varieties of fish, seafood, and thinly sliced meats and cheeses are

How many of these Scandinavian foods have you heard of or tried? — *limpa; gravad lax; plättar; aebleskiver*

This restaurant's cold buffet contains typical Danish foods.

Gingerbread from Bern, Switzerland, being carefully crafted.

offered and never fewer than three different kinds of sandwiches at one time. Cheese is used extensively throughout Scandinavia, and many varieties are available. Selections of foods are garnished carefully with dressings, herbs, and vegetables. The flavours are essentially savoury, never sweet, and their appearance is always fresh, colourful, and appetizing. These sandwiches are eaten from a plate with a knife and fork.

The Scandinavian countries have individual food distinctions. Denmark is noted for its pork and dairy products. Danish cheeses, butter, and bacon are exported to many countries. Since most of Norway is surrounded by water, it is not surprising that fish are a mainstay of Norwegian foods. Lamb and mutton are favoured meats. Norwegian food is not as rich as Danish food and includes more fish and smoked meats than the Swedish diet. Baking in Norway is simpler. Sweden is known for its game and rich desserts. Generally speaking, the universal appeal of Scandinavian food is in the garnish and in the colour and flavour of the natural food rather than in the seasonings used.

## SWISS

*Fondue*, the best-known of Swiss cuisine, is a method of cooking food in a heavy pot over a regulated flame. It originated in the days when all family members worked in the fields and there was little time to prepare meals.

A cheese fondue is made by melting a sharp cheese, such as Gruyère, with a fruit-based liquid in an earthenware pot. Using a long-handled fork, each person skewers a piece of crusty bread and dips it into the melted cheese, turning it until the bread cube is well coated.

*Fondue Bourguignonne* is similar. Small cubes of tender beef are skewered and cooked in hot oil. Various sauces, such as hot mustard, spicy tomato, and Béarnaise, are prepared in advance for dipping the cooked cubes. French bread is served with this meal.

Like their neighbours in Hungary and Austria, Swiss cooks are specialists in preparing elaborate and delicious cakes and desserts. Cooking with sugar has reached high perfection in Switzerland. The endless sweets are derived from French, Italian, German, and Austrian sources and are among the world's finest. Bakers go to endless trouble to produce a variety of cookies, tortes, and other confections. Using chocolate, nuts, *marzipan* (ground almonds), cream, and candied and glazed fruits, these sweets become true works of art. Chocolate is used extensively and the *sachertorte* (a very rich, moist, chocolate cake that originated in Austria) is famous. Numerous folk festivals and holidays encourage the creation of rich masterpieces, and the many hotel schools sponsor contests to encourage these skills.

### Gingerbread From Lucerne

Serves 10–12

| | |
|---|---|
| 450 mL | fresh cream |
| | juice of 3 lemons to sour the cream |
| 120 g | pear purée |
| 200 g | sugar |
| 10 g | mixed spices (star aniseed, cloves, cinnamon, ginger) |
| 5 g | bicarbonate of soda |
| 500 g | whole-wheat flour |
| 150 g | walnuts, roughly crushed |

Add the lemon juice to the cream and leave for a few minutes.
Mix together the cream, pear purée, sugar, mixed spices, and bicarbonate of soda. Add the flour. Mix until well blended and then add the nuts.
   Fill a flan ring or pan (24-cm diameter, 6 cm high) and bake in the oven for 50 minutes at 190°C.
   Serve cold.

SOURCE: Nestlé Canada Inc.

# UKRAINIAN

Primarily of Slavic origin, Ukrainian cookery shares elements from Russian, Polish, and Czeckoslovakian cuisine. Grains form the staple foods for which these people are best known. The Ukraine has long been considered the "bread basket of Europe" with a wide range of breads and

How many of these Swiss foods have you heard of or tried?
— *rösti; muesli; raclette; basel fnutli*

baked goods for all occasions. *Babka* and *kulitsh* are Easter breads rich with fruits, almonds, and egg yolks. The *bagel* is a slightly sour-tasting, compact, flat, round bun with a hole in the centre. In some areas it is a New Year's specialty.

In addition to being used to make many attractive varieties of bread, wheat flour is also used to make noodles and dumplings. Probably best-known and loved of Ukrainian specialties are *pyrohy*. These small envelopes of pasta dough are filled with potatoes, cabbage, mushrooms, or meat mixtures and boiled, fried, or both, before serving. *Kasha* (buckwheat) appears in some other foods.

Dairy products are another staple. Fresh, sweet cream, called *smetanka*, is used generously as an ingredient in desserts and main course dishes alike. *Huslyanka* (clabbered or cultured milk) is used for beverages and in cooking. Pork is the favoured meat used in every possible form from all kinds of sausages to roasts to pickled meats. Vegetables are mainly cabbage, beets, onions, and potatoes. Stuffed cabbage leaves that some Canadians will know as cabbage rolls are called *zakuska*. A hearty soup of beets and/or cabbage, known as *borsch*, originated in the Ukraine. The Russian variation is also called borsch; in Poland it is known as *barshch*.

Caviar wrapped in crêpe-like *bliny* is a Ukrainian delicacy.

Most Ukrainians celebrate two Christmases. December 25th is acknowledged with a tree and gift giving. The more solemn and religious occasion is on January 6th. Symbols of family unity, respect for the dead, and agricultural heritage intertwine to make this the most important family festival. New Year's eve, celebrated on January 13th, is called *Malanka*, or generous eve, and is a time for parties and special foods.

Lent foods prior to Easter are traditionally meatless with cheese and egg substitutes. *Paskha* is a pyramid of pot cheese with fruit and almonds eaten as a thick spread on Easter breads or cakes. Baskets of food and decorated eggs, called *pysanky* and *krashanky*, are traditional at Easter.

For the most part, desserts are reserved for special occasions. Evening or afternoon tea is often served Russian-style with a small dish of sweet jam to spoon up with each sip of tea. Tea is the most important beverage; coffee is considered a luxury.

## Pyrohy With Potato and Cheese Filling

Makes approximately 25

| Pyrohy | | Filling | |
|---|---|---|---|
| 1000 mL | flour | 15 mL | chopped onion |
| 1 | egg | 30 mL | butter |
| 30 mL | vegetable oil | 500 mL | cold mashed potatoes |
| 450 mL | warm water | 250 mL | cottage cheese or grated |
| 2 mL | salt | | cheddar cheese |
| 50 mL | flour | | salt and pepper to taste |

Combine water, oil, egg, and salt and add to 750 mL flour. Mix well. Add 250 mL of flour. Knead on a floured board until dough is smooth and elastic. Cover with a tea towel and set aside for 15 minutes.

Prepare the filling while the dough is resting. Cook the onion in the butter until tender. Combine it with the potatoes and cheese. Season to taste with salt and pepper.

Roll out the dough quite thinly on a floured board. Use a round cookie cutter or the open end of a glass to cut out the dough. Place the round cut-out on the palm of the hand. Place a spoonful of the filling on it. Fold to form a half-circle. Press the edges together with your fingers. Make sure the edges are free from filling and well sealed to prevent the filling from running out. Place the pyrohy on a tea towel, without touching one another. Cover with another tea towel to prevent them from drying out.

Drop a few pyrohy at a time into a large pot of boiling, slightly salted water. Stir with a wooden spoon to prevent them from sticking to the bottom of the pan or to one another. Boil 4–5 minutes. (The cooking time will depend on the size of the pyrohy and the thickness of the dough. They are ready when they are well puffed.) Drain in a colander and place in a deep dish. Drizzle generously with melted butter, and toss very gently to coat them evenly and to prevent them from sticking. Serve hot in a large dish without piling or crowding them.

If desired, serve pyrohy with toasted bread crumbs and sour cream.

**How many of these Ukrainian foods have you heard of or tried?** — *kasha; holubtsi; pyrohy; bublyky; babka*

A sampling of
Vietnamese foods.

# VIETNAMESE

The most distinctive aspect of Vietnamese foods is the care with which they are served. The attractive presentation of a meal is considered almost as important as its flavour, and many hours are devoted to the preparation of the evening meal. Meals are eaten with chopsticks from a rice bowl, except for foods eaten with the fingers. Soup broth is eaten with a spoon, while chopsticks are used for solid food. A table setting is completed with a little pot of *nuoc cham* (a hot blend of mashed chili) and a bottle of *nuoc mam* (the Vietnamese equivalent of Chinese soy sauce). Nuoc mam is the basis of Vietnamese seasoning. It is a light brown colour, thin, and slightly salty with a pungent aroma. Use of seasonings is restrained with few choices: star anise, fresh cilantro or coriander, white pepper, fresh red chili, ginger, garlic, and lemon grass. Other foods used for interest are roasted peanuts, lime juice, brown sugar, and pickled vegetables.

The Vietnamese like to serve many of their main dishes sandwich-style in a wrapper of lettuce or *banh trang* (edible rice paper). Filling includes slivers of cucumber, carrot, radish, leafy herbs, and cooked rice vermicelli. Alternatively, assorted cooked morsels are served with wrappers or lettuce leaves to be rolled at the table. Examples of popular foods for wrapping are *nem nuong* (bite-size, pork meat balls), *bo nuong* (beef balls), and *cha gio* (crisply deep-fried, stuffed rolls wrapped in rice paper). Sauces for dipping range from a tart mixture of lime juice and nuoc mam to sauces that are thick, rich, and sweet.

Vegetables that are not wrapped are arranged with precision in layers on flat platters to serve as *goi* (salad) with assorted meats. A single dish might include sliced pork or beef, shredded cooked chicken pieces, or carefully sliced fried fish and dried squid.

Rice is the staple served at every Vietnamese meal, unless one of the popular noodle, or *mein*, dishes is being included. Noodles are a standard ingredient in *pho* (a popular meal-in-a-bowl enjoyed day or night). Beef is simmered slowly in broth with the addition of rice noodles, bean sprouts, fresh cilantro, and green onions.

Beef and pork are popular meats. Pork is generally simmered with soy sauce and pepper or braised into a richly flavoured stew. *Seven styles of beef* is a banquet of beef prepared for special occasions. Slices, balls, and cubes of meat are each cooked in a special way — braised, fried, simmered, sautéed, grilled, and barbecued — and presented one by one in a particular sequence so that each enhances the other.

Vietnamese enjoy sweet tastes as between-meal snacks rather than as a dessert at the end of a meal. The sweet might be a cake, cookie, or pudding with rice, brown sugar, coconut meat, or milk as the basis. Two contributions of the French colonial era still enjoyed are French-style rolls and excellent coffee.

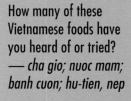

How many of these Vietnamese foods have you heard of or tried? — *cha gio; nuoc mam; banh cuon; hu-tien, nep*

## Pot–fried Rice

Serves 4–6

| | |
|---|---|
| 25 mL | butter |
| 2 | cloves garlic, peeled and finely minced |
| 625 mL | uncooked, long-grain rice |
| 5 mL | salt |
| 625 mL | boiling water |

Melt butter in a saucepan with a tight-fitting lid. Sauté garlic in butter for 3 minutes. Add rice and salt. Stir-fry until rice turns golden.

Pour in boiling water and stir well, then cover. Cook over low heat for 10 to 15 minutes, until rice is soft and water is absorbed.

KEY TERMS

Use the words listed below to complete the following statements in your notebook.

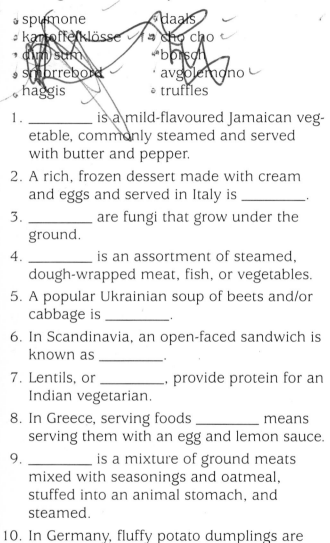

- spumone
- kartoffelklösse
- dim sum
- smörrebord
- haggis
- daals
- cho cho
- borsch
- avgolemono
- truffles

1. _____ is a mild-flavoured Jamaican vegetable, commonly steamed and served with butter and pepper.

2. A rich, frozen dessert made with cream and eggs and served in Italy is _____.

3. _____ are fungi that grow under the ground.

4. _____ is an assortment of steamed, dough-wrapped meat, fish, or vegetables.

5. A popular Ukrainian soup of beets and/or cabbage is _____.

6. In Scandinavia, an open-faced sandwich is known as _____.

7. Lentils, or _____, provide protein for an Indian vegetarian.

8. In Greece, serving foods _____ means serving them with an egg and lemon sauce.

9. _____ is a mixture of ground meats mixed with seasonings and oatmeal, stuffed into an animal stomach, and steamed.

10. In Germany, fluffy potato dumplings are called_____.

 FOCUS YOUR KNOWLEDGE

1. Identify the four main schools of Chinese cooking. Identify two food examples of each school.

2. Identify and describe briefly three traditional foods from each country of the British Isles: England, Scotland, Ireland, and Wales.

3. Describe the grain products used in the various areas of India.

4. Describe how phyllo is prepared and used in Greek cooking.

5. Explain what is meant by the following Japanese terms: sushi, tempura, sukiyaki.

6. Explain the difference between tortillas, enchiladas, and tacos.

7. Describe the ways vegetables may be served in Vietnamese cuisine.

## ☀ DEMONSTRATE YOUR KNOWLEDGE

1. Prepare a chart to show the similarities and differences in the foods grown, and preparation and cooking methods in China, Japan, and Vietnam.

2. Working in small groups, plan and prepare a casserole or one-dish meal from recipes you locate from three different countries. Compare the ingredients, flavour, texture, and appearance of each dish.

3. In small groups, plan a main meal menu from one of the countries discussed in this chapter. Prepare the meal.

4. With a partner, select and prepare one of the recipes included in this chapter.

5. Role play a discussion between a person from Italy and a person from Mexico, focussing on the position — "My country makes the best foods from grain products."

## ☀ APPLY YOUR KNOWLEDGE

1. Prepare a chart of the cheeses found in France, Greece, Italy, and Denmark. Set up a display of some cheeses from each country for tasting.

2. Working in pairs, interview someone originally from a country other than Canada. What foods does he or she eat that are representative of the culture? Have any changes been made in his or her diet since living in Canada?

3. Prepare a class cookbook from class members' recipes that represent the different cultural backgrounds of the students.

4. Visit a supermarket to find the convenience forms of cultural foods available. Classify the foods as canned, frozen, ready-to-eat, or dried for each country.

5. Prepare a list of the restaurants in your community that serve foods from cultures other than Canadian. Classify the restaurants according to country. Note the country represented most frequently.

# Global Food Issues

If you analyzed the daily diet of your grandparents or great-grandparents you would probably notice that they mainly ate foods that were close at hand — locally grown vegetables, fruit, and grains, eggs, meat or game, milk and cheese. Today we are just as likely to eat foods produced in other parts of the world. We eat bananas from Central and South America as well as apples from Canadian apple orchards. We drink beverages made from oranges, chocolate, and coffee, products grown outside Canada. Our supermarkets offer us a wide selection of foods, such as New Zealand lamb and kiwi fruit, tuna and pineapple canned in the Philippines, peanuts from West Africa, sugar and chocolate from the Caribbean, strawberries and fresh vegetables all year round from the United States, Mexico, and South America. Food links people and countries around the world.

When we start to pay attention to where our food comes from, who produces it, how it is produced, and under what conditions, as well as the consequences of our food choices for ourselves and others, we begin to develop a global perspective.

## FOOD PRODUCTION

In earlier times the production of food was centred around small, family farms. Food was considered a basic good, something that was essential for life. Agriculture was a way of life that meant caring for the land. In the cultivation and production of food, farmers developed a relationship to the land that centred on the values of stewardship and co-operation. This means managing and caring for the land in a responsible manner so that it will continue to produce food crops over a long period of time. Family farms were often **subsistence** farms, that is farms that provide almost all of the food required by the farm family to survive. If the family grew more than it needed, the excess was traded for other goods.

A large portion of subsistence crops are known as staple foods. These are foods that are produced in large quantities and form the main part of the diet. Staple foods vary depending on geographic location and conditions such as climate, availability of land, and what crops are suitable for the land. In Canada, wheat, potatoes, and meat are considered staples. In

Asia, rice is a staple food. Protein-rich crops known as *pulses* are part of the staple diet in India. African countries traditionally rely on such staple foods as *millet*, *sorghum*, *cassavas*, yams, and *plantains*. Corn and beans form the main part of the diet in many parts of Central and South America.

How might this family farm in Botswana, Africa, differ from a family farm in Canada?

## Agribusiness and Traditional Farming ◆
Over the years, farming has changed. Instead of producing food for the family, small farms have been expanded to form huge plantations where crops are grown to sell or trade. Such crops are known as **cash crops**, because they are sold to provide money or income for the farm owner rather than to feed the people who cultivate them. Often the farm owner is a large, multinational corporation — one that has operations in many countries. This type of food production, which combines agriculture and big business, is known as **agribusiness**.

Agribusiness treats food as a **commodity**. When food is considered a commodity it becomes an **economic good**, something useful when it can be produced and traded for a profit. The keys to success in agribusiness are efficiency and competitiveness. In order to compete, farms have become larger and larger to produce more and more goods. Now millions of farmers around the world are competing with each other to grow the cheapest food.

Agribusiness has taken advantage of many technological changes.

- The development of new farm machinery.
- Discoveries in the areas of genetics and breeding that produce high-yielding, fast-maturing varieties of plants.
- The formulation of pesticides, fungicides, and chemical fertilizers.
- Faster transportation methods.
- More processing methods.
- The use of computers at all stages of food production and distribution.

Trying to increase food production through scientific advances has been called the **green revolution**. While use of chemical fertilizers, irrigation, pesticides, new seeds, and technology have increased yields, it has not helped the poor. Poor farmers who have little cash are less able to take advantage of the green revolution. At the same time, the wealthy farm owners are able to use their profits to buy up the land of poor farmers.

Agribusiness has affected the lives of people all over the world. Changes in food production have been experienced in both developed and developing countries, but they have had a greater impact in the developing countries.

Canada is considered a **developed country** because most of the people in this country have enough money to meet their basic needs. Developed countries have extensive transportation, energy, communication, education, food processing and storage systems, housing, and health care systems. However, access to these systems can be closed to many people who do not have money. In Canada we have seen the effects of agribusiness. Canadians now have access to a wide variety of reasonably priced food. However, the number of family farms in Canada has been decreasing sharply, while the average size of those farms remaining has been increasing. These large farms tend to concentrate on producing one or two major crops to sell as cash crops. Producing only one crop is called **monocropping**.

**Developing countries** are those where the level of income is well below the world average, and there is little or no industry. These countries lack the necessary resources or supply systems to provide their citizens with basic needs. There are few social support systems such as social assistance, public education, unemployment insurance, health care, or pension plans. As a result, low life expectancy, high birth rates, malnutrition, poor housing, and low literacy rates exist. Because there is little industry, developing countries depend largely on the income from agricultural exports to provide money to import manufactured goods. The prices of agricultural commodities go up and down. Recently the income for exported crops has gone down, while the cost of imported manufactured goods has gone up. To get more money, more and more land is used for cash crops.

As the best land is put into cash cropping, subsistence food producers, mainly women, are pushed into marginal areas; some people are pushed off the land altogether. Marginal areas are not particularly suitable for agriculture. The land is harder to work and produces less.

When land is used for cash crops, there is less land for food crops. Sometimes a country produces agricultural crops for export but not enough food crops to feed its own population. It is then faced with importing food from other countries. The imported foods differ from the staple foods that are normally eaten. They tend to be expensive and often not as nutritionally complete as the traditional foods. Imported foods also tend to be high in refined carbohydrates, sugar, salt, and saturated fats and low in fibre, vitamins, and minerals. High-pressure advertising of these

*The poor are our brothers and sisters...people in the world who need love, who need care, who have to be wanted.*
MOTHER TERESA

foods influences people to change from their traditional foods. Thus, traditional foods begin to decline in importance.

Cash crops like tea, coffee, sugar cane, tobacco, and cotton are worthless nutritionally. Cash crops cannot be eaten to prevent starvation, if the demand for them drops on world markets. Therefore, the people must still purchase their food at the market. Those who do not have money must go without food. Generally, whenever people have no access to land to grow subsistence crops, the poor have become even poorer.

In both developed and developing countries debt has become a normal part of running a farm as a business. To increase productivity and become more competitive, large quantities of high-yielding, fast-maturing seeds, fertilizer, pesticides, machinery, and fuel are required. All of these cost money. Once countries and individuals are in debt, they must continue growing cash crops to pay off their debt.

Many developing countries borrowed money to modernize at a time when interest rates were high. The prices of their agricultural commodities fell, while the cost of production rose mainly due to increases in oil prices. Today, prices for their commodities are still low, and the countries are still in debt. There is no money to feed the poor.

Many subsistence farmers who cannot afford the increased cost of farming are being displaced. When harvests are poor the farmers are forced to sell their land to buy food. Many lose their farms when they cannot pay their debts. These farmers seek work as labourers, often at the farms they once owned. They are called landless agricultural workers. When there is no work in the rural areas, they seek jobs in the overcrowded cities. For those fortunate enough to find jobs, wages are very low. Often there is no work at all. People end up living in slum areas and shanty towns in substandard housing, without basic services such as clean, running water, electricity, and proper sewage disposal.

Women do enormous amounts of farm labour. It is estimated that women grow and process at least half of the world's food. They plant, weed, and harvest food. They care for livestock. They grind grains and market surplus food from their subsistence gardens. They do all of this in addition to caring for their homes and families.

*Must we starve our children to pay our debts?*
JULIUS NYERE (FORMER PRESIDENT OF TANZANIA)

What do you think it would be like to live in a shanty town?

Even though women play such a large part in food production, programs designed to improve agriculture, particularly in developing countries, have been aimed mostly at men. For example, introducing machines to do the ploughing means that the men can plough more land. It is the women who do the planting and weeding by hand. So the ability to plough more land means more work for women. When family land is used for cash cropping, the bulk of the work is done by women and children, but the man is paid for the work of his family.

Seed is the first link in the world's food chain. Agriculture started when people learned to collect and sow seeds from plants. These seeds gradually became domesticated. Each year farmers collected seeds of the most productive plants and planted them the following season. Seeds were also exchanged between farmers and farm communities. With the green revolution and the rise of agribusiness came the demand for seed varieties that produced high yields. Farmers abandoned their own seeds in favour of high-yielding seeds. Increasingly, the world's total food production is relying on fewer crops. Food crop diversity is declining as seeds that are no longer used become extinct. As this trend continues we become more vulnerable. Our food supply depends on an ever-smaller number of species, and if any one of them fails, it could mean hunger for millions of people.

Traditional farming methods included letting some land lie **fallow**. Fallowing is the practice of letting a field rest for a period of time to recover its fertility. Farmers also rotated crops from field to field so that the nutrients of the soil were not depleted. Another practice was **intercropping** — planting different crops in alternating rows in the same field. Intercropping reduces the likelihood of pests attacking and wiping out a whole crop. As well, a proper combination of plants means that some will replenish in the soil nutrients that others extract.

With the rise of agribusiness and the trend to monocropping in both developing and developed countries, the use of these methods has declined substantially. Monocropping depletes the soil of minerals and organic matter. The soil becomes less fertile and gradually farmland becomes less productive. Constant plowing and harvesting expose the soil to the wind and increase soil erosion.

**Desertification** is the term used to describe land that has been lost when a drought strikes and farmland and pasture are turned into desert. The topsoil dries up and is blown or washed away. Desertification can be caused by climatic change or by human activity, which generally involves mismanagement of the land, such as:

- Over cultivation and the prolonged use of heavy machinery.
- Monocropping.
- Overuse of chemical fertilizers and pesticides.
- Improper irrigation.
- Overgrazing.
- Deforestation.

Soil formation is a long and complex process. Once it is gone, it cannot be replaced easily. Prime farmland that is lost to the spread of cities is never replaced.

How do you think this desertification could have taken place?

Pesticides and Fertilizers  ◆  Forty years ago almost no **pesticides** were used. Monocropping and the decline in seed diversity made crops more vulnerable to insect infestation. Thus, chemicals called pesticides have been developed to kill insects and other pests when applied to crops. Over 2.5 billion kg of pesticides a year are used worldwide. Often the pesticides that are banned or restricted in Canada are used in developing countries. It is estimated that as many as 1.5 million people suffer poisoning by pesticides each year, because they do not use the necessary safety precautions to prevent exposure to these dangerous substances.

As the land becomes less fertile farmers rely on more and more chemical **fertilizers** to provide the nutrients the high-yielding seeds need to grow. Like the pesticides, fertilizers contaminate both the air and water. Pesticides and fertilizers seep into the ground water, the source of water that lies underground. When ground water is the only source of water, people, animals, and crops are faced with using polluted water. Much of the nitrogen in fertilizers is converted to nitrous oxide in the soil and escapes into the air where it contributes to acid rain.

Other dangers associated with this growing use of large amounts of pesticides and chemical fertilizers include increased harmful residues in the food we eat and pests becoming resistant to one pesticide or another.

Energy Consumption  ◆  The energy consumed in producing food also affects the environment. Energy is used at every phase of food production to

- Run farm machinery.
- Produce fertilizer and pesticides.
- Transport food to the processor.

*For the first time in the history of the world, every human being is now subjected to contact with dangerous chemicals, from the moment of conception until death.*
RACHEL CARSON

- Run machinery involved in processing.
- Produce packaging.
- Transport food to the distributor.
- Refrigerate food en route and in the store.
- Transport food to homes.
- Refrigerate and prepare food at home.

Such massive energy use has a profound impact on the environment. Most of the energy is derived from burning **fossil fuels**. Fossil fuels are the remains of ancient plants and animals that have been concentrated by heat and pressure over millions of years to form oil, gas, and coal. Once they are used up, it takes millions of years to replace them.

The burning of fossil fuels adds carbon dioxide to the atmosphere. This adds to the **greenhouse effect**. The greenhouse effect occurs naturally when the sun's rays penetrate the earth's surface and certain gases trap some of the earth's warmth. This is similar to how a greenhouse traps heat. However, the greenhouse effect gets *exaggerated* if the concentration of greenhouse gases, such as carbon dioxide, increases. Some scientists predict that the exaggerated greenhouse effect will lead to global warming. This would have a major impact on global food production. Some parts of the world would experience more drought due to the warmer temperatures. Other parts would experience flooding from a rise in the sea level from melting ice caps. This is a topic that is greatly debated among scientists.

One source of energy not derived from fossil fuels is hydro-electric power. However, damming rivers to create this power means much valuable land is flooded, causing extensive changes to the environment. There are alternative renewable energy sources. Solar power, wind power, and tidal power are three examples of energy sources being explored.

We have explored a few of the consequences of agribusiness:

- Displacement of people from the land and resulting poverty.
- Burdens borne by women.
- Alteration of the land that at worst leads to desertification.
- Potential of losing diversity in food crops.
- Environmental effects of chemical fertilizers and pesticides.
- Overuse of energy.

These consequences are interrelated, and you should continue to become aware of their implications, both for your own daily life and for the lives of others.

# FOOD CONSUMPTION

There are many misconceptions surrounding world hunger. Some people believe that it is because there are so many people and not enough food. This is not the case. There is enough food produced in the world to meet the nutritional needs of everyone. If the total world food supplies were divided equally, there would be plenty for everyone. Yet hundreds of millions of people worldwide, including thousands in Canada, go hungry. Food resources are not evenly distributed. Approximately 25 percent of the people consume 70 percent of the food. Food tends to go to the people who have the most money. Food that could feed people is also used to feed farm animals and pets.

Sometimes food is limited because of unexpected circumstances. A recurring drought can cause crop failure. A massive flood may wipe out a crop. An insect plague may consume the food or destroy the plants before they can produce. Civil war can interrupt the food supply. The resulting lack of food from these events is known as a **famine**. During this period people suffer because they are starving, with little or nothing to eat. While the conditions that cause famine are violent at the time, they are temporary.

The majority of hunger deaths are invisible. They are not caused by starvation. These deaths result from nutrition-related sicknesses and diseases. Often there is enough food, but people do not have enough money to buy it or land where they can grow their own. They get some food to eat but it is not enough or the right kind to meet the body's basic need for nourishment. They suffer from **chronic undernutrition**. This condition often lasts a lifetime. It slows the physical and mental development of children and leaves them more vulnerable to illnesses and diseases. Adults lose weight and become progressively weak. This hunger is not experienced equally. Because men are more likely to obtain paid work outside the home they are fed first. Young men are considered more likely to support the family so they get fed before women and girls. Thus, more women suffer from hunger than men, and in times of famine, women and girls may not eat at all.

Hunger and chronic undernutrition are much more widespread than famine but do not receive nearly as much attention because their effects are not as dramatic. Nonetheless, they cause more deaths each year than does famine.

*The war on hunger is everybody's business because it means a world of hunger and chaos in which none of us will be safe and in which individual liberty and security under the law could be wiped out. But the trouble is that everybody's business is nobody's clear responsibility.*
GEORGE McGOVERN

*Hunger is the most degrading of adversities; it demonstrates the inability of existing culture to satisfy the most fundamental human necessities, and it always implies society's guilt.*
JOSUE DE CASTRO

Emergency supplies being delivered in Somalia, Africa.

*One never notices what has been done; one can only see what remains to be done.*
MARIE CURIE

Although it can ease the immediate suffering, emergency food aid will not end hunger. Many argue that the goal should be universal food security. **Food security** means that all people, at all times, have access to enough nutritious food for an active, healthy life, and that this food is obtained in a manner that upholds basic human dignity. Food security addresses the root cause of hunger, the underlying inequities that deprive people, especially poor women, of economic opportunity and thus access to food.

When the goal is food security, aid money goes to reestablishing subsistence crops and promoting greater self-reliance. Aid is useful when it is used to meet the basic needs of the poor. Examples of useful aid would be providing people with access to land to grow food, access to clean, safe, drinking water to prevent disease, and access to health care and education. One way to ensure food security may be to continue trade but only in surplus goods after the basic need of the country has been met.

## TAKING ACTION

Agribusiness and international trade have a major impact on our lives and on the lives of people who are hungry. World hunger is a complex problem, and the solutions are not simple. However, by developing a global perspective on food production and food consumption, each of us can take action in small ways in our everyday lives.

A place to start is to consider five Rs — revalue, refuse, reduce, reuse, and recycle. They provide a useful guide to considering what we can do to create a better world for both ourselves and others.

**Revalue** ◆ Ask yourself what is important. What do you value? If you value justice and fairness, you will ensure that your actions do not contribute to the poverty of others, and you will investigate action that you can take to reduce poverty and hunger in the world.

Start by examining your own consumer habits. Do you really need everything you buy? Do you buy more of something than you need? How do your decisions affect the environment?

One alternative to consider is **sustainable agriculture**. This is agriculture that uses practices to ensure that food will continue to grow on the same land for future generations. One example of sustainable agriculture is **organic farming**. This is farming that uses local resources and practices that do not deplete the soil. Pollution of the land by chemical fertilizers and pesticides is avoided. The use of fossil fuels is kept to a minimum. The emphasis is on producing foods of high nutritional quality.

This may lead you to consider ethical shopping, or shopping for a better world. Ethical shoppers ask critical questions about the product before buying it.

- How is it transported? What are the environmental costs of that transportation?
- Does the company treat its workers in a fair and just manner? Or by buying this product could I be supporting the exploitation of other people?
- How much packaging is involved, and is it necessary?
- What ingredients, additives, and residues does it contain? Is it free of dangerous chemicals?
- What role has advertising played in my decision to purchase?

**Refuse** • Related to ethical shopping is the idea that you do not have to purchase or use food and related products that violate the principles you value. If you value fairness and you know that a certain company does not treat its workers fairly or that they are engaged in other activities that are harmful to people or the environment, then you can simply refuse to buy from them. This is called boycotting. It is also useful to inform the company in question that you are boycotting and explain your reasons for doing so.

If you value the environment, then consider the environmental costs of the products you are considering and refuse to buy those that have high environmental costs. This would include products with too much packaging, too much processing, and with high transportation and refrigeration costs.

If you value health, then refuse to buy products with questionable nutritional value and those that are possibly contaminated. Those produced closer to home are more likely to be fresher and more nutritious and less likely to be contaminated during all the steps of processing and transportation. Those produced by organic farmers are less likely to have chemical residues from fertilizers and pesticides.

Refusing also includes the products that you use to clean your home. Refuse those that are harmful to the environment. Choose instead non-polluting, non-toxic cleaners, such as vinegar, pure soap, baking soda, borax, washing soda, and ammonia.

*We are living beyond our means. As a people we have developed a lifestyle that is draining the earth of its priceless and irreplaceable resources without regard for the future of our children and people all around the world.*
MARGARET MEAD

*We have met the enemy and the enemy is us.*
POGO

Recycling is one way we can all take action. Name three ways you take action.

**Reduce** ◆ You cannot refuse buying things that you really need. However, you can consider packaging and waste. Approximately one-quarter of our food is wasted at the supermarket because consumers refuse to buy food that is not perfect. As well, food is wasted when it is not bought in the proper quantities. If too much is bought it can deteriorate before it is eaten. Food that is spoiled ends up in the garbage. Whenever possible reduce the amount of food wasted.

More money is spent on packaging than the farmers receive for growing the food. Most of that packaging, from drink boxes to tin cans, ends up in the garbage. Whenever possible reduce the waste accumulated in packaging. Try to purchase fewer foods that come in non-renewable, non-recyclable containers. Use your own containers. Carry a bag or knapsack and use it instead of accepting a new plastic bag from the store.

**Reuse** ◆ Reusing simply means using the same item over and over again. It means getting more out of the items you already have. When you cannot avoid purchasing products that come in containers or bags then reuse them. Plastic containers and glass jars can be used to store food. Bags can also be used for storage as well as for carrying lunches and holding garbage.

Reuse also includes repairing household and food preparation equipment when feasible. If you cannot reuse the item yourself, try donating it or trading it with someone who can use it.

Another example of reusing is taking containers with you when you shop at bulk food stores. Can you think of other examples?

**Recycle** ◆ Recycling involves reprocessing wastes into new products. It is not as environmentally sound as refusing, reducing, and reusing because the reprocessing often involves some pollution. However, using this form of recycling ensures that we get the most from our resources and that they do not take up space in landfills.

Many communities have Blue Boxes to collect recyclable materials such as newspaper, cardboard, glass, metal, and plastics. Other communities have depots for such materials.

You can also recycle food wastes at home by starting a compost. Composting is a method of turning kitchen wastes and yard wastes into a material that can be used as a garden nutrient in place of chemical fertilizer. Compost can also be used as a soil conditioner to make the soil darker, richer, and easier to work. As a plant protector, compost works to filter heavy metals from the air and soil. Another type of composting uses worms to eat food waste transforming it into manure, a soil additive that is rich in nutrients. **Vermicomposting** is the technical term for worm composting. The worms, red wrigglers, will eat food waste from vegetables, fruit, and grain.

## Think Globally, Act Locally

Think Globally, Act Locally • Adopting a global perspective on food means contributing to a system of food production and consumption that is fair and just for farmers, consumers, and the environment, both at home and around the world. When considering the problems of food production and consumption, the phrase "think globally, act locally" is used often. This means that we can take action on global problems, such as hunger, poverty, human rights, and the environment, in our local communities.

Thinking about the global problems of cash cropping can lead to producing your own food.

- Grow a vegetable in your yard or in patio containers.

- Plant a herb garden on your window sill.

- Start a school garden.

- Investigate community gardens in your locality.

Thinking about the global concern of the welfare and fair treatment of people and the environment can lead to local action in the supermarket, such as selecting products that:

- Are grown locally to support local farmers and avoid the environmental costs of transportation.

- Are lower on the food chain, that is foods that are not highly processed. Meat and poultry are considered higher on the food chain because vegetables have been fed to them.

- Have minimal packaging.

- Come from companies that have good labour practices and do not exploit their workers. Boycotting those that do not.

- Are least hazardous for cleaning.

In a world where there is so much to be done, I feel strongly impressed that there must be something for me to do.
DOROTHEA DIX

Thinking about the global scale of poverty and hunger can lead to action to reduce poverty and hunger where you live. You can:

• Volunteer at a soup kitchen or food bank.

• Donate time or money to local anti-poverty organizations.

• Investigate the causes of poverty in your community.

• Participate in annual World Food Day activities in October.

Once you begin thinking globally let your views be known. Write a letter to:

• The editor of your local newspaper.

• Companies whose policies are not environmentally sound.

• Your government representatives.

• Obtain information to keep informed.

*The world cannot be changed by one person, but it will take every person to change the world.*
MAURICE STRONG

# KEY TERMS

Use the words listed below to complete the following statements in your notebook.

cash crops
monocropping
composting
staple foods
intercropping
green revolution
ethical shopping
food security
desertification

1. _____ are those foods that are produced in large quantities and form the main part of the diet.

2. _____ are grown to provide money or income for the farm owner rather than feeding the people who cultivated the crops.

3. Trying to increase food production through scientific advances has been called the _____.

4. Producing only one crop is called _____.

5. _____ is when different crops are planted in alternating rows in the same field.

6. _____ is the term used to describe land that has been lost when farmland and pasture are turned into desert.

7. _____ means that all people, at all times, have access to enough nutritious food for an active, healthy life, and that this food is obtained in a manner that upholds human dignity.

8. _____, or shopping for a better world, leads shoppers to ask critical questions about a product before buying it.

9. _____ is a method of turning kitchen and yard wastes into material that can be used as a garden nutrient.

# FOCUS YOUR KNOWLEDGE

1. Explain how the green revolution has affected poor farmers.

2. Briefly discuss the main difference between developed and developing countries.

3. Explain the role of debt in today's farming operations.

4. List the human activity that can lead to desertification.

5. Outline the energy consumed in food production.

6. Briefly describe the causes and results of the greenhouse effect.

7. Explain the importance of food security.

**307**

## DEMONSTRATE YOUR KNOWLEDGE

1. Debate: Agribusiness is causing increased poverty for farmers in the developing countries.

2. Prepare a brief report on the effect of subsistence farming on women.

3. Chart the advantages and disadvantages of monocropping and intercropping.

4. Role play a salesperson from a company that produces pesticides or chemical fertilizers trying to convince a farmer to use the product.

5. Examine the packaging of foods stored in the laboratory. Discuss ways in which the packaging can be reduced, recycled, or reused.

## APPLY YOUR KNOWLEDGE

1. Brainstorm ways to reduce waste in the food laboratory and recycle and reuse products. Put the plan into action.

2. Prepare a concept map showing the effects of agribusiness.

3. Prepare a list of staple foods for Canada, Chile, Hungary, and Zambia. Choose a staple food that is similar for each country, such as rice or flour, and prepare a recipe for each country using that staple food.

4. Locate and read an article on the lives of women and children in the developing countries. Discuss your article with a partner.

5. Debate the ways in which advertising may influence the food you eat.

# Unit Overview

## ☀ REVIEW YOUR KNOWLEDGE

1. List the foods contributed to the Canadian culture by the First Nations peoples.
2. Explain the importance of maple trees to pioneer families in eastern Canada.
3. List one traditional meal for each of the countries in chapter 12.
4. Describe the major grain products for five different countries.
5. Explain the link between agribusiness and fewer food crops.
6. Explain why the majority of hunger deaths are not caused by starvation.
7. List the ways we can put into action our global concern about cash cropping, fair treatment of people, and the environment.

## ☀ EXTEND YOUR KNOWLEDGE

1. Interview a senior citizen to learn how food customs and patterns have changed since his or her childhood. Discuss the effect of transportation, geographic location, technology, and lifestyle.
2. Plan five main meals to reflect the foods of each Canadian region. Prepare one or more meals.
3. Evaluate several popular snack foods from different cultures for convenience, kilojoule content, taste, and nutritional value. (Some examples of snack foods are: cassava chips — Africa; curried potato fries — India; plantain chips — Colombia.)
4. Invite a representative from a non-governmental, international development agency or labour organization to speak to the class on global issues. Evaluate the information to determine any bias of the speaker.
5. Invite guest speakers from a local university, community college, government agency, or food company, who are doing research into food development, to your class. Ask about their current research, particular career paths, and their predictions for future food development.

# The Science of Food

Food provides us with satisfaction when we eat. But, what happens to food as it goes through our system? This is part of the field of study called nutrition. In chapter 14 you will learn how our bodies break down food and how the nutrients are put to use.

Health care is a major concern in Canada. Many people earn their living advising others how to choose food. Like all businesses, some are more responsible than others. How can you tell reliable information from misinformation? This unit will give you some guidelines.

In chapter 15 you will learn which foods and in what amounts are needed by specific populations of people. These groups range in age from young children to seniors and also include people with specific needs, such as athletes and vegetarians. Chapter 16 deals with specific health concerns and how food affects them. Making responsible food choices is something you deal with your entire life.

# How the Body Uses Food

## THE SCIENCE OF NUTRITION

Nutrition as a science is a new and emerging field of study about how the body functions and what nourishment it needs for maximum performance. The study of nutrition in the past was concerned with vitamin deficiency diseases, such as scurvy, rickets, pellagra, beri beri, and malnutrition. Study of these diseases and their possible causes eventually led to more knowledge of nutrients.

The diseases that began the research are now almost unknown in this country. With food more easily obtained than in earlier years, the main focus of nutrient research now is more frequently of conditions caused by an overindulgence in rich, processed food. Examples of some current health concerns are obesity, heart disease, and cancer.

New treatments for life-threatening illnesses and the results of research studies are announced by scientists regularly. Knowledge about how your body works and the nutrients that keep it functioning will help you understand some of these new developments and how they might affect you. Good food choices will help you be healthy and energetic and get the most out of life.

## THE NUTRIENTS

Chapters 1 and 2 gave guidelines for making healthy food choices using *Canada's Food Guide to Healthy Eating*. You were introduced to the four food groups and the nutrients they provide. This section summarizes the essential nutrients and describes their importance to a healthy functioning body. These nutrients are:

- Carbohydrates
- Protein
- Fat
- Vitamins
- Minerals
- Water
- Fibre

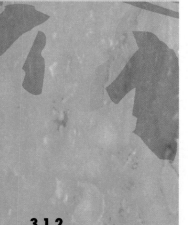

# Carbohydrates

Carbohydrates • **Carbohydrates** include sugars, starches, and fibre and are the body's prime source of energy. They are found mainly in cereal grains and vegetables and fruit. Carbohydrates are the cheapest and most easily digested form of fuel. They are often classified according to their composition — simple and complex.

Giving your body the nutrients it needs is essential to living an active, healthy life.

- **Simple carbohydrates** are all sugars. Some of them are sucrose (cane or beet sugar), lactose (milk sugar), and fructose (fruit sugar). The simplest form is glucose, the form in which carbohydrates are eventually absorbed and transported through the body.

    Simple carbohydrates are sometimes referred to as **disaccharides**, meaning two sugar molecules, and **monosaccharides**, meaning one sugar molecule. Disaccharides are a form of sugar such as sucrose, maltose, and lactose. Monosaccharides are the simplest sugars such as glucose, fructose, and galactose.

- **Complex carbohydrates** are made up of large molecules of simple carbohydrates joined together. Examples are starches, cellulose, glycogen, dextrins. These are digested into simpler forms before they are absorbed by the body for use. They are preferred for good health because they take longer to digest and help maintain a steady blood sugar level. This keeps your energy up for daily activities, and you do not feel tired. Complex molecules having several sugar molecules such as those found in starches and fibre, are sometimes called **polysaccharides**.

    Some complex carbohydrates, such as cellulose, cannot be digested by humans. They do, however, provide bulk to aid elimination.

# Protein

Protein • **Protein** is important for growth and repair of the body's cells and tissues. It is used to make hormones, enzymes, and antibodies. A secondary function is to provide energy. When there are not enough carbohydrates in the diet and fat stores are used up, protein from food is used for energy instead of for building and repair.

Proteins are made up of large numbers of units, called **amino acids**, that are linked together. During digestion, proteins are broken down into amino acids, which are absorbed through the intestinal wall. When the

## SOURCES AND FUNCTIONS OF NUTRIENTS

| Nutrients | Functions | Sources |
|---|---|---|
| Carbohydrates | — supplies energy<br>— spares protein<br>— assists in utilization of fats | Starches: breads, cereals, pastas, potatoes, corn.<br>Sugars: dried and canned fruits, sugars, syrups, jams, honey, molasses. |
| Proteins | — builds and repairs all types of body tissues<br>— regulates body processes<br>— forms antibodies to fight infection<br>— supplies energy | Complete: milk, cheese, eggs, meat, fish, poultry.<br>Incomplete: dried legumes (peas, beans, lentils), nuts, cereals, breads, vegetables. |
| Fats | — supplies energy<br>— transports vitamins A, D, E, K,<br>— protects and insulates body parts<br>— supplies the essential fatty acids | Fish, meat, salad oils and dressing, margarine, butter, whole milk, cream, cheddar cheese, ice cream. |
| Vitamin A | — normal growth and formation of skeleton and teeth<br>— helps eyes adjust to dim light<br>— resists infection by keeping skin and lining layer of body healthy | Dark green and yellow vegetables, yellow fruits, egg yolks, liver, butter, cream, whole milk, cheeses, fortified skim or 2% milk, fortified margarine. |
| Vitamin D | — assists calcium and phosphorus to be deposited in bones and teeth | Fish liver oils and vitamin D enriched milks, infant formulas, margarines. |
| Vitamin E | As an antioxidant:<br>— protects body's supplies of vitamins A and C<br>— maintains membrane health | Vegetable oils (corn and soybean), wheat germ, margarine, and whole-wheat bread. |
| Vitamin K | — normal clotting of blood | Green and yellow vegetables. Synthesized by intestinal bacteria. |
| Thiamin | — releases food energy from carbohydrates<br>— helps nerve, brain, and muscle function | Pork and pork products (including organ meats), dried legumes (peas, beans, lentils), whole-grain or enriched cereals, flours, bread, potatoes, and pastas. |
| Riboflavin | — releases energy to body cells during metabolism<br>— helps maintain a normal nervous system<br>— helps maintain a healthy lining of the nose, mouth, and digestive track | Milk and milk products (except butter), cheese, eggs, meats, (particularly organ meats), salmon, leafy green vegetables, enriched cereals, flours, breads, and pastas. |

| | | |
|---|---|---|
| Niacin | — helps obtain energy from carbohydrates<br>— maintains normal function of the gastro-intestinal tract<br>— normal function of the nervous system | Meat (particularly organ meats), fish, poultry, eggs, enriched cereals, breads and pastas, peas, potatoes, peanuts and peanut butter, milk and cheese. |
| B12 | — maintains healthy blood | Liver, kidney, milk, meat. |
| Folacin | — maintains healthy blood | Liver, asparagus, broccoli, lima beans, spinach, beets, bananas, orange juice, soya flour, cantaloupe. |
| Vitamin C (Ascorbic acid) | — maintains healthy teeth and gums<br>— maintains strong blood vessel walls<br>— helps to form and strengthen the cementing substance that holds body cells together<br>— fights infection | Orange, lemon, grapefruit, lime, tangarine and their juices, vitaminized apple juice, vitaminized fruit drinks, tomatoes and their juice, cantaloupe, strawberries, broccoli, cauliflower, Brussels sprouts, cabbage (green), baked white potatoes, turnips. |
| Iron | — builds hemoglobin in red blood cells to transport oxygen and carbon dioxide<br>— prevents nutritional anemia | Liver, red meats, egg yolks, dried beans, peas and lentils, green leafy vegetables, whole-grain and enriched cereals, precooked infant cereals, flours, breads, and pastas. |
| Calcium | — forms strong bones and teeth and maintains and repairs the skeleton<br>— maintains muscle tone, normal heart beat, and healthy nerve function<br>— aids normal blood clotting | Milk (any type), ice cream, cheese (any type), yogurt, canned salmon and sardines (with bones), broccoli, navy beans (dried), string beans, turnips, carrots, dried apricots, cantaloupe. |
| Phosphorus | — forms strong bones and teeth, and maintains and repairs the skeleton<br>— regulates energy release<br>— helps body produce energy and use nutrients | Meat, fish, poultry, eggs, nuts, milk, cheese. |
| Zinc | — builds protein<br>— helps in wound healing | Seafood, meats, eggs, milk, and whole grains. |

SOURCE: Adapted from *Management and Foods*

body needs to build or repair human tissue, it draws from the pool of absorbed amino acids.

Different proteins contain different forms of amino acids. They can be divided into two types:

- **Essential amino acids** cannot be manufactured by the body so they must come from the food you eat. When all of these essential amino acids occur together in a food the protein is called a **complete protein**. Complete proteins are found in animal foods.

  Some essential amino acids are found in plants. However, plant protein does not contain all of them together in the correct proportion for growth. Proteins that are missing one or more of the essential amino acids are called **incomplete proteins**.

- **Non-essential amino acids** are those that can be manufactured by the body if they are not supplied in sufficient amounts in the food you eat.

Which of these foods contain complete proteins? Which of these foods contain incomplete proteins?

For more detail on proteins refer to page 347, Food for Vegetarians.

Fat • Fats provide heat and energy to the body and support certain organs, for example, the kidneys and the eyes. Some valuable vitamins, A, D, E, and K, are fat-soluble and are found in the fat in food. Fat is also needed for the formation of covers around your nerves, sweat glands in your skin, cholesterol, and steroid hormones. However, when fat is eaten in excess of the amount required for body functioning it is stored as fatty layers in the body.

There are two types of fat — animal fat and vegetable fat.

- **Animal fat** is found in animal products, such as milk, cheese, butter, eggs, and meat. It is also found in oily fish, such as herring, cod, and halibut. All animal sources of protein contain some animal fat. Animal fats are usually solid at room temperature. Lard for cooking is made from animal fat.

- **Vegetable fat** is found in plant foods and products made from them, such as oil. It is usually liquid at room temperature because it is made up of unsaturated **fatty acids** and **glycerol**.

  Fats can be saturated or unsaturated. **Saturated fats**, from animal sources, are usually solid at room temperature and contain **cholesterol**.

For more information on cholesterol see pages 358–359. **Unsaturated fats**, which include **monounsaturated** and **polyunsaturated fats**, come from vegetable sources. They are usually liquid at room temperature and contain no cholesterol.

Unsaturated fats, called oils, can be changed to saturated fats by a process known as **hydrogenation**. This process changes liquid oils to more solid products. Hydrogenation is used in the production of shortening, most margarines, and other foods. The new saturated fat formed this way takes on the properties of animal fat.

| Fat Type | Fat Form | Food Sources |
|---|---|---|
| Monounsaturated | Liquid at room temperature | Olive oil, canola oil, peanut oil, peanuts, peanut butter, avocados |
| Polyunsaturated | Liquid at room temperature | Sunflower oil, safflower oil, corn oil, soybean oil, fish, almonds, pecans |
| Saturated | Usually solid at room temperature | Butter, lard, coconut oil, hydrogenated vegetable oil and shortening, palm oil, meat, poultry, dairy products, cheese, chocolate, egg yolks |

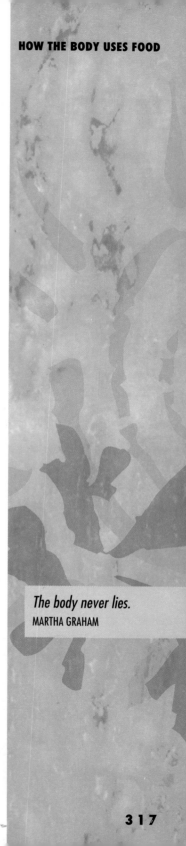

*The body never lies.*
MARTHA GRAHAM

**Vitamins** ◆ **Vitamins** are chemical compounds that are essential for health. As a group they have two main functions — prevention of disease and regulation of body processes. Individually, each vitamin performs specific functions in the body. Vitamins are divided into two main groups based on their solubility. Some are soluble in water and others are found in fat. Vitamins are found in a wide variety of foods.

**Fat-Soluble Vitamins** ◆ **Fat-soluble vitamins** means that these vitamins are found in the fat in food. They are vitamins A, D, E, and K. These vitamins are not easily lost or destroyed during the cooking of food. When your body obtains more than it can use, these vitamins are stored in the body's fat. Taking supplements of vitamins A, D, E, and K is not recommended.

Pumpkin and squash contain vitamin A. What foods do you eat that contain vitamin A?

Extreme vitamin D deficiency causes rickets. This disease most commonly develops in infants and young children during their rapid period of growth and results in stunted growth and deformed bones.

Excessive amounts can build up in the body because extra fat-soluble vitamins cannot be excreted in the urine.

*Vitamin A* ◆ Vitamin A helps the retina of the eye adjust to dim light so that it is possible to see under varying light conditions. Vitamin A is sometimes known as the anti-infection vitamin because it helps you resist infections by keeping the lining of the mouth, nose, throat, and digestive tract healthy. It also keeps the skin healthy and promotes growth.

Vitamin A is found in foods such as egg yolk, fish oils, milk and cheese, fortified margarine, and a wide assortment of dark green vegetables and deep yellow vegetables and fruit.

*Vitamin D* ◆ Vitamin D helps the body use calcium and phosphorus and is therefore needed for healthy, strong bones and teeth. Natural foods, except for fish liver oils, are poor vitamin D sources. For this reason all milk, milk products, margarine, and infant formulas sold in Canada are enriched with vitamin D. Sometimes referred to as the "sunshine vitamin," vitamin D can be manufactured in the body by the action of the ultraviolet rays of the sun.

*Vitamin E* ◆ The main function of vitamin E is to prevent oxygen from destroying the polyunsaturated fats in your body. Vitamin E also helps form red blood cells and maintain the health of moist membranes. Sources of vitamin E include vegetable oils, wheat germ, whole-wheat products, peanuts, and green leafy vegetables.

*Vitamin K* ◆ Vitamin K helps normal clotting of the blood. Most people get enough vitamin K because it can be manufactured in the body by bacteria that are naturally found in the intestine. Food sources are yellow fruits and yellow and leafy green vegetables.

## Water–Soluble Vitamins

◆ **Water-soluble vitamins** are not stored in large amounts in the body. Overdosing on water-soluble vitamins is not a problem because excess quantities are excreted in the urine. Therefore, it is important that enough of these vitamins are provided daily. Water-soluble vitamins are those of the B complex family (thiamin, riboflavin, niacin, B12, folacin, and others) and vitamin C.

*Thiamin* ✦ Thiamin, also known as B1, helps the body use carbohydrates for energy, and it allows the brain, nerves, and muscles to function. Sources include egg yolk, legumes, nuts, whole-grain bread and cereal products, and meat, especially pork and organ meats.

*Riboflavin* ✦ Riboflavin, sometimes known as B2, is important to help break down carbohydrates, proteins, and fats so the body can use energy released from the food. Riboflavin also helps maintain healthy mucous membranes. These are the moist linings inside the body, for example, mouth, nasal passages, and digestive tract, that allow food and body liquids to pass easily. It is important for healthy functioning of the nervous system. Riboflavin is found in leafy green vegetables, milk and milk products, eggs, organ meats, and enriched cereals and bread products.

*Niacin* ✦ Niacin is important for releasing energy to the cells. It helps with growth and reproduction and is necessary for the normal functioning of the gastrointestinal tract and the nervous system. Niacin can be found in eggs, fish, meats, especially organ meats, peanuts, enriched and whole-grain bread products and cereals.

*Folacin* ✦ Folacin helps make collagen and keep it strong. **Collagen** is a protein that is the main support of all cells in the body: bones, teeth, skin, tendons. Folacin also helps form strong **capillaries** that will not bruise easily when you bump into things.

Although other B vitamins are less well known, they all have an important role to play. Readers need to become well-informed consumers who

Nuts are a good source of thiamin. Try to name all the kinds of nuts in this photograph.

A severe deficiency of niacin causes a condition known as pellagra. The symptoms of pellagra are rough and cracked skin, and poor functioning of the gastrointestinal and nervous systems.

Which of these fruits are citrus fruits?

Scurvy is a disease that results when the body does not regularly obtain enough vitamin C. Without vitamin C the body's resistance to infection is reduced, and tissues around the teeth swell and the teeth become loose.

Osteoporosis is a disorder that causes bones to become thin, brittle, and easily broken. The disease is preventable and is directly related to the amount of calcium present in the foods eaten over a long period of time beginning in childhood.

understand food label information. Here are the names of other B vitamins often found on labels: pyridoxine (vitamin B6), vitamin B12, pantothenic acid, biotin.

*Vitamin C* ◆ Vitamin C is also known as ascorbic acid. It strengthens blood capillaries, forms red blood cells, builds antibodies to fight infection, maintains healthy connective tissue, and develops and maintains healthy bones. The best sources are citrus fruit, such as oranges, grapefruit, lemons, as well as other fresh fruit, especially some berries, and green vegetables.

Vitamin C is very unstable so careful handling and preparation of food containing vitamin C is important in maintaining its vitamin C content. For example, when vegetables and fruit become wilted by warmth and exposure to air, their vitamin C content is also reduced. Because it is so easily dissolved in water, proper cooking methods are critical. Use a small amount of water, cook quickly, and eat as soon as the food is cooked.

Minerals ◆ As a group, mineral elements have two main functions. **Minerals** are a part of the body's tissues (4 percent of body mass) and act as a regulator of body functions. The exact role and daily requirement of many minerals are not yet known. However, the three most important minerals are calcium, phosphorus, and iron. When the recommended amounts of these minerals are eaten in food every day, the body's requirement of other minerals are usually met.

*Calcium* ◆ Calcium, in connection with phosphorus and vitamin D, is essential for the maintenance and formation of hard bones and teeth. For this reason it is essential that people of all ages receive an adequate calcium supply. Calcium is also required to maintain normal muscle tone, nerve function, and to aid in blood coagulation.

The amount of calcium you need daily can be obtained by consuming a minimum of two servings of milk and milk products (at least three servings for youths or pregnant women). You also need two servings of other high-quality calcium foods daily. Green vegetables, such as broccoli and spinach, sardines, canned salmon with bones, baked beans, and almonds, are good sources of calcium.

*Phosphorus* ✦ Phosphorus works with calcium and vitamin D to form and maintain healthy bones and teeth. It is also very important in energy metabolism. Because calcium and phosphorus are found together almost always, the importance of phosphorus as an essential nutrient is often overlooked. When there is sufficient calcium in your diet, there is likely to be enough phosphorus in the diet as well. Unless you consume milk products or some animal proteins, it will be difficult for you to get the phosphorus you need.

A healthy smile comes from eating foods that contain phosphorus.

*Iron* ✦ Iron is essential for the formation of **hemoglobin** in the red blood cells. Iron enables the blood to transport oxygen and carbon dioxide throughout the body. When there is insufficient iron the size of red blood cells is reduced and therefore the amount of oxygen carried by the blood is less.

Iron is present in many forms in food. It is found in liver, kidney, red meat, egg yolk, some shellfish, whole-grain products, dried legumes, and green vegetables, such as broccoli, Brussels sprouts, beans, asparagus, and beet greens. The iron in animal products, such as meat and seafood, is absorbed more efficiently by the body than the iron in plants, such as spinach.

Iron from plants is absorbed more fully when eaten with a vitamin C rich food. Careful shoppers need to look for words such as "ferrous" or "reduced iron" on labels, which means that the iron is absorbed more easily by the body than in other forms.

*Zinc* ✦ The importance of zinc has been recognized more recently. Zinc is involved in protein building and is associated with the hormone, insulin. It has been found to play a role in wound healing. Sources are meats, milk, egg yolks, seafood, and whole grains.

Ongoing research has demonstrated the importance of trace elements. They are found in very small amounts in foods. Therefore, it is very important to eat a wide variety of foods balanced from the four food groups. Because processing removes some valuable nutrients, it is recommended that unprocessed foods form the major part of your meals.

Anaemia is the condition that results when the body does not have enough iron to make the hemoglobin in the red blood cells. The person affected may tire easily, be pale and listless. This is because the blood is unable to carry enough oxygen for the person to be energetic.

Water • Water makes up about 60 percent of your body mass. For this reason water plays a very important role in most body functions.

• Water provides the moist environment that is required by all living cells in the body.

• Water is a major component of blood and tissue fluid. It transports substances like vitamins to where they will be used.

• Water takes part in all the chemical reactions that occur inside and outside the body cells.

• Water dilutes and moistens food.

• Water assists in the regulation of body temperature by forming perspiration, which evaporates off the skin and cools the body.

• Water dilutes waste products and toxic substances in the body.

• Water contributes to the formation of urine and feces.

Large amounts of water are lost each day in urine and perspiration. Drinking at least eight glasses of fluids daily, preferably water, is recommended. Foods, especially vegetables, fruit, and milk, provide additional water sources. Liquid substances containing caffeine, such as coffee, tea, or cola drinks, should not be counted in the eight cups of fluids because they actually help to remove fluids from the body tissues.

Fibre • **Fibre** is the indigestible part of the food. Although it is not considered to be a nutrient because it is not metabolized, fibre is necessary for many body functions.

• It gives bulk to the diet and helps to satisfy the appetite.

• It stimulates muscular activity, called **peristalsis**, of the digestive tract.

• It stimulates bowel movement.

• It is associated with prevention of certain diseases and gastrointestinal disorders.

Foods containing fibre are mostly whole-grain products and vegetables and fruit. Most processed foods have a low fibre content.

## Recommended Daily Intakes

The "Recommended Daily Intakes (RDI)," for vitamins and minerals, are reference standards for nutrition labelling. The RDI's are based on the "Recommended Nutrient Intakes (RNI)" for Canadians, established by Health and Welfare Canada.

| Nutrient | Unit | RDI (persons 2 years of age and older) |
|----------|------|----------------------------------------|
| Vitamin A | (RE) | 1000 |
| Vitamin D | (mcg) | 5 |
| Vitamin E | (mg) | 10 |
| Vitamin C | (mg) | 60 |
| Thiamin | (mg) | 1.3 |
| Riboflavin | (mg) | 1.6 |
| Niacin | (NE) | 23 |
| Vitamin B6 | (mg) | 1.8 |
| Folacin | (mcg) | 220 |
| Vitamin B12 | (mcg) | 2 |
| Pantothenate | (mg) | 7 |
| Calcium | (mg) | 1100 |
| Phosphorus | (mg) | 1100 |
| Magnesium | (mg) | 250 |
| Iron | (mg) | 14 |
| Zinc | (mg) | 9 |
| Iodide | (mcg) | 160 |

# THE DIGESTIVE PROCESS

The food you eat contains the nutrients your body needs for growth, maintenance, and energy. The nutrients in what you eat are unlocked and made available to your body by the digestive process.

This process occurs in the **digestive tract**. The digestive tract is also known as the **alimentary canal** or **gastrointestinal tract** and is composed of the mouth, esophagus, stomach, small intestine, and large intestine. The process has three distinct, but continuous, stages. They are **digestion**, **absorption**, and **metabolism**.

Digestion refers to the processes by which the foods you have eaten are changed into their simplest forms. The flow of digestive juices, including saliva, gastric juice, and pancreatic juices, add liquid and enzymes that break complex nutrients into simpler parts. Eventually the nutrients are absorbed in the latter part of the intestinal tract.

Absorption is the passage of the products of digestion through the walls of the intestinal tract into the circulatory system. The body's circulatory system carries the nutrients to cells throughout the body. The chemical process that takes place within the cells, when these nutrients are used by the body, is called metabolism.

Digestion ◆ The process of digestion begins in the mouth. The teeth chew the food, cutting and grinding it into small pieces. The movements of the tongue and mouth muscles mix the food with the juices, or **saliva**, secreted by the salivary glands. The secretion of saliva is a reflex action in response to the stimulus of taste, sight, and smell. These juices moisten the food to allow the soft ball of food, or **bolus**, to pass easily down the **esophagus** or gullet to the stomach.

The **stomach** is a pear-shaped, extremely muscular organ which expands to contain the amount of food eaten. The powerful muscles in the walls of the stomach exert further churning action on the food. This churning mixes the food with the **gastric juices**, which are protein splitting enzymes, and reduces the bolus to a more liquid form known as **chyme**. **Enzymes** are chemical substances that make chemical changes in the substances that they contact.

The flow of gastric juices into the stomach is stimulated by the chemical nature of the food passing into it and also by psychological factors. Worry, excitement, anger, and unpleasant sights and odours stop the flow of gastric juices and hinder digestion.

Food generally remains in the stomach from three to five hours, but this varies with the kinds of foods eaten. Carbohydrate foods tend to leave the stomach sooner than protein foods. Protein foods leave more quickly

A condition known as ulcers can occur in the stomach, duodenum, or small intestine. Ulcers cause pain or discomfort in the pit of the stomach. They may sometimes bleed, noted by blood in the stool, or perforate — eat through the stomach. Spicy foods, extremely hot foods, caffeine, and alcohol all irritate the mucous membrane lining the stomach. Other factors are heredity, nervous strain, poor circulation, and a generally bad diet. Stomach ulcers are treated with alkaline drugs and careful diet. Sometimes ulcers require surgery.

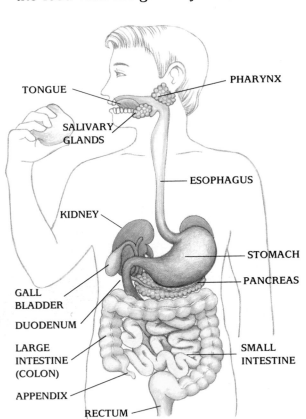

TONGUE

SALIVARY GLANDS

PHARYNX

ESOPHAGUS

KIDNEY

STOMACH

PANCREAS

GALL BLADDER

DUODENUM

LARGE INTESTINE (COLON)

SMALL INTESTINE

APPENDIX

RECTUM

than high-fat content meals. This explains why a meal of protein and fat foods leaves one feeling full and satisfied. However, a snack of easy to digest carbohydrates leaves you feeling hungry again soon.

Small quantities of chyme gradually leave the stomach and enter the **duodenum** (small intestine). Once the acid mixture of partially digested food reaches the alkaline environment of the small intestine, pancreatic juices from the **pancreas** and **bile** from the liver begin to flow. These fluids act on fat, digesting it to the simpler forms of fatty acids and glycerol. Extra bile is stored in the **gall bladder**.

From the glands within the lining walls of the intestine itself, intestinal juices pour onto the chyme as it passes further down the small intestine. Some of these juices complete the final breakdown of all proteins to amino acids. Here, also in the intestine, the double sugars, or disaccharides, are converted to monosaccharides or single sugars of glucose, fructose, and galactose.

The food, or **chyle** as it is now called, is in a very liquid state and is moved along the length of the small intestine by peristalsis. Peristalsis is a wavelike action of the digestive tract that is accomplished by the alternate contraction and relaxation of the muscles within the intestinal walls. All of the chyle that is digestible has been broken down into substances that are simple and liquid enough to pass through the intestinal wall and into the surrounding blood capillaries and **lacteals** of the lymph system. Food that was eaten is now inside the blood or lymph and in a form that can be used by the body.

## Absorption

Absorption into the blood or lymph systems takes place mostly in the small intestine. Within the mucous lining of the intestinal walls are large folds with tiny, hairlike projections called **villi**. These folds exist to give the intestine a large surface area where the digested materials

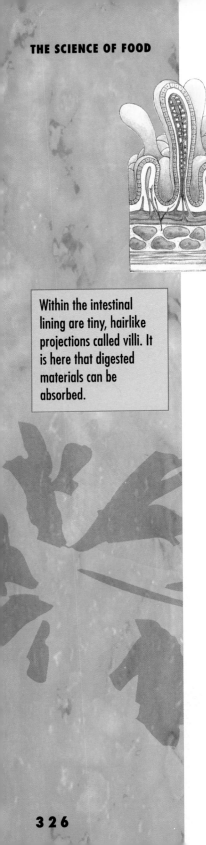

Within the intestinal lining are tiny, hairlike projections called villi. It is here that digested materials can be absorbed.

can be absorbed. Once absorbed into the body's circulation system, nutrients are transported to the part of the body where they will be used.

Each villus is provided with a small lymph vessel called a lacteal and a network of capillary blood vessels. Absorption occurs when these villi are surrounded by chyle containing the digested nutrients in a liquid form.

**Glucose** and amino acids move into the capillaries in the villi and are transported to the liver. Both eventually leave the liver and enter the general circulation system, which takes them to the tissues and organs of the body where they will be used. Fatty acids and glycerol are absorbed in the same way into the walls of the small intestine.

Some minerals, such as sodium and potassium, along with water-soluble vitamins B and C , none of which require digestion, are absorbed from the stomach. For the remaining water-soluble vitamins and all fat-soluble vitamins, absorption takes place in the small intestine. The minerals iron, calcium, and phosphorus are also absorbed in the small intestine.

Excess water-soluble vitamins cannot be stored in the body so they are removed by the **kidneys** and leave the body during urination. Similarly, unusable calcium and excess iron are removed from the body in the feces during a bowel movement.

By the time the food mass reaches the large intestine, all the digestible food has been removed. The material left is mostly fibre and water. Fibre, a starchlike carbohydrate present in bulky vegetable and fruit tissues and in cereal grains, cannot be digested by humans. It is, however, important in the digestive process. It provides bulk, which aids in removing residue materials.

Metabolism • Metabolism refers to the chemical processes that take place within all cells to build tissue or release energy. It is in your cells that the food choices you have made meet their real test. New tissues will be formed during growth, others replaced during maintenance, and your energy needs will then be met if you have supplied your body with all the nutrients it needs.

Glucose in the blood stream, called blood sugar, is your instant available energy supply. It makes your muscles work. As the fuel in the tank of a car makes the motor work, your body's blood sugar level makes it possible for your muscles and organs to do work.

The glucose level, which is normally stable, is controlled by a hormone called **insulin**, secreted by the pancreas. Only a small amount of sugar is stored in the body in the form of animal starch or **glycogen**. Excess glucose can be changed and stored as body fat. This is a more concentrated fuel reserve.

Fat, as well as glucose, is used to carry on the work of the muscles and internal organs of the body. When not needed immediately, fat is stored as body fat. It can later be returned to the blood stream and used as required by the tissues. Since both carbohydrates and proteins can be converted into fat in the body, all foods are a potential source of body fat. About half of body fat is stored directly under the skin; the other half serves as a protective cushion for internal organs, such as the heart and kidneys.

The breakdown of fat in the body, or **oxidation**, is a complicated process. When completely oxidized for energy, fat yields carbon dioxide and water as waste by-products.

Amino acids are the essential compounds for the building of body tissues. When new tissues and organs need to be built or replaced, the body can select from the variety of amino acids present in the blood. Amino acids act as the pool of building blocks, or raw material, from which the body can choose what it needs. Vitamins play an important role in enzymes that help all the metabolism activities occur to keep your body healthy and renewed. But the body needs a constant supply of nutrients to draw upon for its metabolic needs. By following *Canada's Food Guide to Healthy Eating* you will eat a good variety of nutrients to provide the building blocks your body requires.

If your dietary intake of fats and carbohydrates is poorly balanced and there is inadequate carbohydrate, a state known as ketosis results. Some carbohydrate-restricted, high-protein, mass-reducing diets result in this dangerous condition. A balanced diet will include foods from each of the four food groups.

## KEY TERMS

Use the words listed below to complete the following statements in your notebook.

chyle
digestive tract
saturated
glucose
complex carbohydrates

esophagus
amino acids
hydrogenated
duodenum

1. Starches and fibre are two examples of _____.

2. Proteins are made up of _____.

3. Fat from animal sources is _____.

4. When vegetable fat is _____ it becomes solid like margarine and shortening.

5. The mouth, stomach, and intestines are part of the _____.

6. Another name for the _____ is the gullet.

7. The _____ is also known as the small intestine.

8. Food in the liquid state in the intestines is called _____.

9. _____ is an instant source of energy in the blood stream.

## FOCUS YOUR KNOWLEDGE

1. Briefly describe three vitamin deficiency diseases.

2. Identify the two types of carbohydrates and provide examples of each.

3. Explain the difference between essential and non-essential amino acids.

4. List three examples each of animal fat and vegetable fat.

5. What are the two main functions of minerals?

6. Explain why water is important in processing food in the body.

7. Briefly describe what happens in digestion.

8. What is the function of insulin?

## DEMONSTRATE YOUR KNOWLEDGE

1. Plan a day's meals for yourself that include essential nutrients. Prepare a chart showing which nutrients are contained in the foods.
2. Examine a number of processed food products that contain sugar. Determine whether the sugars are disaccharides or monosaccharides.
3. Prepare a chart of fat-soluble and water-soluble vitamin sources.
4. Plan five high calcium snacks for a teen. Prepare one of the snacks.

## APPLY YOUR KNOWLEDGE

1. Locate a recent article on nutrition that interests you. Summarize it in your own words and share the information with the class.
2. Choose a nutrient from those listed in this chapter and prepare a poster showing excellent sources of that nutrient.
3. Record the fats you ate in one day. Chart the source under the headings saturated or unsaturated. Include the approximate amounts you ate, for example, salad dressing — 15 mL.
4. Prepare a concept map showing the process of digestion or absorption.
5. With a partner, each locate and read an article that explores the interrelationship of nutrients in the process of metabolism. Identify the key points in your article. Compare them with your partner's key points. Account for any differences.

# Making Healthy Food Choices

## SOURCES OF NUTRITION INFORMATION

Nutrition information is found in many different locations and forms. Magazines, books, television, radio, newspapers, food labels, and health professionals all offer thoughts on the best eating strategy to achieve maximum health. It is important for your health that the information on which you base your food choices be correct.

To evaluate the accuracy of information you might need, consider what is known about the author or speaker. The fact that a person is speaking on the subject or has written a book does not necessarily indicate any qualifications on the topic. Often it is difficult to distinguish dependable informants from less reliable ones. As with obtaining any goods or services, the caution of "buyer beware" applies with nutrition information also. These are some considerations:

- Does the person hold a recognized degree from an approved institution? Some institutions issue degrees that may be purchased by mail, while others grant honorary degrees based on life experiences or individual work in the field.

- What affiliations does the person hold or has she or he held in the past? Is the person a member of a recognized, nationally based association, such as a Dietetic Association, Nutrition Society, Home Economics Association, or Medical Association? Even though a group is well known it is still worth researching its credibility.

- Is the person a qualified scientist? Scientific background does not ensure reliability, but it can be an indicator. Some journalists have made it their business to present well-researched information.

- Is the person qualified? Anyone can attach the title "nutritionist" to his or her name because the word is neither registered nor protected. In several provinces and in the United States, qualified dietitians may use the letters R.D. or R.D.N., for registered dietitian, after their names. Similarly, in some provinces home economists may use the letters P.H.E. for professional home economist, as well as the degree code after their name. These people are reliable sources.

- Is the reference material tested by research and supported by publication in recognized scientific journals? Reliable writers and speakers will make claims on the basis of research done. They will refer openly to unanswered questions and conflicting research or anecdotal evidence as well.

When considering written material it is also helpful to consider what is known about the publisher or sponsoring group. A reputable publisher will have the manuscript confirmed by several experts on the topic before the printing stage begins. This helps ensure that inaccuracies and misinformation are eliminated. Less reputable publishers may not discourage authors from exaggerating issues with the use of descriptive words such as "miraculous," "life-saving," "amazing," "revolutionary."

A group sponsoring a speaker's visit to the area may be doing so for the best of reasons. On the other hand, it may have a vested interest in the sale or promotion of a certain product or service. To a casual observer it is not always evident that the speaker is also interested in selling a recent book, a weight loss program or preparation, video or audio tapes, or nutrient supplements. Valid information may be presented orally or in written form, but the best advice is to be suspicious and learn all the details first.

Is a speaker who draws a large crowd always a reliable source?

Evaluating Nutrition-Related Advertising ◆ A wise consumer will be suspect of the validity of information provided by advertisements, but especially those related to nutrition. Ask yourself these questions:

- Is it only *implied* that the advertised product is nutritious?
- What misleading methods are being used to convey the message?
- Does the advertisement tell the whole story?

Sources of Reliable Information ◆ A student has many sources available for securing reliable nutrition information. A first stop, after your foods teacher, may well be the school nurse or your doctor. Public health

nurses provide an important link between information on general wellness and more specifically on good nutrition information. Public health nurses and nutritionists can also provide further references. Your doctor should know your health history, which may be helpful. He or she may not have all the detail on food needs that a nutritionist would, but will know where to send you to learn what you need to know.

Here is a short list of places that have reliable information.

1. Community Health Department, Local Health Unit, and Public Health Dietitian — Dietitians here have all kinds of information at their disposal and only credible sources are allowed into their files. Some communities have a Dial-A-Dietitian service that provides answers to your questions by telephone. Check the telephone directory.

2. Community Hospital Dietetic Department — Although staff may be very busy with hospital patients, they will usually offer appointments to out-of-hospital persons. They are especially capable in giving help with special diets.

3. Health and Welfare Canada publications — These are widely available in government offices and health or medical centres. They are provided by the federal government and based on *Canada's Food Guide to Healthy Eating*. They are easy to understand and allow you to compile your personal reference file at no cost.

4. Public Library — Ask the librarian for help in the reference section to find where recognized scientists will be listed. Accredited universities and associations are catalogued in libraries as well. In this way you can confirm the reliability of any author.

## Less Reliable Sources of Information ◆ It is also a good idea to be aware of sources of information that may be unreliable. These are possibilities:

1. Health food stores have been found to be inconsistent in their approach. Some try very hard to distribute only reliable information; others are mainly concerned with selling products. Compare what you are told there with information from reliable sources.

2. Books written by authors who do not give references or footnotes are questionable.

3. Friends who have no nutrition-related credentials may mean well, but you should conduct further research in approved areas to confirm their information.

# FOOD CHOICES OF SPECIFIC POPULATIONS

## Food for Young Children

Have you ever had to make dinner for a young child? Is serving meals to a younger sibling part of your daily responsibility? Earning spending money by caring for children sometimes involves preparing suitable food for them. This section provides general information and helpful hints for those students faced with the responsibility of feeding children.

A baby's need to be held has now been well documented through studies of groups of children over long periods of time. Babies who have been lovingly handled regularly were found to develop normally. Tiny babies have special handling needs. They need to be held close to provide a healthy sense of security. Proper holding is an essential part of the feeding routine and is an important technique to be learned by any caregiver.

Children need a daily routine. Generally, they are happiest when they eat meals and snacks at about the same time each day. Arranging for a "quiet time" by providing a story or music just before the meal may help calm the child and help him or her focus on eating.

Food habits are learned. We are not born with the ability to choose well-balanced meals. Children must be guided in appropriate food selection by their caregivers. You have an important role to play in shaping the eating patterns and habits of the children you assist at mealtime.

A key factor in establishing food habits is appreciating the division of responsibility in feeding. The *caregiver* is responsible for *what* the child is offered to eat and for the physical and emotional setting in which it is offered. The *child* is responsible for the decision of whether or not to eat and *how much*.

Children eat smaller servings than adults, but they usually need to eat more often. Therefore, good snack choices are important. Because eating patterns are established so very early, a poor snack habit can lead to an obese adult. Similarly enforcing a "clean plate" policy can contribute to obesity as well as other eating problems later in life.

Involve children in *choosing* what and how much they will eat. Teach them the food groups, then let them select from what is available. Even at an early age food preferences can be respected while ensuring that each food group is represented. Experience shows that eventually preferences change and more foods will be accepted if the initial experience with a new food is not forced.

Holding a baby properly is one of the first things a mother must learn in caring for her baby.

REMINDER
· · · · · · · · · · · · · ·

*Canada's Food Guide to Healthy Eating* Recommends for Children:

Grain Products
    5 servings
Vegetables and Fruit
    5 servings
Milk Products
    2–3 servings
Meat and Alternatives
    2 servings

**333**

Involve children, as much as possible, in *food preparation*. This may make foods they do not especially like more acceptable. Even at a very young age a child can help in a number of ways. Here are some activities you can encourage them to do. Some will require more supervision than others.

- Put away the groceries.
- Get things from the refrigerator.
- Set the table.
- Wash or put away dishes.
- Stir pudding or other mixtures as they cook.
- Form cookies or other stiff doughs.
- Clean vegetables.

Prepare and serve food that is *easy* for the child *to manage*. Finger food is important for the child who is unable to handle utensils. When the child is ready to use a fork, firm foods can be cut up in advance. Caregivers also need to ensure that liquids, such as soup or hot chocolate, are not too hot.

Prepare interesting food *combinations*. Here are some specific examples, but there are many others.

- Choose a variety of *colour* combinations to make the meal more appealing; for example, yellow and green vegetables with white rice and brown meat.

- Choose various *shapes* to add interest; for example, coin-shaped carrots, meat strips, and round peas.

- Use assorted *flavours* of spicy, bland, sour, and sweet. Examples are chili with biscuits, fruit with custard sauce.

- Select different *textures* such as soft, chewy, smooth, and crisp. Favourite examples are celery stuffed with peanut butter, cream of mushroom soup with whole-wheat crackers.

Serve food in practical *dishes*. Use special utensils suited to the age of the child. Here are a few tips.

- For feeding first solids to the very young a long-handle spoon with a very small bowl for their tiny mouths works well.

> Children usually enjoy helping to prepare food. What kinds of activities in the kitchen did you do as a child?

- For first attempts at self-feeding a special well-rounded spoon with a short handle is best.
- When the child first drinks from a cup alone a covered cup with shaped outlet for drinking can be used.
- A plastic glass or drink cup is safer than glass.
- Metal or plastic plates or wooden bowls are serviceable and less breakable than china dishes.
- You may want to supply a straw for milk or juice.

Help children understand that *treats* come *after* the food needed for *growth* has been eaten and that they will not be served with every meal.
Try to make food fun for young people. Here are some ideas.

- Make blender drinks.
- Bake eggs in a muffin pan.
- Add cheese to hot dogs.
- Decorate open-faced sandwiches with vegetables or fruit.
- Pack a picnic snack.
- Serve lunch outside on a sunny day.
- Make the meal part of an outing to the park or beach.

Snack Suggestions • Because their active bodies require regular nourishment, and young stomachs are small, snacks are an important part of the daily food intake of young children. It is preferable to think of them as mini-meals rather than treats or additions to the meal pattern. This way choices will be balanced better and will be more likely to fulfill the daily requirements of *Canada's Food Guide to Healthy Eating*.

Healthy snacks can still be delicious. Just cut up some favourite vegetables and serve with a dip.

- Prepare a raw vegetable tray for children and adults. Arrange such vegetables as sliced cucumber, cauliflower, broccoli, carrots, turnip, celery, pod peas, and green beans on a large tray with a bowl of dip in the centre. Dip can be made simply by adding curry powder, dill seed, or garlic powder to taste, or half a package of dry onion soup mix to a small container (250 g) of plain yogurt.
- Many children enjoy the fresh taste and firm texture of frozen vegetables such as peas, beans, corn, or mixed vegetables. These can make good snacks.

- Using a divided unbreakable dish, put raisins in one section, peanuts in another, and dried apricots in the third. With a small scoop, children can serve themselves. Or put sliced apples, carrots, and celery sticks in the dish. All children enjoy "finger food."

- Raw peanuts, cashews, sunflower seeds, and other nuts and seeds purchased in bulk can be roasted at home. Place a layer on a cookie sheet and bake at 180°C for about 15 minutes, stirring once or twice. This reduces salt intake and is much cheaper than buying already roasted mixtures.

- Provide a handful of raisins or currants. Currants are not as sweet as raisins and cost about half as much. Try mixing them with nuts and sunflower seeds.

- Offer "ants on a log" made by sprinkling a few raisins or currants on cheese stuffed celery.

- Puffed wheat makes a good, non-sweet snack.

- A jug of water kept in the refrigerator encourages children and other family members to drink this inexpensive, sugar-free beverage.

Children's Parties • Most Canadian children love a birthday party. However, too often the party becomes a binge of eating, primarily of junk foods, leaving the participants feeling sick from too many sweets or from overeating in general. By placing more emphasis on the *fun* and less on the food, both nutritional and lifestyle objectives may be met.

A party can be planned around a sports activity or event, such as swimming, skating, hiking, bowling, or a baseball, hockey or football game. Or arrange the party around some other favourite activity such as a scavenger hunt, a picnic, a boat ride, a hay or sleigh ride, camping, or a trip to a circus, fair, or zoo. Depending on the activity it may be necessary to include fewer guests.

Even on a dull or cool day, a party in the park can be successful. Carry food in a picnic basket or ice chest or wrap it individually for each guest. The package could include an apple, dried banana chips or sports mix, perhaps a sandwich, and a frozen container of juice (it will thaw but stays cold longer).

At home you might serve macaroni and cheese casserole with assorted raw vegetables and biscuits cut into animal shapes. After a complete meal is served, the rich traditional birthday cake will not be as appealing and young guests will be less inclined to "stuff" themselves with dessert. Milk is an acceptable party beverage for most children as long as it is served very cold.

*Faith is the quality that enables you to eat black-berry jam on a picnic without looking to see whether the seeds move.*
ANONYMOUS

A good practice is to let the guests prepare part of the food themselves. When they are involved in fixing the food young people are more likely to eat it without waste. Preparing the food becomes part of the fun and eases the responsibility of entertaining the guests. Including foods from each of the four food groups will give the "Rainbow of Colour" recommended by *Canada's Food Guide to Healthy Eating*.

What kinds of foods do you remember eating at parties when you were a child? Were they healthy foods?

- Plan a "choosing meal" or snack with lots of "good for you" choices. Fix salad greens and then let guests add: various vegetables and fruit from separate bowls; cheese, cooked eggs, beans, or other protein foods; nuts and seeds; choice of dressings; warm biscuits or whole wheat buns.

- Let guests prepare "portrait sandwiches" using: sliced whole-wheat bread; peanut butter; cheese spread; carrot curls, parsley, coconut (for hair), nuts, raisins, apple slices, banana or pineapple chunks (for eyes, nose, and mouth). Cut the bread with a cookie cutter, glass, or knife into round, square, oval, or pear shapes. Spread with peanut butter or cheese. Create faces from bowls of food trimmings placed in the centre of the table.

- Older children can assemble tacos or make individual pizzas. If well supervised they may be able to barbecue their own meat patties or wieners. Kabobs can also be cooked on the barbecue grill. Let the guests make their own by placing favourite vegetables and fruit on a skewer alternately with small pieces of marinated meat.

- Summer party food might rely heavily on raw vegetables and cold meat and cheese nibbles with a spectacular tray of fresh fruit for dessert. To do this, carve a pineapple and arrange slices of cantaloupe, honeydew, watermelon, grapes, banana pieces, and any other fruit in season.

Party Favour Ideas ◆ The party "take home treat" seems to be well established in many communities. There are many interesting alternatives to candy and gum.

- Small bags with dried fruit, nuts, and seeds.

- Homemade nuts and bolts.

- Sugarless gum, fruit-flavoured, sugar-free "gummy bears."

- Popcorn, peanuts in the shell, sunflower seeds.

- A small plant for each guest to take home and tend.

- Small soaps, novelty notepads, jumbo erasers, notebook stickers, personal book labels.

- Place mats or name cards created especially for the party.

- Crafts that the guests have made (pine-cone owls, sea shell creatures, bookmarks, pipe cleaner or chenille crafts).

## Food for Athletes

The nutritional requirement of an athlete is not that different from the food needs of any other healthy individual. However, the more active person needs more food to supply the extra energy used during physical activity. The amount of extra kilojoules that an athlete requires will depend on his or her age, body size and composition, activity, and level of training. Theoretically, exercise does increase the need for vitamins and minerals that are involved with energy metabolism. However, if you are eating a balanced diet these needs will generally be met.

Depending on the type of activity being undertaken, the size and timing of meals and snacks may have to be altered from the typical meal pattern. Despite claims to the contrary, there is no magic to the pregame meal. For example, before a strenuous two- or three-hour activity, an athlete should consume an adequate meal timed to allow digestion before the event. Two to three hours is the time generally recommended to prevent stomach discomfort. But the body's energy stores come from foods eaten hours or days earlier, not from what is consumed in the meal eaten just before exercising.

As a general rule a pregame meal should be high in complex carbohydrates, but not bulky, and low in protein and fat. You should not eat anything, especially not sugary foods or drinks, during the last hour, for they can cause a drop in blood sugar level when you least want it to happen. Athletic events that extend throughout the day or weekend may require frequent small snacks carefully timed to provide the necessary nutrients without overloading the digestive process at any one time. During endurance events, such as long-distance running or cycling, you may need additional nourishment to maintain the blood sugar level that the muscles rely on.

A basic outline for a balanced diet for athletes and other active individuals is not very different from what is recommended for all

Playing football requires energy. An athlete must be sure to maintain a balanced diet.

healthy people. However, athletes are not generic. There is a range of sports from table tennis to marathons and the participants' needs also vary. Here are some specifics that may help to answer your questions.

Recommended breakdown of nutrients of daily food:

| | |
|---|---|
| Carbohydrates | 60 percent–70 percent of total food energy. |
| Protein | 12 percent–15 percent of total food energy. |
| Fat | 25 percent–30 percent or less of food energy. |
| Vitamins | Supplied by a balanced diet. |
| Minerals | Supplied by a balanced diet. |
| Fluids | See page 342 for details. |

*Carbohydrates* ♦ Whether it is glucose in the blood or glycogen in the liver, carbohydrates are the body's main source of energy. Because the body cannot store large amounts of carbohydrates, a few hours of sustained activity will deplete stores. Then the athlete will experience fatigue, weakness, or pain. Sports physiologists have reduced their emphasis on **carbohydrate loading**, which is an attempt to store elevated amounts of glycogen in the muscles and liver in order to postpone the time of exhaustion.

Carbohydrate loading is done by eating an increased amount of foods rich in complex carbohydrates, the starches, such as pasta, bread, and other grains during the two or three days before an endurance event. At the same time, no more than 10 percent–15 percent of the total energy intake should come from simple carbohydrates, which are the sugars. Candy and sucrose tablets, long thought to supply instant precompetition energy, actually upset the balance established by a sensible eating pattern.

*Protein* ♦ Protein supplements, including those containing isolated amino acids, are unnecessary. They are expensive and may contain questionable additives. There is little or no evidence that consuming isolated amino acids offers any advantage over the protein in food, and they may actually be toxic.

It is hard not to get enough protein, even if you are a semivegetarian, because grains, nuts, and legumes contain protein as well as the complete protein found in meat, poultry, fish, and dairy products. A typical Canadian diet of 12 percent to 15 percent of total daily kilojoules from protein is enough for active people.

REMINDER

Athletes requiring large amounts of energy may need:

Grain Products
    12 servings or more
Vegetables and Fruit
    10 servings or more
Milk Products
    4 servings
Meat and Alternatives
    3 servings

Pasta is rich in complex carbohydrates. Add your favourite vegetables or fruit for additional nutrients and flavour.

## CAREER SKETCH

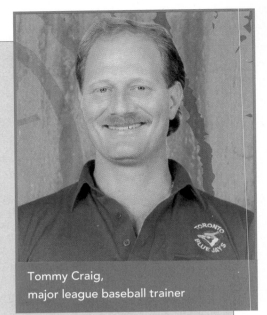

Tommy Craig,
major league baseball trainer

**A**T AGE SIXTEEN Tommy Craig's love of sports pushed him toward a career in athletic training. He set his sights on obtaining a scholarship, a college degree, a trainer certification, and a career in major league baseball or professional football.

In high school Craig became trainer for his high-school football, wrestling, and baseball teams to gain first-hand experience in his chosen career. He went on to attain a BSc in Health and Physical Education with a minor in sports medicine from East Carolina University. He became a certified athletic trainer with the National Athletic Trainers Association and a member of the Professional Baseball Athletic Trainers Society.

Craig started his training career in 1978 at Shelby (A) North Carolina, the Cincinnati Reds farm team. He then moved to the Blue Jays' Knoxville (AA) and then Syracuse (AAA) teams before being named Assistant Trainer for the Toronto Blue Jays in 1985. This was the year the Blue Jays won their first American League East Divisional title. Craig became part of the elite trainers in major league baseball when he was named Head Trainer in February 1987.

He has worked with the Blue Jays ever since. 1991 was an especially difficult year when several key players were hurt and on the disabled list. 1992 was the exciting and rewarding year when the Blue Jays won their first World Series Championship. Receiving the championship ring on Opening Day April 9, 1993 was a highlight of his career. Then 1993 was even more satisfying when the team worked hard and battled through adversity and injuries to win a second World Series.

Craig usually starts his business day at 1:30 or 2:00 pm by writing progress reports and taking care of administrative duties. Around 3:00 he helps get the players ready for batting practice. Sometimes this means giving the players physical therapy, consisting of treatments, strengthening exercises, and taping. He speaks daily to Blue Jays' management Dr. Ron Taylor, Cito Gaston, and coaches, regarding a player's playing status or availability. Occasionally, he talks to the press or public relations department during batting practice about significantly injured or disabled players. After batting practice he and the other certified trainers, Brent Andrews and Geoff Horne, may massage or stretch a pitcher's or player's elbow or shoulder, and retape them to prepare for the game. During the baseball game, Craig and Andrews, along with the medical staff of Dr. Taylor and Dr. Allan Gross tend to injured players. After the game the trainers tend to any injuries incurred during the game and arrange for any further care. Another part of the trainers' duties is keeping precise medical reports and daily logs for any injured player's medical file. It is usually after midnight before the trainers' day ends.

Another part of the trainers' job is to educate the players on the importance of nutrition and their choice of foods. Especially important are the meals they eat prior to playing on a daily basis and the need to replenish through food energy the kilojoules the players burned off during the game. In Tommy Craig's own words, "Too often people treat their cars better than their bodies. Most athletes do not know they play *Saturday's game on Thursday's food*. The three important facets [of performance] are sufficient rest, excellent nutrition, and consistent exercise." However, it is ultimately up to the players to take care of their food needs.

Once Craig's days in baseball are complete, he plans a partnership interest in a Sports Medicine and Fitness Clinic. An induction into the East Carolina University Sports Hall of Fame as Trainer would top off a fantastic career in baseball.

*Fat* ◆ Athletes do not need any more fat than other people. High-fat foods might take the place in your meals of the carbohydrates you need for high intensity exercise. Even lean people have enough stores for energy production. Avoid fatty foods right before exercising. It takes a long time and valuable energy to digest and absorb fat.

*Vitamins* ◆ Most devoted athletes are faced regularly with evaluating promises of great benefits from vitamin and mineral supplements. A cautious approach will advise against such intake. Choosing foods based on *Canada's Food Guide to Healthy Eating*, with plenty of fresh vegetables and fruit, will supply all the nutrients the body needs. In addition, a body that has been properly nourished daily on a long-term basis will have adequate nutrient reserves for optimal performance potential.

*Minerals* • The key minerals for physically active people are outlined below.

*Iron* is needed for the blood to transport oxygen, which is of tremendous importance to most strenuous activity. **Sports anaemia** refers to iron depletion that impairs performance. It may be caused by several factors including increased elimination of iron and breakdown of red blood cells during prolonged exercise. If they are physically active, dieters, menstrual women, and strict vegetarians need to be doubly careful to consume enough iron.

*Sodium* and *potassium* help to maintain the body's water balance. Losses through perspiration are actually quite small and are usually replaced by normal eating. Additional salt is not required except in the case of prolonged vigorous activity undertaken in hot temperatures.

Sports drinks actually contain only small amounts of potassium. They are nutritionally similar to diluted juice or soft drinks but more expensive. Which drink you choose depends on your preference.

*Chromium* is important to carbohydrate and fat metabolism and the regulation of blood sugar. Good sources are whole wheat, apples, peanuts, mushrooms, oysters, and prunes.

*Zinc* is involved with energy metabolism. Athletes may have a zinc shortfall since increased zinc is lost in sweat and urine. Good food sources include meat, eggs, seafood, and whole-wheat products.

*Calcium* for strong bones is particularly important for female athletes who are at risk of osteoporosis later in life.

*Magnesium* plays a part in muscle contractions. Supplements appear to have no effect on muscle activity or athletic performance.

*Fluids* • The most important advice is to drink plenty of water, even if you are not thirsty. After a workout or competition it is important to replenish liquids with water, juice, or milk. Thirst will be satisfied long before you have replenished lost fluids. It is possible to loose 2 L of water before you notice your fluid loss.

Avoid drinking carbonated beverages. They may seem to be thirst quenching at the time, but they actually contribute to dehydration. Other dehydrating beverages include tea, coffee, cola, and chocolate beverages, and alcohol.

Whether an athlete is in a competitive or recreational sports program, there are several well-established principles to follow to maximize health and performance potential. Athletes should:

• Eat a variety of foods from all food groups daily to ensure that they get all the required nutrients.

> ...when you become hooked on cycling you tend to become more diet conscious. You realize that you need the proper foods to feed your two-wheel habit and you watch what you eat.
> STEVE BAUER

- Eat more whole grains and vegetables and fruit. Choose at least twice as much from these two groups as from the other two groups. These supply the nutrients required for energy production.

- Reduce to a minimum those foods having low nutritive value so that all food consumed will contain important nutrients without "empty" energy value. Omit, for example, pastry, soft drinks, potato chips, and candy. Cut down on sugars, honey, jams, jellies, and sweetened drinks.

- Choose foods that are as close to their natural state as possible. Generally, the more processed the food, the fewer the nutrients it will contain. A baked potato will provide better nutritive value than French fries; an apple is a better choice than apple juice or applesauce.

- Drink more water, especially after a workout. The most common cause of fatigue is dehydration. Fluids are always needed to compensate for body water losses in sweat and urine. Thirst alone will not indicate how much fluid is needed. Good advice is: "Drink until your thirst is satisfied, then drink some more."

Cyclists usually carry water bottles on their bicycles to replenish the liquid they lose as they ride.

## Food for Pregnant Women

A pregnant woman is responsible for her baby's health as well as her own. From conception, the developing fetus depends on the mother to provide a daily supply of healthy foods. It is equally important that a woman, especially a young person who is not fully grown, eat carefully and develop a healthy, well-nourished body, before she becomes pregnant.

By 12 weeks the fetus will have all the systems and organs a full-term baby would have. During the next three months the mother's appetite will usually increase. The quantity of food needed by the fetus will also increase. By the beginning of the last three months the fetus will usually weigh between 1 kg and 1.5 kg, and after that time will gain about 30 g per day.

The current thinking is that a woman should aim for a gain of 11 kg to 14 kg during her pregnancy, which is a higher range than previously recommended. The Food Guide For Pregnant Women on page 345 may seem to be more than a reasonable amount of food to eat daily. However, the serving sizes are smaller than most people eat at one time. The total amount of food is not as great as it seems. For example, an average purchased muffin is equal to two grain servings; most people eat the equivalent of three grain servings of pasta at one meal. Women who have smaller appetites can have the smaller number of servings recommended. The larger number of servings indicated in *Canada's Food Guide to Healthy Eating* are meant for women who are physically active.

It is important to remember that eating more does not mean eating more fat. For example, skim milk, 1%, and 2% milk have less fat than whole milk but have the same amount of vitamins, minerals, and protein. See Tips For Lowering Fat Intake on page 359.

Many women find it difficult to eat enough iron-rich foods needed by the fetus to build red blood cells. Also the baby will need an extra supply of iron to last until his or her diet can include iron-rich foods. Good iron sources are red meat and dried beans. Iron is also found in whole-grain and enriched cereals, as well as in dark green and leafy vegetables. A food rich in vitamin C, such as citrus fruit or tomato, needs to be eaten at the same meal to get the full benefit.

Pregnant women have a special need for calcium. The fetus draws calcium from the mother's body to harden and strengthen developing bones and teeth. Vitamin D helps the body absorb the calcium. Milk, cheese, and yogurt are excellent sources to supply calcium requirements. In fact, milk and milk products are an important part of the pregnant woman's eating plan because of the calcium, phosphorus, and vitamin A they supply. If for some reason these foods are not eaten daily, the woman should consult her doctor immediately.

Studies have demonstrated the special importance of women of child-bearing age obtaining adequate folate in their food. Its function in the body is not well understood, but it is known that folate is a component of tissues. It is essential for forming both white and red blood cells. Low folate supplies have been linked to a variety of birth defects and physical disabilities. Good sources of folate are green vegetables, especially asparagus, Brussels sprouts, spinach, and broccoli. Other sources include cauliflower, oranges, melons, baked beans, chick peas, lentils, sunflower seeds, peanut butter, and eggs. A doctor will advise on the need for folate supplements.

Fluids are also important, and 1.5 L to 2 L of water, juice, milk and/or soup are recommended daily. As food intake increases, the need for water also increases. It carries nutrients throughout the body and works with fibre to prevent constipation. A safe level of alcohol intake during pregnancy is not known. It is,

Why does a glass of milk make a good snack for a pregnant woman?

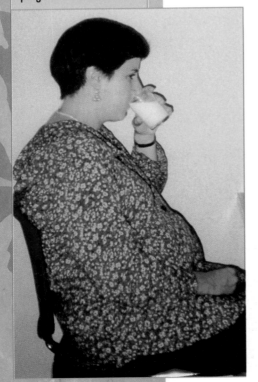

therefore, best to avoid alcohol completely. It is also wise to limit caffeine intake during this time because it interferes with iron absorption.

The guidelines for healthy eating during pregnancy are similar to those for other healthy individuals:

• Eat a variety of foods from the four food groups.

• Eat fewer highly processed foods.

• Do not drink alcohol.

• Make good food choices, avoiding extras with little food value, so that both mother and baby will be well nourished.

Young women whose bodies are still developing will need to be doubly concerned that they are eating food that will be adequate to both themselves and their babies.

## Food for Ageing Populations

Most of you have regular contact with a person who is in the later stages of life. It may be a grandparent, a neighbour, or someone that you meet regularly while you are employed or volunteering. Recent Canadian statistics indicate we have an ageing population and that services will need to be extended for seniors over the next several decades. One day you will be in this category. The information provided here will explain why your eating habits today are important to your later years.

Eating habits later in life are a natural extension of a long pattern of eating that, for most people, will be hard to change. Indeed, changes in an older person's dietary habits, along with differences in physical appearance and body mass, can be a clue to psychological illness. Most people normally experience a reduced appetite with the advancing years and this, together with a less active lifestyle, will usually affect daily food intake. It is important that all seniors be encouraged to attend to their nutritive needs.

Although a carefully chosen diet cannot prevent the problems that are part of the normal ageing process, it can reduce significantly the risk of osteoporosis, diabetes, heart disease, obesity, and some cancers. More important to seniors who have none of these serious conditions is that food continues to be one of life's greatest pleasures. Eaten alone, with a life partner, or with friends, good food can help maintain the joy of living. To a senior, being

Meals on Wheels provides seniors with a hot, nutritious meal. Do you know of any seniors who receive this service?

healthy means more than just not being sick or disabled. It means feeling good with the courage to adapt to the many physical changes that come with additional years. Here are some suggestions.

*Shopping* ◆ For some seniors, just getting to a grocery store is a major challenge. Usually there are opportunities for transportation to be shared between seniors and their friends and relatives, if the need is known. In some communities volunteer drivers can be arranged or a local seniors' association may have other suggestions. Family, friends, and caregivers have discovered that some local stores provide a delivery service. A student might assist the senior to find such a store.

Better service is always available when stores are less busy. Shoppers can take time to read labels and compare products, and there is more room to move between the aisles. Many seniors take advantage of mid-week discount days to stretch their budget.

*Cooking* ◆ Usually a reduced appetite and some dietary restrictions means that favourite recipes will need to be adapted. Making smaller portions using less fat, salt, sugar, and more fibre are not difficult, but changing lifelong habits may be harder to accomplish. Trying new recipes and ideas may be easier. Some seniors prefer to eat smaller meals and snacks throughout the day. Others find that eating the main meal at noon is better for their digestion. The pattern is not important as long as a variety of foods meet daily nutritional needs.

The example of a lonely senior existing on toast and tea is certainly to be discouraged. Here are some ideas to prevent this from happening. Volunteer to help a senior.

- Offer seniors a cooking class. Encourage sharing of recipes and ideas.
- Form a gardening club, even if the only soil available is in pots. Growing food, working together in the fresh air, then sharing produce will make the resulting meals more interesting and appetizing.
- Have seniors cook with friends. They can plan and prepare the basis of several meals to share and freeze for a future meal.
- Suggest making more of the recipe than can be eaten at one meal, then freezing the extra in serving sizes for another day.

*I'm not interested in age. People who tell you their age are silly. You're as old as you feel.*
ELIZABETH ARDEN

Spending time with a senior can be enjoyable for both of you. Think of activities you could do with a senior you know.

• Make arrangements for seniors to eat out for a change. The place might be a restaurant that serves ethnic food they may otherwise not try or a favourite place that they can no longer get to alone. Accompany them or arrange return transportation.

## Making the Most of Mealtime

• Make meals pleasurable as well as a source of nourishment by providing seniors with an opportunity to relax and socialize with others. Having an older person or a couple to your house for a meal may well be the highlight of their week. Or you might take the time to visit their home taking part of the meal with you. Neighbours or friends might start a "potluck" group in which everyone brings a prepared dish. Local agencies will know if the neighbourhood provides meals for others at a community centre, place of worship, or school. Such meals would not only offer adequate nutrition but a chance to be with other people in a social setting.

Making the most of mealtime can be more difficult for seniors who live alone. To break up the routine of eating alone, they might try eating in different places in the house or apartment, such as the living room or on the porch or patio. Caregivers in nursing homes, however, need to be sensitive to some residents' desire to have an assigned place at the table. In the face of many physical and personal losses, this special spot may be one stable aspect that he or she has retained.

For a single senior, especially one who has difficulty getting out, home delivery of a hot meal may be an option. Most communities have an agency that sponsors "Meals on Wheels." Volunteers usually deliver these meals near noon. Their visits are as welcome as the nourishing meals they provide. Alternatively, family members can agree to take turns bringing a hot meal one day a week.

## Food for Vegetarians

Like everyone's food habits, vegetarian eating patterns vary widely. Vegetarian diets differ in the types of foods eaten, but the main differences are in the way each eating plan supplies the body's protein requirement.

**Vegans**, or total vegetarians, obtain needed protein from plant sources only. In addition to vegetables, total vegetarians eat fruit, nuts, seeds, grains, and legumes. They completely avoid all foods of animal origin including meat, fish, poultry, eggs, all dairy products, gelatin, and honey.

**Lacto vegetarians** get much of their protein from plant sources with the addition of dairy products. Other animal source foods, including eggs, are avoided.

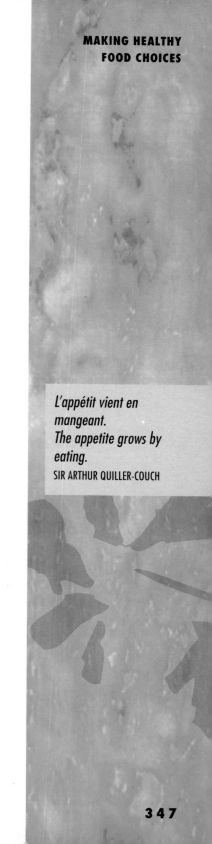

*L'appétit vient en mangeant.*
*The appetite grows by eating.*
SIR ARTHUR QUILLER-COUCH

**Ova lacto vegetarians** avoid meat, fish, and poultry, referred to by some as "flesh foods." They do, however, eat eggs and dairy products.

Another group of people, including millions of Asians, allow fish in their diets. Called **pesco vegetarians**, they live on staples of rice, fish, and vegetables. Similarly, **pollo vegetarians** eat poultry such as chicken, duck, and game birds, while omitting red meat. Throughout much of the world, a form of vegetarianism is the norm rather than the exception.

There seems to be an increasing number of Canadians adopting a vegetarian eating pattern. As numbers increase there are more restaurants offering vegetarian entrées and a greater assortment of vegetarian recipe books and magazines are available. Some of the reasons expressed for vegetarian eating are:

- Health — Vegetarian style food can be low in saturated fat and generally lower in total kilojoules. Including more fibre-rich vegetables and grains in meals will improve the functioning of the digestive tract and, in some cases, may actually reduce risk of disease. Carefully planned, vegetarian meals supply required nutrients and vitality for health.

- Economy — Meat, fish, and poultry tend to be more expensive than vegetables and grains. Gram for gram, plant foods are more economical choices than meat.

AS THE ULTIMATE VEGETARIAN, THE ONLY SPORT THAT KRISTEN EVER PLAYED WAS SQUASH.

- Ecology — The grazing land and water required to rear red meat animals, and the energy and raw materials required for processing and packaging are major concerns for some people. They choose vegetarianism as their personal contribution to preserving ecosystems and limited natural resources of the world.

- Ethics — Some people take the position that it is morally wrong to kill any animal for any reason. Their vegetarianism is a statement against cruelty and is based on the belief that it can help to save the lives of animals.

- Cultural — There are many religions, both ancient and contemporary, that prohibit the eating of flesh foods. Hinduism and Buddhism are two. In many cultures vegetarian eating is not a new idea and may stem from beliefs, ethics, or health considerations.

- Personal taste — Many people do not enjoy the taste of red meat or other non-vegetarian protein foods. Since a taste for most food is acquired, those who never acquire a taste for meat are naturally drawn to vegetarianism.

Vegetarians can easily meet their nutritional needs by following *Canada's Food Guide to Healthy Eating* as suggested for the appropriate age and activity level. The only change is to include several servings of meat alternatives each day instead of meat. Meat alternatives include legumes, beans, nuts, seeds, tofu, peanut butter, other nut and seed butters, and also eggs, if they are not excluded from the diet.

If all animal products are left out of the diet, vegetarians should be careful to choose plant foods that are rich sources of calcium, iron, and other essential minerals and vitamins found in meat. A dietitian can provide assistance. This advice may be critical during childhood, adolescence, and pregnancy.

The main concern for vegetarians is obtaining adequate amounts of four nutrients: calcium, iron, vitamin B12, and protein.

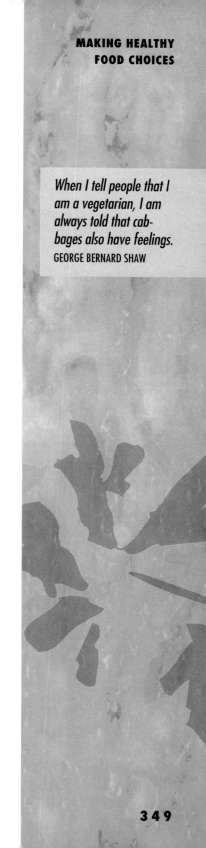

> *When I tell people that I am a vegetarian, I am always told that cabbages also have feelings.*
> GEORGE BERNARD SHAW

- Calcium — Milk products are important for the calcium they provide. If dairy products are excluded from the diet, other calcium-rich, non-dairy foods must be included. Some of these are dark green, leafy vegetables, broccoli, kale, chard, almonds, Brazil nuts, sesame seeds, tahini, molasses, and firm tofu made with calcium.
- Iron — Sources of iron include lentils, split peas, beans, molasses, tofu, and egg yolks, if eggs are allowed. These are foods that people of the Middle East, Africa, Asia, Central America, and South America have used traditionally for centuries. Iron absorption is increased when a food containing vitamin C is eaten with an iron-rich food.
- Vitamin B12 — When dairy products or eggs are not part of the diet, a supplement from fortified brewers yeast, fortified soymilk, and other soy products is advisable. A reliable source is nutritional yeast that has been grown on a vitamin B12 enriched substance.
- Protein — Although most people in Canada get plenty of protein, it is a good idea to fully understand the different kinds and how to combine them to advantage.

Meat, fish, poultry, milk products, and eggs all supply complete proteins. The term complete protein means that the food contains all of the essential amino acids. Amino acids are the building blocks of protein. Some twenty-two amino acids have been identified. Of those, eight must be supplied in sufficient amounts by food because they cannot be manufactured by the body. Incomplete proteins, as the name implies, are lacking or low in one or more of the essential amino acids. During digestion the amino acids from all the foods eaten at the same meal get mixed up and the body puts them together in the right proportions.

The amino acid selections in different protein foods can supplement one another when eaten together. If incomplete protein foods are eaten with complete protein foods, they can perform their function as effectively as complete proteins alone. In fact the two types of foods together offer more amino acids in ideal proportions than either food by itself.

For a person on a vegan diet, combining plant protein foods, which are all incomplete, is a little more complicated. Each vegetable protein provides a specific amino acid profile and in order to supply the body with the essential amino acids at a single meal, the right plant source proteins need to be eaten together. By using them in combination, those amino acids that are deficient in one food, may be supplied by another vegetable protein. This is the principle of **complementary protein combinations**. Further assistance for pregnant and nursing women and feeding infants and children on vegetarian diets can be obtained from your local registered dietitian or nutritionist.

Familiar combinations from around the world that provide a balance of incomplete protein sources include:

• Peanut butter sandwich (North America)

• Baked beans and corn bread (eastern United States)

• Pea soup with a bread roll (France)

• Lentil soup with crackers (Middle East)

• Tofu with rice and stir-fried vegetables (China)

• Humus and pita bread (Middle East)

• Tortilla and refried beans (Mexico)

• Falafel (Middle East)

• Dahl and chapatis or rice (India)

If you are carefully following *Canada's Food Guide to Healthy Eating* you should be meeting your nutritional needs. However, the following chart will make it easier for you to combine complementary proteins from incomplete protein sources.

A vegetarian diet revolves around whole grains, seeds, whole-grain breads, legumes, vegetables (especially green and orange vegetables), and all fruit. Usually more small meals and healthy snacks form an important part of the dietary plan.

*Bread is better than the song of birds.*
DANISH PROVERB

The foods eaten by a vegetarian usually contain more polyunsaturated fats than a conventional diet. If dairy products are included, a person can safely enjoy more milk products and eggs than a meat eater because overall their cholesterol and saturated fat intake is generally lower.

Depending on the choices made, a vegetarian diet can be high in bulk but low in kilojoules. It is important that meals and snacks contain enough food energy. When they do not the body will use its own protein for energy, and protein reserves will be lowered.

Salads containing a variety of vegetables are one option for vegetarians. Think of some other possible vegetarian meals.

## COMPLEMENTARY PROTEIN COMBINATIONS

| | |
|---|---|
| Wheat flour | Wheat germ |
| Whole-wheat flour | Peas |
| Bran | Soybeans |
| Brown rice | Kidney beans |
| Oatmeal | Chick peas |
| Barley | Lentils |
| Millet | |
| | |
| Peanuts | Legumes, not with peanuts |
| Cashews | Wheat germ |
| Black walnuts | Spinach |
| Brazil nuts | Sesame seeds and soybeans |
| Pistachio nuts | |
| | |
| Broccoli | Mushrooms |
| Cauliflower | Millet |
| Brussels sprouts | Sesame seeds |
| Green peas | Parboiled rice |
| Lima beans | Brazil nuts |
| | |
| Kidney beans | Wheat |
| Navy beans | Wheat bran |
| Black beans | Barley |
| Chick peas | Rice |
| Lentils | Millet |
| Soybeans | Corn, only with soybeans or black beans |

SOURCE: *Management and Foods*

To maximize the amino acid content of the meal, any food from a grouping on the left can be eaten with any food from the corresponding group on the right side.

## ☀ KEY TERMS

Use the words listed below to complete the following statements in your notebook.

accreditation          Meals on Wheels
vegan                  dehydration
buyer beware           caregivers
affiliation            ova lacto vegetarian
potluck                credibility

1. An _____ is developed when groups of people with a common interest form organizations.

2. To have _____ a group must be recognized by their peers as being knowledgeable in an area.

3. Water stations are provided for marathon athletes to prevent _____.

4. Information that is worthy of belief is said to have _____.

5. People who provide services for seniors, children, or sick people are called

   _____.

6. A _____ describes a social gathering where the participants bring a food to share.

7. _____ is a program that delivers a daily meal to those who have difficulty providing for themselves.

8. Those people who eat no animal products of any kind are called _____.

9. A person who will eat eggs and milk products but no other animal products is called a _____.

10. _____ is good advice when deciding what nutrition information to believe.

## ☀ FOCUS YOUR KNOWLEDGE

1. What are appropriate questions to ask when determining whether nutrition information is reliable?

2. Locate an advertisement for a food product. List the claims it makes. Make a judgement about its truthfulness. Share your judgement with the class.

3. Prepare a poster for the school gym that shows what athletes need to do to maximize performance.

4. Prepare an organizer of the categories of vegetarians. List the foods each group excludes.

5. Briefly describe a pregnant woman's special nutritional needs.

6. What are three of the ways a child's food needs differ from an adult's?

## ☀ DEMONSTRATE YOUR KNOWLEDGE

1. Prepare a display of finger foods appropriate for young children. Include vegetables, fruit, or cereals.

2. Prepare an easy dish suitable for seniors to make for themselves.

3. Role play a parent and child as the parent introduces a new food. Have the class evaluate how the parent handled the situation.

4. Demonstrate a table setting for a two- or three-year-old using appropriate dishes and utensils.

5. Prepare a meal in which two incomplete proteins are combined to make a complete protein meal.

## ☀ APPLY YOUR KNOWLEDGE

1. Interview a senior living in an apartment or house. Identify his or her shopping and eating habits.

2. Graph the weight gain for a typical foetus from 12 weeks to term. See your math teacher for help in graphing.

3. Plan a party with activities and nutritious food for a six-year-old.

4. Interview a coach of a sport team about nutrition. Prepare a report on the suggestions he or she gives to the team members.

5. Have a potluck at school and invite seniors in your neighbourhood to participate. Have participants bring the recipe for the dish they brought.

6. Plan a day's menus for a vegan, making use of complementary proteins.

Why must female teens be especially careful to eat foods rich in iron?

# Health Risks and Food

Currently there is a welcome trend in Canada for citizens to take responsibility for their own health. Costs of medical care are a drain on the financial resources of both the country and its residents. With a volatile world economy and a developing awareness of environmental impacts on health, everyone needs to take responsibility for his or her own wellness, and as early in life as possible. It is not acceptable to indulge in unhealthful practices and then expect the doctor, with surgery or pills, to repair the damage.

## IRON DEFICIENCY

**Iron deficiency** is the most common worldwide nutrient deficiency problem. It is a complex condition that is not always detected by the usual laboratory tests, until the situation reaches serious levels.

Iron is a necessary part of hemoglobin in red blood cells. It carries oxygen to the tissues needing it. Seventy percent of the body's iron is found in hemo-

globin. Two-thirds of our iron is stored in the liver, and the rest is held in a more insoluble form. The fact that iron can be stored means that our intake can be sporadic. Daily minimum amounts of iron from food are not required, as long as the required amounts are retained in our iron reserves by a regular total intake.

Males generally do not have a problem with iron deficiency except in rare cases during the teenage years. Young children, teens, and premenopausal women do. Maintaining the required iron level is essentially a female problem, partly because some iron is lost monthly during menstruation.

When iron-rich foods are not eaten, iron levels can be depleted by stages to very dangerous levels. Two-thirds of iron is stored as **ferretin**, making it the indicator of our stores of iron. Unfortunately, a ferretin plasma test, which would detect iron deficiency even before there is clinical evidence, is not the test normally used when a hemoglobin count is ordered. A person can show quite normal iron in the blood while having virtually no iron stores in the liver. A standard test will show no anaemia, the iron-carrying capacity will still be all right, and the hemoglobin count will be normal, but there will be no remaining stores of iron.

A current problem is that many people, especially young women, are simply not eating enough food to supply them with the necessary iron. In an effort to be thin, they frequently limit their food intake to less than 5000 kJ. In order to get enough iron, these people need to eat more, specifically iron-rich foods. The simple inexpensive addition of whole-grain or enriched cereal with milk to the foods eaten daily goes a long way to improve total iron stores. A regular exercise program will use up the energy value of foods eaten.

In athletes, a low iron level will influence the body's oxygen-carrying capacity and therefore affect their athletic performance. A low body mass is recommended for many sports. Competitors in these sports need specific nutritional knowledge to be sure they get sufficient available iron. During the growth spurts associated with adolescence, iron needs of adolescent athletes will be even greater.

Absorption is an important factor to the body's use of available iron. Continuing research has shown that some nutrient combinations aid and others interfere with the absorption process. Vegetarians especially need to be aware of foods that will assist their iron absorption level. People who eat very little meat often have a low ferretin level. We now know that meals that include meat contribute more to iron absorption. People who limit their intake of red meat because of the fat content need to remember that the grading of meats has changed dramatically in Canada since 1969. The standard for pork and red meat has a much healthier composition of lean with very low fat levels allowed.

Including a vitamin C food, such as orange juice, with a breakfast of cereal will improve iron absorption. However, any recommended calcium supplements should be taken at a different time from the

Why will the iron in this breakfast be absorbed well?

355

iron rich-food or between meals, since they interfere with iron absorption. For generally healthy people, the best advice is to practise moderation and follow *Canada's Food Guide to Healthy Eating*.

# CARDIOVASCULAR DISEASE

**Cardiovascular disease** is the number one cause of death among Canadian adults today. It claims about 80 000 lives each year. Often the first indication people have of the presence of this disease is a **heart attack**, which is fatal one out of three times.

Cardiovascular disease includes all diseases of the heart and blood vessels. The two most common forms of cardiovascular disease are heart attack and **stroke**. Both involve a narrowing of passageways supplying blood to the heart and brain. When a coronary artery to the heart is blocked, the tissues of the heart normally fed by this blood are starved for nutrients and oxygen, and a heart attack occurs. When there is a blockage of blood flow to the brain, a portion of the brain does not get enough blood, and a stroke occurs. In each case a portion of the organ deprived of life-giving blood, the heart or brain, dies, and the recovering patient is left with less capability than before the attack. Understanding how this disease develops is helpful in knowing how to prevent or combat it.

## Cardiovascular Disease Warning Signs

### Heart Attack

Any combination of the following symptoms may be a signal of a heart attack about to happen:

- Heaviness, pressure, squeezing, fullness, burning, discomfort, or pain in the centre of the chest which may spread to neck, jaw, shoulders, arms, and back; these symptoms may not be severe.
- Shortness of breath, paleness, sweating, or weakness.
- Nausea, vomiting, and/or indigestion.
- Fear, anxiety, denial.
- Symptoms may come and go.

### Stroke

- A sudden temporary weakness or numbness in the face, leg, or arm.
- Temporary loss of speech or trouble speaking or understanding speech.
- Episodes of double vision.
- Unexplained dizziness, headaches, etc., in conjunction with other symptoms.

### What to do?

**Act immediately.**

- Have victim stop activity and sit or lie down.
- Expect denial; take charge; do not rely on the victim's opinion of whether medical help is required.
- If the victim has known heart disease, assist the victim in taking his/her nitroglycerine as prescribed.
- Call your emergency telephone number.
- Take action to get to the nearest hospital with 24-hour emergency care. More Canadians who die each year of heart attacks or strokes could have been saved if they had reached a hospital within hours of the signals of the event.

SOURCE: Heart and Stroke Foundation of Canada

Heart health rests primarily on three factors.

1. **Genetic history**
   This refers to the characteristics of the genes and chromosomes inherited from your parents and their family members. Because genetic make-up is a given at conception and is not altered normally, we have no choice in this matter.

2. **Gender**
   Statistics show that more men than women have cardiovascular disease. This is primarily related to stress of traditional male occupations. As more women move into these male-dominated occupations, they are also moving into high-risk categories, and their chances for getting the disease are also increasing.

### 3. Lifestyle

Individuals have the most control over this factor because they have a great deal of choice in how they manage their health. Understanding the risk factors associated with heart disease is a first step in prevention.

## Lifestyle Habits and Involved Risks

- **Smoking**
  Tobacco smoke contains nicotine and carbon monoxide. While the nicotine stimulates the heart to beat faster, the carbon monoxide deprives the heart of the oxygen it needs to function. Smoking tobacco is the major risk factor for cardiovascular diseases in Canada and attributes to about one-third of all cardiovascular-related deaths.

- **High Blood Pressure**
  A major risk factor for cardiovascular disease is an elevated blood pressure, experienced by one in every five Canadians. Risk of developing high blood pressure is associated with smoking, obesity, stress, physical inactivity, and high levels of sodium (salt) and alcohol in the diet. All of these can be controlled by the individual.

On the left is a healthy artery; on the right is an artery that is "hardening." How are the two arteries different?

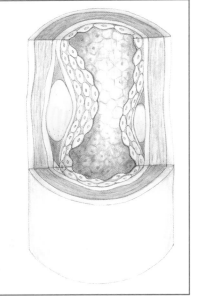

- **Low Physical Activity**
  Regular physical activity keeps the heart working at its best. Chances of cardiovascular disease increase for individuals who are not active enough to give this system a regular workout.

- **Excess Mass**
  Additional mass beyond a healthy range places more strain on all the body's systems and increases risks for chronic disease. Heart disease is one of those.

- **High blood cholesterol levels**
  Cholesterol is a waxy substance produced primarily by the liver. It is essential for life and is a normal part of all body tissues. When too much cholesterol circulates in the blood, it deposits as **plaque** on the internal surfaces of the arteries. This narrows these passageways and makes the arteries thickened and stiff. This is the condition referred to as **hardening of the arteries**.

Blood cholesterol levels come from two sources:

- 80 percent is manufactured in the body.
- 20 percent comes from the foods we eat.

There has been much written about HDL, or "good" cholesterol, and LDL, or "bad" cholesterol. Here it is sufficient to understand that LDL cholesterol increases the risk of plaque development and clogging of arteries and other blood vessels. Total fat intake has a far greater influence on total blood cholesterol levels than eating foods containing cholesterol.

Also important are the terms saturated and unsaturated as they relate to fat. Saturated fat comes from animal sources, such as in meat, dairy products, and eggs. Because these foods are also excellent sources of many nutrients they should not be eliminated from the diet. However, they should be chosen less frequently, in smaller portions, or from low-fat varieties. Unsaturated fat comes from plant sources such as vegetable oils. Elevated blood cholesterol can be cut by reducing the intake of all fat and especially saturated fat. The following table compares typical and recommended intakes of fat.

| Fats as a Percentage of Total Kilojoules | | | |
|---|---|---|---|
| | Total Fat (%) | Saturated (%) | Unsaturated (%) |
| Typical intake | 40 | 15–20 | 20–25 |
| Healthy intake | no more than 30 | no more than 10 | no more than 20 |

## Tips for Lowering Fat Intake

1. Choose lean cuts of meat and trim all fat from the edges. Remove skin and fat from poultry.

2. Grill or broil meats over a drip pan, so the fat can escape.

3. Substitute low-fat or skim milk dairy products for full-fat dairy products.

4. Choose lower-fat foods for breakfast, such as cereals, breads, and fruits.

5. Eat fewer high-fat baked goods, such as croissants, doughnuts, and other pastries.

6. Eat fewer fried foods, such as French fries, deep fried fish, or poultry.

7. Limit meat, poultry, or fish portions to the size recommended in *Canada's Food Guide to Healthy Eating,* about 100 g.

8. Skim the hard fat layer off the top of cooled homemade soups and stews before reheating to serve.

9. Limit high-fat snack foods, such as potato chips, mixed nuts, cookies, and chocolate.

## CANCER

Environmental and lifestyle factors are estimated by scientists to be the cause of as many as 80 percent of cancers in the world. This means that theoretically these cancers are preventable. According to the Canadian Cancer Society, diet is the lifestyle factor responsible for up to 35 percent of cancer in the world. Statistics like these make it even more important to take a positive approach to maintaining your health. You have some control over the risk factors.

Because both cancer and nutrition are so complex it may never be possible to prescribe a 100 percent cancer-preventing diet for everyone. However, the Canadian Cancer Society provides these diet guidelines:

1. Reduce your total daily fat intake to no more than 30 percent of total energy.

    Research results indicate that both saturated and unsaturated fats seem to be associated with cancer. It is the total fat consumption that is the important factor in cancer prevention. See Tips For Lowering Fat Intake page 359.

2. Eat more fibre-containing foods.

    Fibre is the part of vegetables, fruit, and cereals that is not digested and, by absorbing water, increases the bulk of waste products leaving the bowel. Researchers believe that fibre dilutes concentration of cancer-causing substances and also speeds their movement from the body. Foods with the most fibre are whole grains, vegetables, and fruit.

3. Have several servings of vegetables and fruit each day.

    Several studies have shown encouraging evidence of the importance of vitamins A and C in lowering the risk of some cancers. Scientists believe that vitamin A may reduce the tendency

You will enjoy eating several servings of vegetables and fruit each day more if you choose many different kinds to eat.

for malignant cells to multiply. They are not sure whether it is the **carotene** or another component in the foods that is responsible. Carotene comes from dark green and deep yellow or orange vegetables and fruits. A welcome surprise of cancer diet research is the finding that vegetables of the cabbage family (Brussels sprouts, broccoli, cauliflower) may reduce the incidence of some types of cancers.

4. Keep your mass close to ideal.

It is not clear whether it is the mass itself or the total foods eaten that is responsible for the increased risk of cancer. However, people who are 40 percent or more above their ideal mass have a cancer risk higher by as much as 50 percent in some studies. The best way to maintain ideal mass is to balance energy intake with energy output. That means that people should eat less and exercise more.

5. Limit alcohol consumption.

There is an unusually high risk of cancers of the mouth, esophagus, and throat for heavy drinkers. The risk increases dramatically if the person also smokes. Liver damage caused by excessive alcohol may lead to liver cancer.

6. Minimize your consumption of smoked, nitrate-cured, and salted foods.

Cured meats are high in both fat and salt, which are linked to cancer and hypertension. It is prudent, therefore, to limit how much you eat of smoked hams and fish, cold cuts, sausages, and other cured foods.

## DIABETES

**Diabetes** is a disorder that prevents the body from producing insulin or from using the insulin that it does produce. Insulin is essential in moving glucose, or sugar, from your bloodstream to your cells. This is how your body gets energy.

Heredity may play a role in people developing diabetes. People who have a history of diabetes in their families have an increased risk of inheriting the tendency to get diabetes.

There are two types of diabetes. Type 1 diabetes occurs when the insulin-producing cells of the pancreas have been damaged or destroyed. The body produces little or no insulin. This type of diabetes is called "juvenile" diabetes because it is more likely to occur in children or young adults. The onset of type 1 diabetes is sudden and the symptoms often severe. Because the body can no longer produce insulin, people with type 1 diabetes must take insulin injections.

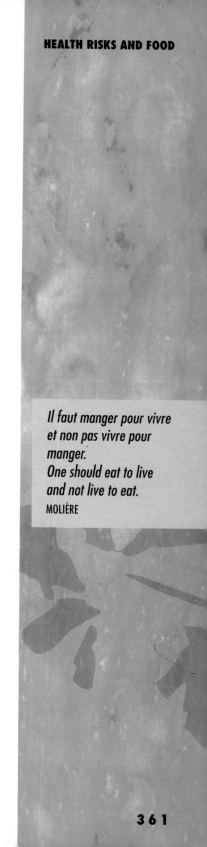

*Il faut manger pour vivre et non pas vivre pour manger.*
*One should eat to live and not live to eat.*
MOLIÈRE

People of all ages enjoy walking as part of their daily exercise.

Type 2 diabetes, also called "maturity onset," usually occurs in people over 40 years of age. More than 80 percent of people with diabetes have this type. In type 2 diabetes, the body still produces insulin, but it is unable to use it. The onset of type 2 diabetes can take months or even years, and its symptoms are often mild or even absent. Because the body is still producing insulin in type 2 diabetes, medication (pills) may be taken that help the body to produce more insulin or use it better.

Whether an individual has type 1 or type 2 diabetes, diet, meal planning, and exercise are part of a daily routine. Monitoring blood sugar levels, weight control, and lifestyle adjustments may also be required. The general guidelines for food choices provide a healthy approach to eating that benefits everyone.

- Enjoy a variety of foods.
- Whole-grain breads, cereals, rice and pasta, legumes (peas and beans) are a fabulous choice because they are high in starch and fibre.
- Vegetables and fruit are best eaten unpeeled if possible and be sure to pick the dark green vegetables and orange vegetables and fruit more often.
- Try using small amounts of butter, margarine, oil, and salad dressings. This will help decrease the amount of fat in meals.
- Skim milk, or 1% or 2% milk is a great way of producing calcium and protein with less fat compared with whole milk.

## OSTEOPOROSIS

Because of the high incidence of this disease and of our ageing population, many young people will have knowledge of someone who is older and affected with **osteoporosis**. Osteoporosis is a bone disease in which there is a reduction of bone mass through a loss of calcium. This causes bones to become thin, brittle, and easily broken. It has become a serious health problem, affecting over 850 000 Canadians, mostly older women. Some younger women and some men are also affected.

Have you ever seen a person with a hump at the back of the neck that makes them appear stooped? This is an indicator of a severe case of osteoporosis. Osteoporosis affects one in four women over the age of 50, rising

*Think of the skeleton as a bank. It's during the growing years, adolescence, and young adult years that we can make deposits into this bone mineral account. Then, we all start making withdrawals.*
DR. DON BAILEY

to one in two women 70 years of age or older. At this time, there is no cure. However, prevention is possible. Attention to diet at an early age and regular physical activity are important for the prevention of osteoporosis and its consequences. Women under 35 years of age should eat dairy products to build up calcium stores.

As the disease progresses a person affected can fracture a bone while sneezing or have a rib cracked by a strong hug. Progressive results are height loss and fractures of the spine, hip, or wrist. Associated symptoms can include fatigue, chronic pain, and loss of mobility.

Many factors contribute to osteoporosis. Some are controllable, others are not. For a better understanding of the condition we must focus on these factors:

1. Ageing

   Bone strength and shape are formed during early growth and development. The total amount of bone and bone mass continues to grow and to replenish until a person reaches 35 years of age when bone growth slows. Bone mass is no longer replenished. It slowly declines, although the rate of decline varies with different people. Thus the normal process of ageing places people at risk for the development of osteoporosis.

2. Heredity

   Smaller people have less bone mass and therefore cannot afford to lose much of it. Often a small frame is inherited. There may also be a family history of osteoporosis. Small-boned people, usually women, are more likely to develop osteoporosis than people who have more bone space for calcium storage.

3. Exercise

   Complete inactivity or prolonged immobility caused by paralysis or illness may result in a rapid loss of bone mineral content, even in young people. Bone is living tissue. With exercise, the stretching and contracting of muscles applies stress to the bone which responds and becomes stronger. This counteracts the natural tendency of idle bone to lose calcium. Regular physical activity is essential to good health for anyone. An exercise program may specifically prevent or reverse bone loss. Those with osteoporosis find that exercise, such as swimming, helps strengthen muscle support and improve flexibility. This, in turn, reduces the risks of falls and fractures. Weight-bearing exercises, such as walking, dancing, and low impact aerobics, help maintain strength.

Eleanor Mills is the founder of the Osteoporosis-Canada Relay Walk Foundation. Two of her goals are to alert Canadians to osteoporosis and to demonstrate to those suffering from the pain and deformities of this disease that a return to active life is possible.

Keeping active is easy if you enjoy the form of exercise you choose. Which of the physical activities you enjoy now will you continue as you grow older?

**4. Estrogen Loss**

Low hormone levels affect calcium metabolism and contribute to a more rapid loss of bone density. At **menopause**, the rate of bone loss increases sharply, and may be as much as six times the rate in men. This rate of loss slows again after about age 65, but by then a woman may have lost a substantial amount of bone. Surgical removal of the ovaries before menopause may also hasten the development of osteoporosis.

**5. Diet**

Calcium is essential for normal bone development and maintenance for all ages. Especially important in children and teens, a good diet will assure adequate calcium metabolism. Foods rich in calcium are milk and milk products, canned salmon with bones, sardines, almonds, and to a lesser degree, dark green leafy vegetables and broccoli. Where calcium intake is insufficient because of food intolerance or preference, a calcium supplement is recommended. Research studies consistently support the value of having plenty of calcium, on a regular basis, as a preventative measure.

**6. Habits**

Excessive intake of alcohol, tobacco, or caffeine may interfere with the ability to absorb and retain calcium, thus increasing the rate of bone loss.

## FOOD ALLERGIES AND FOOD INTOLERANCES

It is very important to know the difference between **food allergies** and **food intolerances**. People with food allergies have an unusually sensitive immune system. Food allergies can be very serious. For someone with a peanut allergy, one bite of a cookie containing ground peanuts can be life threatening.

For reasons as yet unknown, swallowing a protein from a particular food triggers the allergic person's **antibodies** to attack the foreign substance. This starts a chain reaction of chemical changes that cause swelling and irritation in certain parts of the body.

The Canadian Dietetic Association advises, "Don't guess. If you suspect you have a food allergy, have it properly diagnosed by a doctor, then obtain dietary advice from a registered dietitian." Some obvious symptoms of food allergy are:

- Swelling in the lips, throat, tongue, or face
- Skin irritations in the form of hives or a rash
- Coughing, wheezing, or difficulty breathing
- Stomach cramps
- A sudden drop in blood pressure.

A food intolerance causes digestive discomfort for people in ways that do not involve the immune system. People with **lactose intolerance**, for example, do not have enough of the enzyme, lactase, to digest the lactose, or milk sugar, in milk. People with **celiac disease** cannot digest wheat protein. Other people have an intolerance to caffeine, chili peppers, horseradish, or hot sauce.

The main difference between the two conditions is that a person with an allergy must avoid even the smallest amount of the offending food to avoid any ill affects. A person with a food intolerance may be able to eat some forms of the food. For example, even the milk protein found in baked goods should be avoided by a person allergic to milk, but some cheeses and certain modified milks may be accepted by a person with a lactose intolerance.

Food allergies are most common in young children. During their first year of life many infants display sensitivities to foods such as cow's milk, eggs, and soy. For this reason most doctors now advise that mothers breast-feed and not give infants any solid foods prior to six months. Babies who are breast-fed avoid the allergies related to cow's milk or infant formulas. Fortunately, most young children outgrow these sensitivities. It is advisable to add new foods slowly to avoid the problem in the first place. Most doctors and dietitians would agree with the following suggestions:

BY A SHEER STROKE OF LUCK FOR CLARENCE, THE GREAT WHITE SHARK WAS LACTOSE INTOLERANT.

1. Continue breast-feeding the baby for nine to twelve months. Do not give regular cow's milk until the baby is at least nine months old. If you cannot breast-feed seek professional advice on how to give your baby a good start. A doctor can recommend a formula that is less likely to cause an allergic reaction.

2. Give the baby solid foods gradually. It is preferable not to start solids until the baby is at least four months old. Then introduce new foods one at a time beginning with a single grain cereal, such as rice. Later, vegetables and fruit can be added, followed by meats.

3. Delay feeding the baby orange juice until the baby reaches at least six months of age. Do not introduce egg white and peanut butter until twelve months of age.

There are some interesting facts about food allergies that everyone who prepares foods for others should understand.

- Only six foods cause most allergies: milk, wheat, soy, egg, peanut, and fish. Very few people are allergic to more than three foods. Allergies are usually to only one or two foods.

- Usually it is not necessary to avoid an entire food family. For example, people who are allergic to lobster can often tolerate shrimp and crab. Even children with a life-threatening peanut allergy are rarely sensitive to other legumes, such as soybeans and lentils.

- Milk is not usually the cause of a child's runny nose. Children need the protein, calcium, and vitamins in milk. Until a doctor has done a thorough examination of the problem, milk should not be eliminated from the child's diet.

- Reactions to food additives are rare. Only a very few people are sensitive to certain additives, such as the preservative, sulphite, and the flavour enhancer, monosodium glutamate (MSG).

People with a food allergy are advised to take the following steps:

1. Talk to a dietitian to review foods that may have a bad effect. Some may be present as hidden ingredients. Get help so that you can avoid the foods that cause problems.

2. Learn how to read food labels carefully. For example, someone allergic to milk protein will need to look for sodium caseinate or casein on the ingredient list. These words refer to the main protein in milk.

3. Ask about ingredients in foods *before* tasting. For example, "Are there any nuts in this cake?" Some restaurants display the "Allergy Aware" symbol. In these places, senior staff will be able to answer questions about food ingredients.

4. Be safe, rather than sorry. If you are not sure what is in a food, then *do not* try it.

5. Be prepared. People who have a mild reaction to foods, such as local-ized itching and swelling, are advised to carry an antihistamine with them. With a severe attack, an allergist should be consulted about car-rying and using an adrenaline kit for emergency purposes.

# WEIGHT MANAGEMENT

Canadians seem to be preoccupied with body shape and mass. A hasty look through the yellow pages of any telephone directory, a quick survey of magazines at any newsstand, a walk through any bookstore, or even a few hours watching television or listening to radio will support this statement. And a quick glance does not include the self-help clubs and commercial enterprises that do not have offices. These organizations sell weight-loss preparations in drugstores, by door-to-door salespeople, through printed advertising, or by mail. Weight management is big business in Canada.

Various diet strategies, many considered unhealthy, have come and gone over the years. Most weight control strategies are based on a reduction of kilojoules in the food eaten. Some simply involve fasting, with or without nutrient supplements. You will probably be able to recognize a diet currently being advocated in your community as one of these:

- High carbohydrate
- Low carbohydrate
- High protein
- Vegetarian
- Low calorie
- Liquid diet
- Meal replacements

There is little reliable information on success rates of adver-tised commercial diet plans. Those who have attempted studies have had difficulty obtaining accurate figures from the groups included in their studies. In some cases, a large percentage of par-ticipants do not lose significantly; in others, participants soon regain what they lost. Advertisers are not interested in having negative results like these published.

Desirable weight-loss programs are nutritionally sound and result in maximum losses in body fat and minimum losses of

People who are preoccupied with body shape and mass often turn to diets. How many people do you know who are on a diet right now?

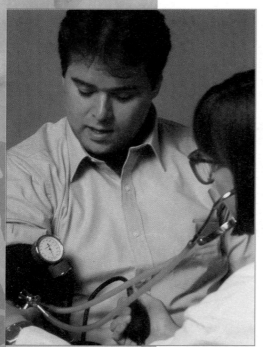

Remember to talk to your doctor before you start a weight management program.

muscle tissues. Programs with a **behaviour modification** component firmly in place seem to be getting the best results. This means the behaviour or pattern of eating is changed for the better.

Undesirable weight-loss programs are not nutritionally sound and result in large losses of fat-free muscle tissue. Most pose potentially serious medical complications and cannot be followed for long-term maintenance of body mass.

To help you evaluate the variety of weight management strategies currently being used and discussed, ask the following questions.

1. Does the program recommend that you talk to your *doctor before* beginning the program?

   It is important to find out if weight loss could be a risk to your health. Talking to your doctor also gives you an opportunity to find out about any medical conditions or special needs you may have. In general, children, teens, and pregnant and nursing women should not be following a weight reduction program.

2. Is a *registered dietitian* available to talk with people who are following the program?

   A registered dietitian should be involved with the program. This professional is specially trained to bring the science of nutrition together with established guidelines for healthy eating. A dietitian can sort nutrition fact from fiction and communicate the truth to the public. With this information he or she can design healthy eating plans to help you achieve a healthy mass.

3. Is the program based on *Canada's Food Guide to Healthy Eating* with *all* of the food groups included?

   In order to get all of the more than 50 nutrients required daily for health, we need to eat a variety of foods from each of the food groups every day. It should be possible to get all of the nutrients without vitamin, mineral, or herbal supplements.

4. Does the program provide at least 5000 kJ per day for women and 6500 kJ per day for men?

   It is very difficult to get all the nutrients the body needs from food containing fewer kilojoules than this. A dietary plan with fewer kilojoules should be undertaken only under medical supervision.

5. Does the program recommend a *loss of* more than 1 kg per week?

   When a program aims at a very quick loss or starvation, the body's survival instinct kicks in. Kilojoule use slows right down and reduction of body mass will grind to a halt. Then when more food is added, the mass returns quickly and may even reach a greater level than before the loss. A gradual reduction of 0.25 kg to 1 kg per week is safe and sensible.

6. Does the program allow for *personal eating patterns* within individual nutritional needs?

   A perfect menu plan for an individual needs to consider cultural food choices as well as individual likes and dislikes. If the plan does not include any favourite or familiar foods, it will not be followed for long. Individual needs based on age, sex, and physical activity must also be considered.

7. Does the program encourage regular enjoyable *physical activity* suitable to lifestyle and physical condition?

   The equation is simple. If more energy than can be used is taken in, in the form of food, there will be an increase in mass. Loss of mass occurs if more energy is burned through activity than is taken in. Therefore, not only should food intake be lowered, but activity should be increased to burn more energy. The added benefit of regular activity is that, combined with a slow mass reduction, it helps with fat loss instead of muscle loss.

Playing a sport on a team is one kind of physical activity. Name five other ways to burn kilojoules.

8. Does the program depend on *special foods*, products, supplements, or treatments?

   Only a permanent change in eating habits and activity will keep off lost mass. Unusual food combinations or special foods or treatments such as injections will not help. With a balanced diet there is no need for vitamin and mineral supplements which add unnecessary expense to a weight loss program.

9. Are high pressure *sales techniques* or spectacular claims characteristic of the program?

   There should be no strong pressure to buy something. If it sounds too good to be true, then it usually is. There is no magic way to trim down. Wholesome, tasty food combined with regular activity is a dependable prescription for achieving a healthy mass and a good feeling.

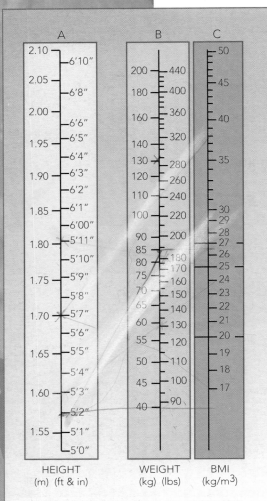

A — HEIGHT (m) (ft & in)
B — WEIGHT (kg) (lbs)
C — BMI (kg/m³)

## HOW TO FIND YOUR BMI — IT'S EASY

1. Mark an X at your height on line A.
2. Mark an X at your weight on line B.
3. Take a ruler and join the two X's.
4. To find your BMI, extend the line to line C.

**FOR EXAMPLE:**
- If Michael is 1.80 m and weighs 85 kg, his BMI is about 26.
- If Irene is 1.60 m and weighs 60 kg, her BMI is about 23.

SOURCE: Body Mass Index, Health Canada, 1993. Reproduced with permission of the Minister of Supply and Services, Canada, 1993.

10. Does the program use the **Body Mass Index** (BMI) to help set healthy and realistic goal weights?

   Being underweight can be just as harmful to health as being overweight. The Body Mass Index is a ratio of height and weight that helps a person find a healthy range. In general, a normal BMI, in the 20 to 25 range, reflects a positive relationship of weight to health. A BMI in the 25 to 27 range reflects the beginning of an unhealthy weight to health ratio. A BMI over 27 or under 20 indicates an increased risk of health problems in relation to weight. The BMI is used in combination with waist and hip ratio and should be interpreted by a registered dietitian.

The Body Mass Index does not apply to those under 20 years or over 65 years of age, nor is it appropriate for athletes. This guideline is not suitable for use by teens. However, it is important for you to be introduced to it now since it is the recommended measure for your adulthood.

## General Guidelines for Weight Control

- Realize that obesity is due to many factors, all of which must be considered. Some are biological; some are psychological.

- Weight reduction must be shaped to individual tastes, metabolism, and lifestyle. No one program suits all.

- Weight loss should be gradual, not more than 1 kg weekly. It took years to put on the mass, it should not be lost too quickly.

- Dismiss "quick" cures that promise rapid reduction. Most of it is water loss and is regained quickly.

- **Diet** means usual food and drink. Abandon the idea that diet assumes "going on" and therefore "going off" a regime.

- Aim for permanently improved eating patterns. These habits are forever and cannot be given up once weight is lost.

- Recognize that the main goal is not to lose weight but, by making healthy choices, to keep weight off.

- Incorporate a daily exercise program for active living into your life.

## Getting on the Right Track

Improving your eating habits may not be as difficult as you think.

- Do not cut out, cut back. Train yourself to eat smaller portions, especially of meat, by cutting back a little at a time.

- Think of lower kilojoule substitutes when you are cooking or preparing food. How about yogurt for sour cream in dips and on baked potatoes? Try skim milk instead of whole milk in recipes. Every little change helps.

- Although at first you might miss lots of fat and sugar in your food, it is surprising how quickly your taste buds will adjust. Enjoy the crunch of raw vegetables instead of the crackle of potato chips and the natural sweetness of ripe fruit instead of the sticky sweetness of cake.

- Zap your taste buds with non-fattening flavourings such as lemon juice, garlic, mustard, herbs, spices, curry powders, chili sauce, and salsa.

- Do not make any food taboo. You can eat anything you want, but in moderation. Eating a doughnut once in a while will not make you fat.

- Switch your mealtime thinking by eating more starchy foods, such as potatoes, pasta, rice, bread, and dried beans. Starchy foods are filling, but low in fat.

- If you are on the run, most convenience stores offer some basics for a good meal or snack. Milk or juice, yogurt, bran muffins, and fresh fruits are all good choices.

- Best choices for a main meal in a restaurant are a small grilled steak, poached fish, roast chicken, pasta, or a fruit salad plate. Avoid dishes with rich sauces or gravy. Ask for your salad dressing and coffee cream to be served on the side so you can control how much you use.

SOURCE: *Healthy Weights*, published by the Ministry of Health, province of Ontario.

*Character contributes to beauty. It fortifies a woman as her youth fades. A mode of conduct, a standard of courage, discipline, fortitude, and integrity can do a great deal to make a woman beautiful.*
JACQUELINE BISSET

**371**

# EATING DISORDERS

Increasingly, eating disorders are becoming a serious problem. Ten to twenty percent of females in Canada engage in behaviours associated with eating disorders, including anorexia, bulimia, and compulsive eating. And these frightening numbers appear to be on the rise.

The National Eating Disorders Information Centre reports that 90 percent of Canadian women are dissatisfied with their bodies. That means that only 10 percent have a healthy perception. No wonder sales of diet preparations and memberships in fitness studios are such big business.

Many teens are not happy with their body image. Sometimes the effort to change that body image can lead to eating disorders.

Long thought to be a problem only among adolescents, eating disorders are now being diagnosed in children as young as five years old and among women nearing menopause. Females account for approximately 90 percent of those affected. However, males are becoming increasingly susceptible to the disease. National Eating Disorders Information Centre figures say that 10 percent of those with eating disorders are men.

**Anorexia nervosa** is a condition of drastic weight loss from excessive dieting or self-imposed **starvation**, usually combined with other compulsive weight-loss behaviours, such as strenuous exercise. Beginning as an attempt to control some part of their lives through their weight, the illness and related behaviour eventually control the patient.

**Bulimia nervosa** is a serious disorder that involves **binge eating**, or gorging on food, followed by attempts to purge the food from the body using various artificial means, such as forced vomiting or laxatives. The cycles of binging, followed by **purging**, occur repeatedly until the patient feels completely out of control.

Because they have common symptoms, bulimia and anorexia nervosa are considered to be closely related. Victims of both disorders, for example, share an intense fear of becoming fat, and often they are obsessed with dieting. They have both accepted the common belief that thinness is a highly desired goal. Comments from their peers on their appearance, more specifically their thinness, are seen as a welcome reward worth striving for.

Both groups of people seem preoccupied with food and are very knowledgeable about nutrition. In an attempt to control their lives, they usually strive for perfection in other areas, such as academic achievement or exercise programs. In the attempt to achieve perfection, they tend to be compulsive about the knowledge they are acquiring.

There are, however, key differences between the two disorders. Bulimics usually have a normal or slightly above normal body weight; anorexics, on the other hand, typically have a lower than normal body weight. The primary characteristic of the former is binge eating. With the latter it is starvation.

When therapists interview those suffering from an eating disorder, different feelings about food are expressed. Bulimics love food; anorexics hate it. Both may envy others who are able to stay thin, and both attempt some form of control over their body proportions. In fact, the one word that comes the closest to characterizing what eating disorders are all about is "control."

While experts often disagree about causes and treatment, they do agree that eating disorders can kill. Of the so-called mental illnesses, mortality rates in Canada for anorexia and bulimia are estimated to be between 15 percent and 25 percent. Even when an eating disorder does not kill, it can cause long-term or permanent physical damage. For example, life-long constipation and other digestive problems have been the result of misuse of laxative preparations; dental erosion results from frequent vomiting.

## Anorexia Nervosa

The statistics of anorexia nervosa are alarming to say the least. An estimated 1 percent to 2 percent of Canadian women aged 14 to 25 suffer from anorexia and some reports say up to 5 percent. Doctors and therapists are beginning to see more men with the condition, but percentages are not available. The illness is described as a relentless pursuit of thinness resulting in "skeletons covered with skin." Mortality rates are as high as 15 percent to 23 percent of those afflicted, even after treatment.

Of all cases 90 percent have occurred in females and generally symptoms begin about the time of adolescence. Some investigators have generalized about family background saying sufferers come from well-educated and financially successful families. Although not always so, importance is typically placed on physical appearance in these families. Generally, the mother is dominant and the daughter has little control over her own life.

When challenged about their thinness, anorexic patients deny there is a problem. It seems that part of the problem is that the person has a distorted sense of self. While in reality patients may be very thin, to them the mirror shows an overweight image. Anorexics take pleasure in losing mass because taking control of their bodies gives them a noble feeling. Being slim is a demonstration of willpower.

*"How long does getting thin take?" Winnie the Pooh asked anxiously.*
A. A. MILNE

More often than not, the behaviour of anorexics toward food at times seems bizarre. Some prepare terrible concoctions that other people would not consider eating. Anorexics generally prefer not to have people around when they eat; frequently they stash food where it will not be found easily. There seems to be a preoccupation with simple sugar-containing foods. While they may spend a lot of time baking sweet foods which they encourage other family members to eat, anorexics usually do not sample the baking themselves.

Physicians tell us that hormonal and metabolic profiles of anorexic patients are the same as those of starvation cases. Feeding the patient will cause vomiting and intravenous feeding has not been too successful. Behaviour modification treatment produces the best results. Cardiac arrest is typically the cause of death.

## Bulimia Nervosa

The word bulimia is derived from the Greek concept meaning "ox hunger" or "insatiable appetite." In the search for the perfect thin image, bulimics resort to vomiting to control mass. An estimated 3 percent to 5 percent of Canadian women aged 14 to 25 suffer from bulimia. Approximately 5 percent to 10 percent of reported cases of bulimia are male.

There is a fairly typical cycle noted in bulimia. First, the impulse to eat can be triggered by depression, stress, or some other factor from which the bulimic seeks relief. The person eats more than a person normally would and then feels guilty about it. Because of the fear of weight gain from keeping the extra food in the system, vomiting or purging is induced. The person feels shame, disgust, and a loss of self-control and resolves not to eat that way again. The resolution is short-lived when appetite or stress triggers the next binge and the cycle begins once more. Some studies show that this cycle of binging and purging may occur up to five times per day.

Binging is usually associated with stress, rather than hunger. In addition, consumption is so quick that there appears to be no pleasure associated with food intake, only relief. The binge usually takes place when the individual is alone and may last several hours. The food chosen is specific to the individual but is most likely to be sweet: a dozen doughnuts, a whole cake, chocolate bars, sweet rolls.

The other aspect of bulimia, purging, varies from individual to individual. Most bulimics are embarrassed or even disgusted about the way they attempt weight control. Self-induced vomiting seems to be the most common choice. Other means to eliminate the effects of a binge are dieting or

*Unnecessary dieting is because everything from television and fashion ads have made it seem wicked to cast a shadow.*
PEG BRACKEN

fasting, enema, laxative or diuretic abuse, and excessive exercise. Long-term effects from these are severe. Patients experience internal bleeding and lacerations of the esophagus from vomiting, dental erosion, stomach ulcers, colon hemorrhoids, heart palpitations, heart attack, and even death.

Once the pattern of binging and purging has been learned, the cycle must be consciously interrupted and broken by the sufferer. Personal recognition and acknowledgment of the problem is the first crucial step toward successful treatment. Once that stage is reached it is recommended that further discussion of the eating itself be avoided. Instead the emphasis should be placed on discovering and learning to cope with the pressures that lead to the behaviour. This is a very serious illness and a physician should be consulted as soon as possible.

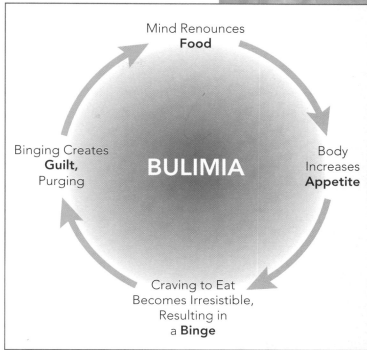

The bulimia cycle

## Compulsive Eating

While most of us occasionally eat when we are not hungry, compulsive eaters do so consistently. For them, food is a comfort to help overcome feelings of depression, inadequacy, anxiety, or loneliness. Compulsive eaters may binge but instead of purging, they tend to engage in yo-yo dieting. Sometimes they use diet pills or fad diets that can lead to high blood pressure, heart conditions, and in severe cases heart attacks.

Compulsive eaters find it difficult to manage their weight. It is often a diet that triggers compulsive eating in the first place. The diet usually backfires completely, and the compulsive eater becomes heavier than before the diet.

For those caught or controlled by an eating disorder, recognizing and acknowledging the problem can be difficult. Reaching out for help can be even harder. It is important that we all learn to recognize the symptoms of eating disorders and appreciate the close relationship between eating disorders and a preoccupation with body image. Once we understand the factors that are involved, we can learn how to reduce their influence. The National Eating Disorder Information Centre offers suggestions to family and friends of people with food and weight problems. Their guide has been adapted for use here.

## CAREER SKETCH

Jadine Cairns, dietitian

JADINE CAIRNS, a clinical dietitian at British Columbia's Children's Hospital, specializes in adolescent eating disorders. Her objective is to help teens overcome their phobias about food and body image and become happier with themselves. While it can be a frustrating struggle, it can also be rewarding when she sees them overcome their eating disorders.

When a patient is admitted to the hospital with a very low weight or an unstable medical condition, Cairns' job begins. She assesses the patient's nutritional status and determines whether or not the patient will eat. Occasionally he or she must be fed through a tube. Cairns sets a plan for the patient and follows his or her progress. She and the rest of the eating disorder team — a doctor, nurse, social worker, psychologist, and occupational therapist — work together to help the teen become better. Cairns would like to be able to shorten the hospital stay and get the patient home more quickly. For this reason, research is a major interest for her

Cairns must find creative ways to get her patients to eat. Often this involves working around allergies, religious or cultural restrictions, or personal preferences. Cairns teaches the teens exactly what happens to their bodies when they do not eat. She applies all the knowledge she has gained through her years of experience, as well as recent medical advances. Once patients are released, Cairns follows them on an outpatient basis. Teens who have finished high school but still have an eating disorder are transferred to an adult program.

Cairns feels strongly about her patients. She is always looking for better ways to help teens with eating disorders. She finds it frustrating when outside forces, such as the home environment or medical conditions, prevent a teen from getting better. She would like to see a support system established within the province. At this time, Cairns receives referrals for teens with eating disorders for the entire province of British Columbia.

In addition to her work at the Children's Hospital, Cairns is a consultant to the Adolescent Eating Disorder Summer Camp and teaches a nutrition class at Pearson Hospital Education Centre. She has published recent papers on the topic of adolescents and nutrition.

Cairns feels that any student thinking of becoming a dietitian must have an interest in food, especially in all kinds of cultural foods. The sciences, particularly biology and chemistry, are important courses to take as nutrition and dietetics are based on the sciences. "Ask dietitians in your area about their work; what it is like. Get them to share their experiences."

## What You Can Do for a Person With an Eating Disorder

1. Know the warning signs of anorexia nervosa and bulimia nervosa. See the list provided.

2. Express your concerns in a preliminary way with the person to decide if he or she does have an eating disorder.

3. Do some research. Discuss your concerns with any resources available to you, the counselling department at your school, a teacher, or a doctor. Gather information about the problem from the library or local support or information groups. Know what to do in an emergency.

4. Discuss your concerns with the person. Be informal, compassionate, and open so that your approach does not seem like an interview by a "professional." Express your concern for the person's health while respecting his or her need for autonomy and privacy. Often the behaviour is a cry for help. Let the person know that you care and are willing to talk when he or she is ready.

5. Avoid comments related to appearance — do not focus on loss of mass or body size. Let the person know that you are available to help and mention the ways you might be able to do so (by gathering literature, finding the name of a therapist, going to the counsellor or doctor with the person), but do not make promises you cannot keep.

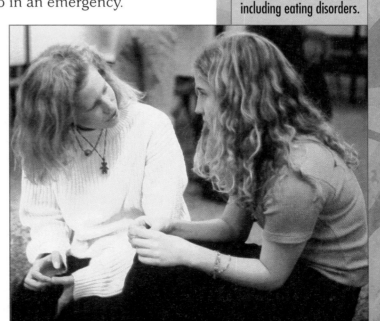

Good friends should be able to discuss any topic, including eating disorders.

6. Be patient. Expect to be rejected at first. Be prepared for the possibility that your discussion about the problem may not lead to any immediate change in attitude or behaviour. Appreciate that it is frightening to think of admitting you have a problem and even more frightening to consider giving up the behaviour. Realize that only the person affected can make the decision to get help and decide what kind of help will be acceptable.

7. Know your own limits. Avoid becoming over-involved in trying to offer advice. Do not try to be a substitute for professional care. Eating disorders are very complicated, dangerous, difficult to treat, and beyond the scope of most people. Generally a whole-team approach by professionals is required for successful treatment of long-lasting duration.

## Signs of Anorexia Nervosa or Bulimia Nervosa

- Preoccupation with food, mass, dieting, and/or kilojoules in food.
- Frequent weighing.
- Claims of being fat when mass is normal or below normal.
- Evidence of binge eating.
- Hoarding food.
- Guilt or shame about eating.
- Secretive vomiting (leaving for the bathroom after a meal).
- Use of laxatives, diuretics, and/or emetics.
- Moodiness, irritability, and/or depression.
- Low self-esteem.
- Need to be perfect.
- Extreme concern about appearance, physical and behavioural.
- Social withdrawal, intolerance of others.
- Sensitivity to criticism.

## Specific Signs of Anorexia Nervosa

- Significant loss of mass with no related illness.
- Significant reduction of eating and denial of hunger.
- Dieting when not overweight.
- Signs of starvation — thinning or loss of hair, lanugo (fine hairs on skin), bloated feeling, yellow coloured palms of hands and soles of feet.

- Stopping of menstruation.
- Unusual eating habits — compulsively arranging food, unusual mixtures, preference of certain colours, textures.

## Specific Signs of Bulimia Nervosa

- Habitual overeating in response to stress.
- Frequent mass fluctuations of 5 kJ or more.
- Evidence of binge eating — observing it, reports of it, large amounts of food missing, stealing of food or money.
- Evidence of purging — vomiting, laxative and diuretic use, frequent fasting, excessive exercising.
- Swelling of the glands under the jaw from frequent vomiting results in a "chipmunk" appearance of the face.
- Frequent and unusual dental problems.

KEY TERMS

Use the words listed below to complete the following statements in your notebook.

insulin
diuretics
hemoglobin
osteoporosis
cardiovascular disease
purging

anorexia nervosa
hardening of the
 arteries
food allergies
obese

1. Iron is a necessary part of _____ in red blood cells.

2. All diseases of the heart and blood vessels are called _____.

3. Cholesterol deposits in the arteries cause a condition known as _____.

4. People with diabetes often take _____ to control the disease.

5. _____ is a bone disease that most commonly affects older women.

6. People with _____ have an unusually sensative immune system.

7. Grossly overweight people are said to be _____ .

8. Forced vomiting or use of laxitives is called _____ .

9. Drastic weight loss from self-imposed starvation is called _____ .

10. Medications that reduce the fluids in the body are called _____ .

FOCUS YOUR KNOWLEDGE

1. What is the function of iron in the body?

2. Explain the role of insulin for a diabetic.

3. Briefly describe the factors that contribute to osteoporosis.

4. What are the key differences between a food allergy and a food intolerance?

5. Describe the importance of body image for a person with an eating disorder.

6. What role does exercise play in a weight management program?

## ☀ DEMONSTRATE YOUR KNOWLEDGE

1. Plan and prepare a low-fat dinner meal.
2. Plan and prepare an iron-rich breakfast meal.
3. Plan and prepare a lunch meal excluding wheat products.
4. Create a brochure or poster giving information on how to identify eating disorders.
5. Role play a doctor discussing cancer, osteoporosis, iron deficiency, or weight management with a patient. The patient should prepare questions to ask the doctor.

## ☀ APPLY YOUR KNOWLEDGE

1. Keep a record of foods you eat in a week. Also record your lifestyle decisions, for example, the amount you exercise. Based on that record assess your risk of developing osteoporosis, heart disease, or an eating disorder.
2. Prepare a chart showing the processed foods to avoid if you are allergic to one of the following foods: milk, wheat, soy, egg, peanuts, or fish.
3. Using periodicals locate and read the latest research on osteoporosis. Prepare a report and present your findings to your classmates.
4. Interview a person who has suffered from a cardiovascular disease to determine which facts the person believes caused his or her disease.
5. Plan a day's meals by following the Canadian Cancer Society's guidelines.

# Unit Overview

 ## REVIEW YOUR KNOWLEDGE

1. Name three current health concerns that are related to the overindulgence of food.
2. Describe the role that the small intestine plays in the digestive process.
3. Describe how to determine whether nutrition information is reliable.
4. How might a senior's food needs differ from those of a child?
5. What are seven ways to lower fat intake?
6. What are the differences between anorexia nervosa and bulimia nervosa?

## EXTEND YOUR KNOWLEDGE

1. Conduct library research to determine how the body manufactures vitamin D from ultraviolet light. Prepare and present to the class a report on your findings.
2. Volunteer your services at your local senior centre and keep a journal. Record your observations about seating arrangements, variety of meals, choices of foods, serving sizes, preparation techniques, and appetites. Prepare a brief summary of your observations.
3. Survey your classmates, friends, and family to find out which food allergies or food intolerances they might have. Prepare a report on the most common condition identified. Include in your report the symptoms reported, which foods need to be avoided, and how the condition has affected eating patterns.
4. Research a career as a dietitian. Determine the necessary education required, where you might find employment, what is involved in daily activities, and what interests you about the career. If possible, interview a dietitian to hear his or her point of view as well.

# Glossary

**Absorption**   The passage of the products of digestion through the walls of the intestinal tract into the circulatory system, which carries the nutrients to body cells.

**Agribusiness**   Food production that combines agriculture and business.

**Air cell**   The area between the shell and the egg white that forms by evaporation of the egg white as the egg ages.

**Al dente**   The Italian term used to describe the correct consistency for cooked pasta, tender but still chewy.

**Albumen**   Another name for egg white.

**Alimentary canal**   System that comprises the mouth, esophagus, stomach, small intestine, and large intestine. (*See* Digestive tract or Gastrointestinal tract.)

**Amino acids**   The building blocks of all protein foods used by the body to build and repair tissue.

**Anaemia**   An insufficiency of hemoglobin or of red corpuscles in the blood caused by lack of iron, which is required to transport oxygen; the patient has little energy and is constantly tired.

**Animal fat**   *See* Saturated fat.

**Anorexia nervosa**   A serious eating disorder that results in drastic loss of body mass from excessive dieting or self-imposed starvation.

**Antibodies**   Various proteins, produced in the blood, that attack foreign bodies and prevent illness that they may cause.

**Appendix**   A small organ situated between the small and large intestine.

**Bacteria**   Microorganisms that multiply by cell division under ideal conditions. Some produce spores that are highly resistant and can survive until conditions are more favourable. Under unfavourable conditions some also produce deadly toxins.

**Barbeque**   A dry-heat method of cooking food by exposing it to heat from hot coals, briquettes, electricity, or gas flames and generally is done outdoors.

**Basal metabolism**   The food energy needed for the body to perform the basic functions that keep your body alive: breathing, blood circulation, digestion, assimilation, growth.

**Beat**   Vigorous action to combine ingredients using a spoon, fork, whisk, rotary beater, or mixer.

**Behaviour modification**   A program that encourages individuals to permanently change the patterns surrounding their eating, such as what, when, and where, so that body mass can be gained, reduced, or maintained, depending on the objective.

**Beri-beri**   A deficiency disease caused by insufficient thiamin in the diet.

**Bile**   A substance produced by the liver that is involved in fat digestion.

**Binge eating**   A regular spree of gorging on food with little pleasure associated with the actual eating.

**Blanch**   To subject vegetables or fruit to hot water or steam just long enough to retard action of the natural enzymes that cause spoilage.

**Blend**   To mix very thoroughly until ingredients that do not dissolve readily in each other are combined.

**Bloom**   A thin, natural coating on fresh eggs that prevents penetration by air.

**Body Mass Index (BMI)**   A ratio of height and weight to assist individuals of 20–65 years to find a healthy range. It is not appropriate for athletes or people under 20 years of age.

**Bolus**   The name given to the softened food ball that passes along the esophagus to the stomach.

**Botulism**   Acute food poisoning caused by a potent toxin produced by a bacterium in food that is improperly preserved.

**Braise**   A moist-heat method of cooking meat by browning it on both sides in hot fat, then adding a small amount of liquid and simmering in a covered pan until tender. The resulting juices are usually thickened before serving to make a tasty sauce or gravy.

**Bran**   The outer layer of a grain that remains after the husk, which protects it, has been removed.

**Broil**   A dry-heat method of cooking food by exposing it to direct heat on one side, then on the other side.

**Bulima nervosa**   A serious eating disorder that involves binge eating followed by purging to remove the food from the stomach before it has a chance to increase body mass.

**Butterfat**   The fat in whole milk that rises as cream naturally or is dispersed throughout the liquid in homogenized milk.

**Caffeine**   A drug found in coffee, tea, chocolate, cola drinks, and some medications that stimulates the nervous system.

**Candling**   A commercial method of rotating an egg before a bright light to reveal how the contents compare with a required internal standard.

**Capillaries**   Tiny extensions of the blood circulation system.

**Caramelize**   To melt sugar over low heat until it becomes golden brown, or to heat or bake foods containing sugar until browned.

**Carbohydrate loading**   Eating an increased amount of complex carbohydrate-rich foods for two to three days before an endurance event in an attempt to store elevated amounts of glycogen to postpone exhaustion during the event.

**Carbohydrates**   The main energy source for body activities in the form of sugar, starch, or fibre.

**Cardiovascular disease**   Any disease of the heart and blood vessels.

**Carotene**   The dark green and deep yellow-orange pigment of vegetables and fruit that indicates a vitamin A source.

**Casein**   The main complete protein found in milk that forms the curd from which cheese is made.

**Cash crops**   Crops sold to provide income to the farmer rather than to feed the people who cultivate them.

**Celiac disease**   The condition that occurs when a person cannot digest wheat protein.

**Chalaza**   Whitish, twisted cords in the albumen that attach the egg yolk to the egg white and keep the yolk in the centre of the shell.

**Chlorophyl**   The substance manufactured in plants, with the help of light, that gives them their green colouring.

**Cholesterol**   A waxy substance produced naturally by the liver and ingested in fatty foods. When too much is circulating in the bloodstream, it can settle on the inside wall of blood vessels, clogging them and interfering with efficient blood circulation. (*See* Hardening of the arteries.)

**Chronic undernutrition**   Insufficient nourishment over a lifetime.

**Churning**   Vigorous mixing of cream that makes the fat particles cluster together and form butter, leaving the surrounding liquid as buttermilk.

**Chyle**   The name given to what remains of the undigested liquid food as it passes through the small intestine.

**Chyme**   The name given to what remains of the undigested food after it has been made more liquid in the stomach.

**Coagulate**   The process of firming or solidifying a protein substance, such as egg, when heat is applied.

**Collagen**   (1) A tough, elastic connective tissue in meat that softens, eventually becoming tender, and converts to gelatin during cooking. (2) A protein that supports all cells in the body: bones, teeth, skin, tendons.

**Commodity**   Food that can be produced and traded for profit.

**Complementary protein combinations**   Combining foods that contain different amino acids so that all of the essential amino acids are eaten together. (*See* Essential amino acids.)

**Complete protein**   Protein that contains all of the essential amino acids.

**Complex carbohydrates**   Large molecules of simpler carbohydrates, such as starches, cellulose, glycogen, and dextrins, that take longer to digest because they are joined.

**Conformation**   The shape of an animal or bird used for meat determined by its bone structure and distribution of flesh.

**Connective tissue**   Tough, elastic strands that provide the framework for the muscle fibres that constitute meat.

**Convection oven**   An oven that cooks food with heated air driven by a powerful fan. A convection oven has no element or flame like a conventional oven; it also cooks food faster.

**Cream**   To mash, stir, or beat a solid fat, such as shortening, butter, or margarine, so that it absorbs air and becomes light and fluffy.

**Crystallization**   The formation of ice crystals when a liquid freezes; also the formation of solid crystals when a solution has reached the correct chemical nature to do so. For example, sugar solution to sugar crystals, maple syrup to maple sugar crystals.

**Curd**   The firm part of coagulated milk that is removed from the whey in the first step in making cheese.

**Curdle**   Separation of the liquid from the solids of milk when it is overheated or under acid conditions.

**Dehydration**   A condition that occurs when there is insufficient water in the body tissues either because of excessive water loss from perspiration, vomiting, or diarrhea or from the use of foods that have a diuretic effect, such as carbonated beverages.

**Desertification**   Land that has been lost to drought or human activity when the topsoil dries up and is blown or washed away.

**Developed country**   A country with extensive transportation, energy, communications, education, food processing and storage, housing and health care systems in which most of the people's basic needs are met.

**Developing country**   A country with little or no industry and insufficient resources or supply systems to provide citizens with basic needs.

**Diabetes**   A disorder that prevents the body from producing insulin or from using the insulin that it does produce. (*See* Insulin.)

**Diet**   (1) A person's usual pattern of food and drink. (2) A special selection of food and drink consumed in an attempt to adjust body mass.

**Digestion**   The processes whereby the foods eaten are changed into their simplest forms.

**Digestive tract**   System that comprises the mouth, esophagus, stomach, small intestine, and large intestine. (*See* Alimentary canal or Gastrointestinal tract.)

**Disaccharides**   Carbohydrates made up of two sugar molecules.

**Dressing**   A poultry-grading term referring to the presence or absence of discolouration, bruises, pinfeathers, skin tears, or other blemishes.

**Dry ingredients**   The dry and powdery or granular substances used in a recipe.

**Duodenum**   The first part of the small intestine immediately below the stomach.

**Economic good**   Something useful produced and traded for profit.

**Elastin**   A very tough connective tissue in meat that is extremely resistant to tenderizing by any cooking method. It is normally removed before cooking.

**Emulsifiers**   Ingredients that permit tiny globules of one liquid to be dispersed in another, such as oil in vinegar for salad dressing.

**Emulsifying agent**   A substance, such as egg, that is used to surround oil droplets to prevent them from separating from a mixture.

**Endosperm**   The largest part of any cereal grain that contains mainly starch and some vegetable protein. In nature it furnishes nourishment for the developing plant.

**Entrée**   The main course; the substantial part of a meal.

**Enzymes**   Chemical substances produced within the living tissues of all plants and animals that speed changes of normal ripening or maturing. In meat, the enzyme activity breaks down muscle tissue, making it more tender; in vegetables and fruit, their activity causes continued ripening to spoilage if not curtailed in some way.

**Esophagus**   The passageway for food moving from the mouth to the stomach. It is sometimes referred to as the gullet.

**Essential amino acids**   Building blocks of protein required for growth and repair of body tissue that cannot be manufactured in the body.

**Extractives**   Liquid in the muscle fibres that gives meat its characteristic flavour.

**Fallow**   To allow land to rest for a period of time to recover its fertility.

**Famine**   Lack of food resulting from events such as crop failure, drought, flood, insects, or war.

**Fat-soluble vitamins**   Vitamins that are found or stored in the fats of food, principally vitamins A, D, E, and K.

**Fatty acids**   A group of organic acids found in vegetable fat.

**Feast**   A celebration of relationships among people through sharing of plentiful food at a large or elaborate meal.

**Fertilizers**   Chemicals applied to crops to enhance production.

**Fibre**   The undigestible part of food that is eliminated in the feces.

**Finish**   The visible layer of fat on a cut of meat that lies directly under the skin.

**Fleshing**   A poultry-grading term referring to the distribution and amount of flesh in specific areas.

**Fold**   To gently combine two or more mixtures with a vertical motion, using a spoon or rubber spatula.

**Food additives**   Substances added to food in small amounts to add or improve certain desirable qualities.

**Food allergy**   A physical demonstration of an unusually sensitive immune system, which makes a person ill when he or she injests even a small amount of the offending food.

**Food intolerance**   The physical demonstration that a person cannot metabolize or tolerate a specific food in a particular form.

**Food security**   All people at all times having access to enough nutritious food for an active, healthy life while upholding basic human dignity.

**Fortification**   Enrichment of foods by the addition of vitamins and minerals. Government regulated.

**Fossil fuels**   The remains of ancient plants and animals concentrated by heat and pressure for millions of years to form oil, gas, and coal.

**Freeze drying**   Subjecting food to both low temperature and drying conditions at the same time to preserve it.

**Gall bladder**   A small organ adjacent to the stomach that stores bile produced by the liver until it is needed.

**Garnish**   An edible item added to prepared food to improve its appearance.

**Gastric juices**   Protein-splitting enzymes found in the stomach.

**Gastrointestinal tract**   System that comprises the mouth, esophagus, stomach, small intestine, and large intestine. (*See* Alimentary canal or Digestive tract.)

**Gelatinization**   The swelling of starch granules in hot liquid to thicken the mixture.

**Germ**   (1) The small, nourishing part of the grain from which a new plant grows. (2) A small, light-coloured spot on the surface of an egg yolk that, if fertilized, develops into a young chick.

**Glucose**   The simplest form of sugar (called blood sugar) as it is found in the blood stream and used by the body as a source of energy.

**Gluten**   Elasticlike strands of protein formed when wheat flour and a liquid are mixed. Gluten becomes the framework for any flour mixture when the protein hardens upon heating in the oven.

**Glycerol**   A sweet liquid found in fats and oils. Also known as glycerin.

**Glycogen**   A starchlike substance that is stored in the liver and body tissues and can be changed into glucose when needed.

**Grazing**   Constant snacking on whatever food is available with no advance planning or consideration of healthy food choices.

**Green revolution**   The attempt to increase food production through scientific advances.

**Greenhouse effect**   A natural occurrence of penetration of the sun's rays in the earth's surface so that certain gases trap some of the earth's warmth.

**Hardening of the arteries**   Narrowing of the passageways that supply blood to the heart and brain caused by deposits of plaque on the interior of artery walls. This scientific term for this is arteriosclerosis. (*See* Cholesterol.)

**Heart attack**   A condition that occurs when a coronary artery to the heart is blocked and a portion of the heart tissues do not receive oxygen and nutrients. It can be fatal.

**Hemoglobin**   A component of red blood cells that carries oxygen to body tissues and carbon dioxide away for elimination. Iron stored in the hemoglobin assists with that transport.

**Homogenized**   Milk that has been forced through very small holes under pressure to break the fat globules (butterfat) into small enough particles that they remain in suspension throughout the liquid.

**Husk**   The outermost protective layer of a cereal grain that is removed and not eaten.

**Hydrogenation**   The process that changes a liquid vegetable fat to a solid product having the same properties as an animal fat. Examples are margarine and shortening.

**Incomplete proteins**   Proteins that are missing one or more of the essential amino acids.

**Instantizing**   Clustering powdered dried food by slightly moistening and further drying. The resulting product disperses more quickly in water.

**Insulin**   A hormone secreted by the pancreas that enables the body to use sugar and other carbohydrates. (*See* Diabetes.)

**Intercropping**   Planting different crops in alternating rows in the same field to reduce pest attack and balance the nutrient content of the soil.

**Iron deficiency**   A blood condition caused by inadequate intakes of iron over an extended period of time.

**Irradiation**   Exposure of food to ionized energy to extend its shelf life without appreciably altering texture, flavour, or food value.

**Kidneys**   Body organs that are involved in the formation of urine, the liquid waste products of digestion.

**Lacteals**   Vessels in the wall of the intestine that carry chyle into the bloodstream.

**Lacto vegetarian**   A vegetarian who consumes dairy products in addition to foods from any vegetable source.

**Lactoalbumin**   A complete milk protein found in the whey that remains after the curd is removed to make cheese.

**Lactoglobulin**   A complete milk protein found in the whey that remains after the curd is removed to make cheese.

**Lactose**   The form of sugar found in milk.

**Lactose intolerance**   The condition that occurs when a person does not have enough of the enzyme lactase to digest the lactose or sugar in milk.

**Leavening agent**   An ingredient or combination of ingredients that makes a flour mixture rise and become light and porous. Examples are: baking powder, baking soda, yeast, steam, and air.

**Legumes**   The dried seeds of a family of plants that produce their seeds in pods, including beans, lentils, and peas. (*See* Pulses.)

**Leverage**   A principle that allows greater power to be exerted to lift something or force it open when a bar or other device is pivoted on a fixed point (the fulcrum).

**Lifestyle**   A way of life that includes habits, recreation, attitudes, food choices, and all behaviour affecting one's health.

**Liquid ingredients**   The fluids in a recipe, such as milk, juice, water, egg, and puréed vegetables or fruit.

**Magnetron**   The device that converts electricity into microwave energy in a microwave oven.

**Marbling**   Microscopic white streaks of fat in the red part of meat.

**Menopause**   The time in the life of a female when menstruation ceases permanently.

**Meringue**   A stiffly beaten mixture of egg whites and sugar (1) spread on the top of a pie and usually browned in the oven, (2) baked as a type of cookie or shell, or (3) folded into other ingredients to make a light dessert, such as chiffon pudding or sponge cake.

**Metabolic rate**   The speed at which the body uses food energy to maintain basal metabolism.

**Metabolism**   The chemical processes that take place within all cells to build tissue or release energy.

**Microorganism**   A living organism that cannot be seen by the naked eye.

**Microwave**   Energy waves that excite the molecules in food and cause them to vibrate against each other, creating friction that produces heat, which cooks the food.

**Minerals**   Elements that are part of the body's tissues and act as regulators of the body functions.

**Monocropping**   Production of only one crop.

**Monosaccharides**   Carbohydrates made of one sugar molecule.

**Monounsaturated fats**   Unsaturated fat from vegetable sources having only one hydrogen bond and containing no cholesterol.

**Moulds**   Microorganisms that occur as a fine growth of fungi forming on food (sugar, starch, protein) when exposed to air that contains their spores.

**Muscle fibres**   Meat composed of long, hollow cells bound by a connective tissue called collagen.

**Myosin**   A protein found in tender meat.

**Non-essential amino acids**   Building blocks of protein that can be manufactured by the body.

**Nutrients**   Chemical substances the body needs to function, grow, repair itself, and produce energy.

**Organic farming**    Farming that uses products that do not deplete or pollute the soil.

**Osteoporosis**    A bone disease in which there is a reduction of bone mass, through loss of calcium, that causes bones to become thin, brittle, and easily broken.

**Ova lacto vegetarian**    A vegetarian who consumes dairy products and eggs in addition to foods from any vegetable source.

**Oven poach**    A method of cooking that involves placing the dish or casserole of uncooked mixture into a larger pan and surrounding it with hot water. Recommended for any egg, milk, or cheese mixtures.

**Oxidation**    (1) The discolouration of the surface of vegetables and fruit caused by exposure to the air combined with enzyme action. (2) The breakdown of fat in the body that yields carbon dioxide and water as waste by-products.

**Pan fry**    A dry-heat method of cooking food quickly in an uncovered pan containing a small amount of fat.

**Pancreas**    An organ that produces insulin that regulates blood sugar levels.

**Papain**    An extractive from the papaya tree that contains a protein-splitting enzyme used in meat tenderizer.

**Paralytic shellfish poisoning**    Poisoning caused by a toxin produced by the "red tide" organism ingested by shellfish, which are subsequently eaten by humans. No amount of cooking will make the food safe to eat.

**Pasta**    Any macaroni, noodle, or spaghetti product made from a basic formula of flour and water and the possible addition of egg.

**Pasteurization**    Quickly heating milk to 71°C for a few seconds followed immediately by chilling, so that harmful bacteria are destroyed and storage time is extended.

**Peristalsis**    Muscular action of the walls of the intestine that moves undigested food along the digestive tract.

**Pesco vegetarian**    A vegetarian who consumes fish in addition to foods from any vegetable sources.

**Pesticides**    Chemicals applied to crops to kill insects and other pests.

**Plaque**    Deposits of cholesterol on the internal surfaces of the arteries that thicken the artery walls and narrow the passageway. (*See* Hardening of the arteries.)

**Pollo vegetarian**    A vegetarian who does not consume red meat but will consume poultry in addition to foods from any vegetable sources.

**Polysaccharides**    Complex carbohydrates made of several sugar molecules; found in starches and fibre.

**Polyunsaturated fat**    Unsaturated fat from a vegetable source missing many hydrogen bonds and containing no cholesterol.

**Pot roast**    A moist-heat method of slowly cooking a large piece of meat, called a roast, in a covered pan.

**Potlatch**    A lavish feast given by First Nations people of Canada's northwest coast during which the best food is served in traditional ways and gifts are presented by the host to all guests.

**Prestige**    Good reputation, social status, or influence derived from past achievements or wealth.

**Protein**    A component of food that is important for growth and repair of body tissues.

**Pulses**    The dried seeds of a family of plants that produce their seeds in pods, including beans, lentils, and peas. (*See* Legumes.)

**Purging**    Purposefully emptying the stomach through use of enemas, laxatives, and diuretics or by forced vomiting.

**Ramadan**    The ninth month of the Muslim year when Muslims fast between sunrise and sunset.

**Recommended Daily Intake (RDI)**    A calculation of the daily amounts of vitamins and minerals required by an individual so that the nutritional contribution of a specific food to that RDI can be expressed as a percentage. This enables the consumer to compare the nutrient value of foods more easily.

**Red Tide**    *See* Paralytic shellfish poisoning.

**Rennin**    An enzyme that coagulates milk, separating the curds from the whey in the first step of making cheese.

**Roast**    A dry-heat method of cooking tender cuts of meat or vegetables in an open pan in the oven.

**Rotisserie**    A dry-heat method of cooking a large piece of meat by rotating it on a spit in the presence of heat, either in an oven or from a barbeque or grill.

**Roux**    Equal parts of fat and flour cooked together as a first step in making a thickened sauce.

**Saliva**   Fluid produced by salivary glands in the mouth in response to stimulus of sight, smell, or taste. Its function is to moisten the food so that it can begin its passage down the esophagus.

**Satiety**   A satisfied feeling of having a full stomach after having eaten a meal.

**Saturated fat**   Fat from animal sources, such as meat, dairy products, and eggs, that is solid at room temperature and contains cholesterol. It includes the maximum quantity of hydrogen.

**Sauté**   A dry-heat method of cooking rapidly in a large, open pan with a small amount of hot fat. The pan is kept in motion throughout cooking.

**Scald**   Heating milk to just below the boiling point, about 82°C. Milk has reached the correct temperature when bubbles form around the edge of the pan.

**Shell**   The firm, porous outer protection of an egg composed of calcium.

**Shell membrane**   A thin tissue covering the inside of the egg shell.

**Simple carbohydrates**   Carbohydrates that are all sugar, such as sucrose (cane or beet sugar), lactose (milk sugar), and fructose (fruit sugar). The simplest form is glucose, the form eventually absorbed and transported through the body.

**Snacks**   Small amounts of food eaten between meals.

**Spores**   Single cells that are formed and released by some bacteria, yeast, and moulds when their environmental conditions become unfavourable for life. The spores are capable of developing new life. For example, some bacteria form spores when high heat is applied.

**Sports anaemia**   Depletion of iron stores that impairs athletic performance. The cause may be a breakdown of red blood cells during prolonged exercise and normal elimination of iron. (*See* anaemia.)

**Spray drying**   Dehydration of liquid food, such as milk, by spraying it into a heated cylinder.

**Stabilizers**   Ingredients that keep particles from separating from a mixture and settling to the bottom, such as chocolate in chocolate milk.

**Staphylococcal food poisoning**   Food poisoning caused by toxins from a bacteria that is naturally found in the body. When the toxin is eaten in food, it causes cramps, nausea, vomiting, and diarrhea.

**Starvation**   A condition of inadequate food supplied to the body. (*See* Anorexia nervosa.)

**Status**   A person's or object's position or rank in relation to others.

**Sterilization**   Application of sufficient heat to food or utensils to destroy both enzymes and microorganisms, including spores.

**Stew**   A moist-heat method of cooking seasoned cubes of meat by first browning in hot fat, then simmering in liquid until the meat is tender. Vegetables are generally added later and the sauce thickened to complete the dish.

**Stir**   To mix ingredients with a utensil such as a spoon, whisk, fork, spatula, or other similar utensil.

**Stomach**   A pear-shaped, muscular organ that receives food eaten and assists in breaking it down into parts that are usable to the body tissues.

**Stress**   Mental or physical circumstances that place strain on the body systems. Some stress is important to efficient functioning; too much stress has a detrimental effect on health.

**Stroke**   A condition that occurs when there is a blockage of blood flow to the brain, and a portion of it dies because it does not get enough blood.

**Subsistence**   For farms, those that provide almost all of the food required by the farm family to survive.

**Sun drying**   A method of food preservation, using the sun to dry food.

**Sustainable agriculture**   Agricultural practices that ensure that food can be grown on the same land for future generations.

**Taste buds**   Small sensors on the tongue that perceive the flavour of food.

**Temper**   The process of heating and working steel until it has the proper degree of hardness and toughness. When used in knives, the temper of the steel determines their ability to retain sharpness.

**Thickeners**   Food additives that regulate the consistency of foods, such as jams and jellies.

**Tofu**   The curd made from soy milk that is a soy bean product. Also called bean curd.

**Toxins**   Tasteless, odourless poisons produced by bacteria that cause no visible changes in appearance of the food but are life threatening when ingested.

**Trichinosis**   Illness caused by eating meat infected by the larvae of a parasite sometimes found in animals. Thorough cooking will destroy the larvae.

**Unsaturated fat**   Fat from a plant source that is liquid at room temperature and contains no cholesterol. It is missing some hydrogen bonds. Unsaturated fat can become saturated when it is hydrogenated as when vegetable oil is made into shortening or margarine.

**Vegans**   Strict vegetarians who eat only foods from vegetable sources.

**Vegetable fat**   *See* Unsaturated fat.

**Vermicomposting**   Composting using worms to turn garden and kitchen waste into fertilizer.

**Villi**   Hairlike projections of the intestinal wall where digested materials are absorbed.

**Vitamins**   Complex organic substances required for normal growth and nourishment of the body and essential for protection from diseases.

**Water-soluble vitamins**   Vitamins distributed in body fluids and eliminated regularly in the urine. Since they are not stored, they must be supplied daily. Principal ones are those of the B complex and C.

**Whey**   The liquid that remains after the curd has been removed from curdled milk during the making of cheese.

**Whip**   To beat rapidly to incorporate air and expand ingredients.

**Yeasts**   Microscopic organisms that grow in the presence of sugar, warmth, and moisture and produce carbon dioxide, water, and alcohol as by-products.

**Yolk**   The yellow-orange part of the egg containing the greatest proportion of nutrients.

# Works Consulted

*A Guide to Good Cooking.* 23rd ed. Montreal: Lake of the Woods Milling Company, Limited, n.d.

Barer-Stein, Thelma. *You Eat What You Are: A Study of Ethnic Food Traditions.* Toronto: McClelland & Stewart Inc., 1979.

*The Canadian Encyclopedia.* Edmonton: Hurtig Publishers Ltd., 1988 ed.

*Diabetes: What Every Canadian Needs to Know.* Toronto: Canadian Diabetes Association, n.d.

Elliot, Rose. *The Complete Vegetarian Cuisine.* London: William Collins Sons & Co. Ltd., 1988.

Dickason, Olive Patricia. *Canada's First Nations: A History of Founding Peoples from Earliest Times.* Toronto: McClelland & Stewart Inc., 1992.

*Facts on Cancer & Diet: Your Food Choices May Help You Reduce Your Cancer Risk.* Toronto: Canadian Cancer Society, 1986.

*Food and Drink in China: A Visitor's Guide.* Beijing: New World Press, 1986.

*Food Guide Facts: Background for Educators and Communicators.* Ottawa: Health and Welfare Canada, 1992.

Haskew, Paul and Cynthia H. Adams. *Eating Disorders: Managing Problems with Food.* Mission Hills: Glencoe, 1989.

*Healthy Habits—Healthy Weight.* Ottawa: Heart and Stroke Foundation, n.d.

Jarvik, Lissy and Gary Small. *Parentcare: A Common Sense Guide for Adult Children.* New York: Crown Publishing Group, 1988.

Lindsay, Anne. *Lighthearted Everyday Cooking.* Toronto: Macmillan of Canada, 1991.

Lindsay, Anne. *Smart Cooking.* Toronto: Macmillan of Canada, 1986.

*Native Foods and Nutrition: An Illustrated Reference Resource.* Ottawa: Minister of National Health and Welfare, Minister of Supply and Services Canada, 1987.

*Panasonic Microwave Oven Cookbook.* Matsushita Electric Industrial Co., Ltd. Secaucus, NJ, 1980.

"Recipes: Latin American Cooking." *Foods of the World.* New York: Time-Life Books, 1968.

"Recipes: The Cooking of Japan." *Foods of the World.* New York: Time-Life Books, 1969.

Rombauer, Irma S. and Marion Rombauer Becker. *Joy of Cooking.* Indianapolis/New York: The Bobbs-Merril Company, Inc., 1975.

*Secrets of Better Cooking.* Montreal: The Reader's Digest Association, 1973.

Siebert, Myrtle. *Management and Foods.* Victoria: Government of the Province of British Columbia Department of Education, 1975.

*Stop Osteoporosis...Stop the fractures.* Vancouver: Osteoporosis Society of B.C., n.d.

"The Cooking of the British Isles." *Foods of the World.* New York: Time-Life Books, 1969.

*The Inuit Way: A Guide to Inuit Culture.* Ottawa: Inuit Women's Association, 1989.

*Using Food Labels To Choose Foods for Healthy Eating.* Ottawa: Health and Welfare Canada, 1993.

*Using the Food Guide.* Ottawa: Health and Welfare Canada, 1992.

Visser, Margaret. *Much Depends on Dinner.* New York: Macmillan, 1988.

Visser, Margaret. *The Rituals of Dinner: The Origins, Evolution, Eccentricities & Meaning of Table Manners.* New York: Grove Press Inc.,1991.

Wattie, Helen and Elinor Donaldson. *Nellie Lyle Pattinson's Canadian Cook Book.* Toronto: The Ryerson Press, 1991.

# Photo Credits

page 3 Reproduced with the permission of the Government of Canada and copyright © the Ministry of Government Services, 1993; page 4 Courtesy of Newfoundland Department of Tourism and Culture; page 6 Dick Hemingway; page 9 CIDA photo/Pierre St. Jacques; page 10 Fleischmann's Yeast is a product of Specialty Brands, a division of Burns Philp Food Ltd.; page 11 Courtesy of Winnie Chu; page 13 Courtesy of Frank Petracca; page 16 Dick Hemingway; page 17 Courtesy of Variety Village; page 18 The Province of British Columbia; page 22 National Archives of Canada/C-30165; page 23 Tessa Macintosh/Government of Northwest Territories; page 27 © Minister of Supply and Services Canada, 1992. Cat. H39-253/3-1992E, ISBN 0-662-20073-X; page 28 Courtesy of Teresa Camardo; page 29 Courtesy of Wanita Watson-Rhodes; pages 32 and 33 Courtesy of the Beef Information Centre; page 34 Dick Hemingway; page 36 Fleischmann's Yeast is a product of Specialty Brands, a division of Burns Philp Food Ltd.; page 37 Superstock/Rivera Collection; page 38 Thermos ® insulated lunch bag. ® Registered trademark of Canadian Thermos Products Inc.; page 42 Dick Hemingway; page 43 Courtesy of Yvonne Pinnock; page 46 Dick Hemingway; page 47 Photo courtesy of Red Lobster Canada; pages 51–54 Reprinted with permission of Keg Restaurants Ltd.; page 59 Fleischmann's Yeast is a product of Specialty Brands, a division of Burns Philp Food Ltd.; page 60 Courtesy of the Bracciale family; page 61 Toast-R-Oven/Broiler by Black & Decker; page 61 Deep Dutch Skillet by Black & Decker; page 61 Power Pro ™ Hand Mixer by Black & Decker; page 62 Food Processor courtesy of Moulinex Canada Ltd.; page 62 Rival ® Crock-Pot ® is a registered trademark of The Rival Company; page 63 Cookware from Regal Ware, Inc., Kewaskum, Wisconsin; page 65 Beautiful elmwood kitchen cabinetry from the kitchen court in the Pickering Home and Design Centre; page 86 Courtesy of Vince Barrett; page 89 Courtesy of mmmarvellous mmmuffins; page 90 Superstock/P.R.

Production; page 95 Lucerne Foods Ltd., Vancouver, B.C., V6B 4E9; page 95 Fleischmann's Yeast is a product of Specialty Brands, a division of Burns Philp Food Ltd.; page 96 CIDA photo/David Barbour; page 97 Photo courtesy of the Dairy Bureau of Canada; page 97 Photo courtesy of Newfoundland Department of Fisheries; page 98 CIDA photo/Dilip Metha; page 99 Courtesy of the Beef Information Centre; page 101 Reproduced with the permission of Nabisco Brands Ltd., Toronto, Ontario, Canada. DEL MONTE ® is a trade mark of Nabisco Brands Ltd., Toronto, Canada, © all rights reserved, used under license from Del Monte Corporation; page 105 Health Canada, K88-00007-36; page 107 Glenbow Archives, Calgary, Canada, NA-3729-23; page 112 Photo: K.A. Seifert, Agriculture and Agri-Food Canada; page 114 Photo courtesy of Bernadin of Canada Ltd.; page 118 Canadian Egg Marketing Agency; page 119 Photo compliments of Ontario Turkey Producers' Marketing Board; page 123 Superstock/ Rivera Collection; page 129 Dick Hemingway; page 131 Courtesy of Canada Catering Co. Limited; page 132 Courtesy of the Ontario Turkey Producers' Marketing Board; page 137 The Image Bank/Pat LaCroix; page 138 Superstock/William D. Adams; page 143 USA Rice Council; page 146 Borden Catelli Consumer Products; pages 147, 149, 150, 152, 154 Fleischmann's Yeast is a product of Specialty Brands, a division of Burns Philp Food Ltd.; page 155 Frank Petracca; page 160 Courtesy of Fresh For Flavour Foundation; page 167 Prince Edward Island Potato Board; page 171 Photo courtesy of B.C. Salmon Marketing Council; page 174 CIDA photo/David Barbour; pages 180, 182, 184 Courtesy of the Dairy Bureau of Canada; page 187 Prince Edward Island Potato Board; page 189 Photo compliments of American Dairy Association®; pages 195 and 197 Courtesy of the Beef Information Centre; page 198 Compliments of Canada Pork Inc.; page 199 Courtesy of the Ontario Sheep Marketing Agency; page 200 Courtesy of the Beef Information Centre; page 201

# Text Credits

pages 87, 108–110, 152, 163–165, 196, 202–203, 206–207, 209, 314–315 Adapted from *Management and Foods*, published by the Government of the Province of British Columbia Department of Education, 1975. Reprinted with permission by the Ministry of Education. pages 214–220 With assistance from the Canadian Egg Marketing Agency; page 234 Adapted from *Food Guide Facts — Background for Educators and Communicators*, Health Canada, 1992. Reproduced with permission of the Minister of Supply and Services Canada, 1993; page 323 *Canada Gazette*, Part II, Vol. 122, No. 24, pp. 4630-4652, November 23, 1988. Published under authority of the Statutory Instruments Act, Minister of Supply and Services Canada 1988, Queen's Printer for Canada, Ottawa, 1988; pages 343–345 Portions of this section were adapted from *Baby's Best Chance* (Macmillan Canada, 1992). Used by permission; pages 345–351 Information adapted from "Choices" fact sheets produced by the Canadian Dietetic Association; page 351 From *Management and Foods*, published by the Government of the Province of British Columbia Department of Education, 1975. Reprinted with permission by the Ministry of Education. pages 356–360 Adapted from *Get a Taste for the Healthy Life*. Reprinted with permission from Kellogg Canada Inc. ©; pages 362–364 The information on osteoporosis has been provided courtesy of OSTOP, Osteoporosis Society of B.C.; pages 364–367 Information adapted from "Choices" fact sheet produced by the Canadian Dietetic Association; pages 367–370 Information adapted from "Choices" fact sheet produced by the Canadian Dietetic Association; pages 372–379 This information was adapted from resources at the national Eating Disorder Information Centre, College Wing 1–304, 200 Elizabeth Street, Toronto, Ontario M5G 2C4.

# Index

(CS) = career sketch; (R) = recipe